Holden Kass

CALIFORNIA

Prentice Hall

AMERICA

HISTORY OF OUR NATION

Independence Through 1914

Interactive Reading and Notetaking Study Guide

PEARSON
Prentice Hall
Upper Saddle River, New Jersey
Boston, Massachusetts

PEARSON
Prentice Hall

ISBN 0-13-119997-8

18 V011 15 14 13 12

Contents

How to Use This Book vii

Unit 1: Foundations of American History 1

Chapter 1: American Roots (Beginnings to 1732) 2

Section 1: Roots of Democratic Government 2
Summary 2
Notetaking Study Guide 4
Section 2: An Age of Exploration 5
Summary 5
Notetaking Study Guide 7
Section 3: Commerce and Colonies 8
Summary 8
Notetaking Study Guide 10
Section 4: The 13 English Colonies 11
Summary 11
Notetaking Study Guide 13
Chapter 1 Assessment 14
Chapter 1 Notetaking Study Guide 15

Chapter 2: From Colonies to Nation (1680–1783) 16

Section 1: A Tradition of Liberty 16
Summary 16
Notetaking Study Guide 18
Section 2: Impact of the Enlightenment 19
Summary 19
Notetaking Study Guide 21
Section 3: Declaring Independence 22
Summary 22
Notetaking Study Guide 24
Declaration of Independence Notetaking Study Guide 25
Section 4: A New Nation 27
Summary 27
Notetaking Study Guide 28
Chapter 2 Assessment 29
Chapter 2 Notetaking Study Guide 30

Unit 1 Pulling It Together Activity 31

Unit 2: The Constitution of the United States 33

Chapter 3: Creating the Constitution (1776–1790) 34

Section 1: Governing a New Nation . . . 34
Summary 34
Notetaking Study Guide 36
Section 2: The Constitutional Convention 37
Summary 37
Notetaking Study Guide 39
Section 3: Debating the Constitution . . 40
Summary 40
Notetaking Study Guide 42
Chapter 3 Assessment 43
Chapter 3 Notetaking Study Guide . . . 44
Constitution Notetaking Study Guide . 45

Citizenship Handbook 47

Section 1 47
Summary 47
Constitution Notetaking Study Guide . 49
Section 2 50
Summary 50
Branches of Government Notetaking Study Guide 52
Section 3 53
Summary 53
Amending the Constitution Notetaking Study Guide 55
Section 4 56
Summary 56
Governments and Citizens Notetaking Study Guide 58
Citizenship Handbook Assessment . . . 59
Citizenship Handbook Notetaking Study Guide 60

Unit 2 Pulling It Together Activity 61

Unit 3: The New Republic 63

Chapter 4: First Steps (1789–1800). 64

Section 1: Launching a New Nation ... 64
Summary 64
Notetaking Study Guide............ 66
Section 2: The Birth of Political Parties . 67
Summary 67
Notetaking Study Guide............ 69
Section 3: Troubles at Home and Abroad 70
Summary 70
Notetaking Study Guide............ 72
Section 4: The Presidency of John Adams 73
Summary 73
Notetaking Study Guide............ 75
Chapter 4 Assessment 76
Chapter 4 Notetaking Study Guide ... 77

Chapter 5: The Era of Thomas Jefferson (1800–1815) 78

Section 1: Jefferson Takes Office 78
Summary 78
Notetaking Study Guide............ 80
Section 2: The Louisiana Purchase and Lewis and Clark 81
Summary 81
Notetaking Study Guide............ 83
Section 3: A Time of Conflict 84
Summary 84
Notetaking Study Guide............ 86
Section 4: The War of 1812 87
Summary 87
Notetaking Study Guide............ 89
Chapter 5 Assessment 90
Chapter 5 Notetaking Study Guide ... 91

Chapter 6: A Changing Nation (1815–1840). 92

Section 1: Building a National Identity. 92
Summary 92
Notetaking Study Guide............ 94
Section 2: Dealing With Other Nations. 95
Summary 95
Notetaking Study Guide............ 97
Section 3: The Age of Jackson......... 98
Summary 98
Notetaking Study Guide 100
Section 4: Indian Removal 101
Summary 101
Notetaking Study Guide 103
Section 5: Finance and States' Rights . .104
Summary 104
Notetaking Study Guide 106
Chapter 6 Assessment 107
Chapter 6 Notetaking Study Guide . . .108

Unit 3 Pulling It Together Activity....109

Unit 4: The Nation Expands and Changes 111

Chapter 7: North and South Take Different Paths (1800–1845) 112

Section 1: The Industrial Revolution . .112
Summary 112
Notetaking Study Guide 114
Section 2: The North Transformed 115
Summary 115
Notetaking Study Guide 117
Section 3: The Plantation South 118
Summary 118
Notetaking Study Guide 120
Section 4: Americans Move Westward.121
Summary 121
Notetaking Study Guide 123
Chapter 7 Assessment 124
Chapter 7 Notetaking Study Guide . . .125

Chapter 8: An Age of Reform (1820–1860) 126

Section 1: Improving Society.........126
Summary 126
Notetaking Study Guide 128
Section 2: The Fight Against Slavery . .129
Summary 129
Notetaking Study Guide 131
Section 3: A Call for Women's Rights. .132
Summary 132
Notetaking Study Guide 134
Section 4: American Literature and Arts 135
Summary 135
Notetaking Study Guide 137
Chapter 8 Assessment 138
Chapter 8 Notetaking Study Guide . . .139

Chapter 9: Westward Expansion (1820–1860) 140
Section 1: The West. 140
Summary 140
Notetaking Study Guide 142
Section 2: Trails to the West. 143
Summary 143
Notetaking Study Guide 145
Section 3: Conflict With Mexico 146
Summary 146
Notetaking Study Guide 148
Section 4: A Rush to the West 149
Summary 149
Notetaking Study Guide 151
Chapter 9 Assessment 152
Chapter 9 Notetaking Study Guide . . . 153

Unit 4 Pulling It Together Activity . . . 154

Unit 5: Civil War 156

Chapter 10: The Nation Divided (1846–1861) 157
Section 1: Growing Tensions Over Slavery 157
Summary 157
Notetaking Study Guide 159
Section 2: Compromises Fail. 160
Summary 160
Notetaking Study Guide 162
Section 3: The Crisis Deepens. 163
Summary 163
Notetaking Study Guide 165
Section 4: The Coming of the Civil War 166
Summary 166
Notetaking Study Guide 168
Chapter 10 Assessment 169
Chapter 10 Notetaking Study Guide. . 170

Chapter 11: The Civil War (1861–1865) 171
Section 1: The Call to Arms. 171
Summary 171
Notetaking Study Guide 173
Section 2: Early Years of the War 174
Summary 174
Notetaking Study Guide 176
Section 3: The Emancipation Proclamation 177
Summary 177
Notetaking Study Guide 179
Section 4: The Civil War and American Life. 180
Summary 180
Notetaking Study Guide 182
Section 5: Decisive Battles 183
Summary 183
Notetaking Study Guide 185
Chapter 11 Assessment. 186
Chapter 11 Notetaking Study Guide . 187

Chapter 12: Reconstruction and the New South (1863–1896) 188
Section 1: Rebuilding the Nation. 188
Summary 188
Notetaking Study Guide 190
Section 2: The Battle Over Reconstruction 191
Summary 191
Notetaking Study Guide 193
Section 3: The End of Reconstruction. 194
Summary 194
Notetaking Study Guide 196
Chapter 12 Assessment. 197
Chapter 12 Notetaking Study Guide. . 198

Unit 5 Pulling It Together Activity . . . 199

Unit 6: An Age of Industry . . 201

Chapter 13: The West Transformed (1860–1896). 202
Section 1: Miners and Railroads 202
Summary 202
Notetaking Study Guide 204
Section 2: Native Americans Struggle to Survive 205
Summary 205
Notetaking Study Guide 207
Section 3: Cattle Kingdoms 208
Summary 208
Notetaking Study Guide 210
Section 4: Farming in the West 211
Summary 211
Notetaking Study Guide 213
Chapter 13 Assessment. 214
Chapter 13 Notetaking Study Guide . 215

Chapter 14: Industry and Urban Growth (1865–1915) 216

Section 1: A New Industrial Revolution 216
Summary 216
Notetaking Study Guide 218
Section 2: Big Business and Organized Labor 219
Summary 219
Notetaking Study Guide 221
Section 3: Cities Grow and Change 222
Summary 222
Notetaking Study Guide 224
Section 4: The New Immigrants 225
Summary 225
Notetaking Study Guide 227
Section 5: Education and Culture 228
Summary 228
Notetaking Study Guide 230
Chapter 14 Assessment 231
Chapter 14 Notetaking Study Guide . 232

Chapter 15: Political Reform and the Progressive Era (1870–1920) 233

Section 1: The Gilded Age and Progressive Reform 233
Summary 233
Notetaking Study Guide 235
Section 2: The Progressive Presidents . 236
Summary 236
Notetaking Study Guide 238
Section 3: The Rights of Women 239
Summary 239
Notetaking Study Guide 241
Section 4: Struggles for Justice 242
Summary 242
Notetaking Study Guide 244
Chapter 15 Assessment 245
Chapter 15 Notetaking Study Guide . . 246

Chapter 16: The United States Looks Overseas (1853–1915) . . . 247

Section 1: Eyes on the Pacific 247
Summary 247
Notetaking Study Guide 249
Section 2: The Spanish-American War . . 250
Summary 250
Notetaking Study Guide 252
Section 3: The United States and Latin America 253
Summary 253
Notetaking Study Guide 255
Section 4: World War I 256
Summary 256
Notetaking Study Guide 258
Chapter 16 Assessment 259
Chapter 16 Notetaking Study Guide . . 260

Unit 6 Pulling It Together Activity 261

Epilogue: The United States in the Modern World 263

Section 1 263
Summary 263
Faces of America Notetaking Study Guide 265
Section 2 266
Summary 266
Economics, Workplace, and Civil Rights Notetaking Study Guide 268
Section 3 269
Summary 269
Opportunities and California Democracy Notetaking Study Guide 271
Epilogue Assessment 272
Epilogue Notetaking Study Guide 273

Ideas to Build On 274

How to Use This Book

The *Interactive Reading and Notetaking Study Guide* was designed to help you understand the content in your *America: History of Our Nation* textbook. It will also help you build your notetaking and historical-thinking skills. Please take the time to look at the next few pages to see how it works.

The unit opener page prepares you to read and think about the chapters in each unit. Section Summary pages provide an easy-to-read summary of each section.

Unit 1

Connecting with Past Learnings: The Foundations of American History

What You Will Learn

Chapter 1 European exploration led to colonization and settlement of the Americas. The 13 British colonies formed governments that were based on traditions of democracy and representative government.

Chapter 2 Tension between the 13 colonies and Britain rose during the mid-1700s. In 1776, the 13 British colonies declared independence from Great Britain and fought a war to win it.

Focus Your Learning As you study this unit and take notes, you will find the information to answer the questions below. Answering the Chapter Focus Questions will help build your answer to the Unit Focus Question.

Chapter 1 Focus Question
How did the American colonists establish their own way of life with strong roots in the past?
(page 2)

Chapter 2 Focus Question
How did the growth of democratic ideals in the colonies lead to the American Revolution?
(page 16)

Unit 1 Focus Question
How did the foundations of the American nation reflect both continuity and change?
(page 31)

Brief summaries of the chapters in the unit prepare you for what you will learn.

Unit, chapter, and section focus questions help you to think about the big ideas in your reading.

This paragraph provides a summary of the section's most important ideas.

Vocabulary Builders expand your understanding of important terms.

Key Terms from your textbook, set in blue, are defined in the summary.

Chapter Standards
History-Social Science 7.11.4, 7.11.5, 7.11.6, 8.1.1, 8.1.2, 8.1.3, 8.1.4, 8.3.7

Key Events

- 1735 John Peter Zenger found not guilty of libel.
- 1776 Americans declare independence from Britain.
- 1783 American Revolution ends with the signing of the Treaty of Paris.

Vocabulary Builder
A proprietor is an owner of a business or a colony. The word is closely related to the word *property*.

✓ Checkpoint
Name a form of self-government used in New England.

____

Chapter 2

From Colonies to Nation (1680–1783)

What You Will Learn

American colonists developed traditions of self-government, freedom of religion, and freedom of the press.

Chapter 2 Focus Question
As you read through this chapter, keep this question in mind: **How did the growth of democratic ideals in the colonies lead to the American Revolution?**

Section 1

A Tradition of Liberty

Section 1 Focus Question
How did the traditions of liberty take hold in the colonies? To begin answering this question,
- Find out how the colonies became self-governing.
- Understand the significance of the Great Awakening.
- Learn about the importance of freedom of the press.

Section 1 Summary

Self-government in colonial America was strengthened by religious ideals and freedom of the press.

Self-Government in the Colonies
American colonists were subjects of the British monarch who were expected to obey English law. However, the distance separating Britain from North America made it hard for England to govern its colonies. As a result, the early English colonists set up forms of self-government. The Jamestown colonists, for example, set up the first colonial legislature. New Englanders developed the town meeting, a gathering in which residents meet once a year to make decisions for the community.

A more complex system was needed for governing an entire colony. Each colony had a governor, usually appointed by the king or the proprietor of the colony. Colonies also had their own legislatures to create and pass laws. Most legislatures were made up of two houses: an upper house and a lower house. ☑

The Great Awakening
Religion had always played an important role in the 13 English colonies. However, by the 1700s the Puritan tradition was declining in New England. Still, churches were centers of faith and community life.

16 Unit 1 Chapter 2 Section 1

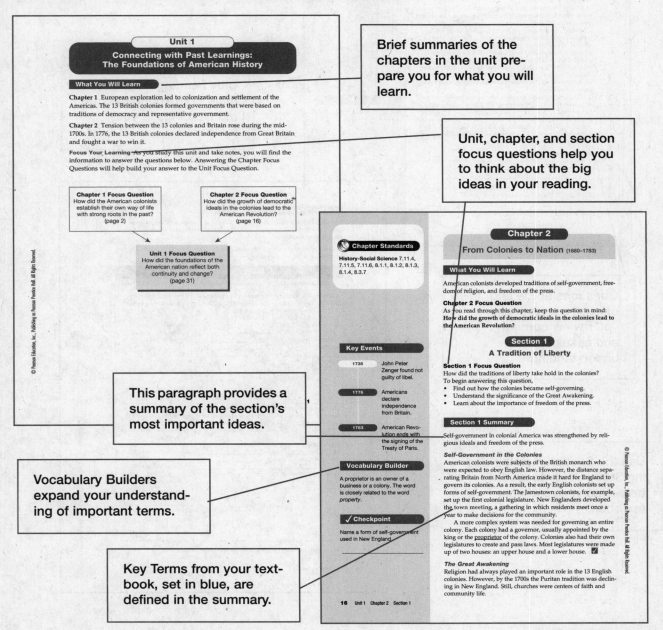

Questions and activities in the margin help you recall information from the summary. Section Notetaking Study Guides help you take notes as your read your textbook.

A passionate Christian movement swept through the colonies in the 1730s and 1740s. This period of religious revival is called the Great Awakening. It was a response to the belief that religion was becoming less important in colonial life.

Massachusetts preacher Jonathan Edwards called on people to commit themselves to God or risk being "sinners in the hands of an angry God." Other forceful preachers quickly spread the ideas of the Great Awakening throughout the colonies. One such speaker, the English minister George Whitefield, held outdoor meetings from Georgia to Massachusetts. The huge crowds who came to listen to his sermons heard him call on all sinners to reform.

The Great Awakening led to the rise of many new organized churches. This increased tolerance of religious differences. The Great Awakening was also one of the first movements to involve people in many American colonies. It affected the way people viewed their political rights, because they realized that if they could decide how to worship God, they could also decide how to govern themselves. ☑

✓ Checkpoint

Name the Massachusetts preacher who was a major figure of the Great Awakening.

___

Freedom of the Press

In 1734, an important court case helped establish the right to a free press. Freedom of the press is the right of newspapers and other public media to publish articles believed to be accurate.

Printing presses had been established throughout the colonies, leading to the emergence of many publications. Newspapers, for example, began to appear in the early 1700s. Benjamin Franklin had established *Poor Richard's Almanac* during this period. Then in 1734, John Peter Zenger, publisher of the *Weekly Journal* in New York City, was arrested for printing articles that showed the governor in a bad light. Zenger was charged with libel, the publishing of statements that unjustly damage a person's reputation.

Zenger's trial was a sensation. His lawyers proved that the statements he published were true. Therefore, Zenger could not be convicted of libel. The case helped establish that a democracy depends on well-informed citizens, and that the press has a right and responsibility to inform the public of the truth. Today, freedom of the press is considered to be one of the most important American liberties. ☑

✓ Checkpoint

Why was John Peter Zenger arrested?

___

Check Your Progress

1. How did the Great Awakening influence people's political views?

___

2. What principle did the Zenger case establish?

___

The Checkpoint prompts you to recall details in the summary. The checkmark tells you when to stop and read the Checkpoint.

Blue headings in the summary correspond to large red headings in your textbook.

Questions at the end of each section help you review content and assess your understanding.

Use the Section Notetaking Study Guide to record details as you read your textbook.

Section 1 Notetaking Study Guide

Question to Think About As you read Section 1 in your textbook and take notes, keep this section focus question in mind: **How did the traditions of liberty take hold in the American Revolution?**

► Use this chart to record key information from the section. Some of the information has been filled in to get you started.

Moving Toward Liberty

Self-Government	Freedom of Religion	Freedom of the Press
Situation: Colonists subject to British rule, but everyday decisions in each town couldn't be addressed quickly enough by London. **Response:** Colonists developed the ______/______. Villagers gathered to ______ and ______ local issues.	**Situation:** The Great Awakening movement in 1730s and 1740s led to many new organized churches. **Response:** ______	**Situation:** John Zenger printed articles showing the governor in a negative light. **Response:** Zenger was charged with ______, and put on trial.
Situation: A more complex system of government was needed for each colony as a whole. **Response:** Colonists created ______ to make laws. Each colony set its own ______ for electing representatives.	**Situation:** The Great Awakening showed people that they could decide for themselves how to worship God. **Response:** ______	**Situation:** Zenger wins his case. **Response:** The principle was established that a ______ depends on well-informed ______, so the press has a right and ______ to keep the public informed of the ______. This right is known as ______.

Refer to this page to answer the Chapter 2 Focus Question on page 30.

18 Unit 1 Chapter 2 Section 1

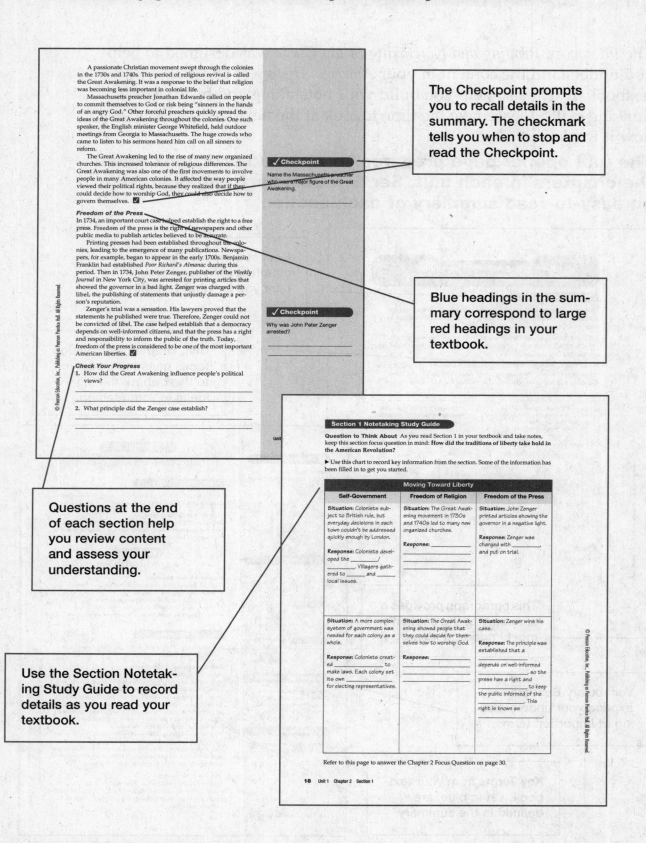

Questions help you to assess your progress. Chapter Notetaking Study Guides help you to pull together the notes you took for each section and focus on important ideas.

Chapter 2 Assessment

Directions: Circle the letter of the correct answer.

1. Which idea did the Zenger trial help establish?
   - **A** The press has a right and responsibility to accurately inform the public.
   - **B** The government should be divided into three branches.
   - **C** Taxation without representation is not fair.
   - **D** Society is governed by unchanging natural laws.
2. How did the Scientific Revolution influence Enlightenment thinking?
   - **A** Natural laws could be measured and described.
   - **B** If natural laws existed in nature, they must exist in society, too.
   - **C** Absolute monarchs provided their people with natural rights.
   - **D** Natural rights must be given to scientists so they could do their research.
3. Why did colonists believe they should not have to pay British taxes?
   - **A** because they were boycotting British goods
   - **B** because the taxes were so high people couldn't afford basics
   - **C** because British citizens in England didn't have to pay taxes
   - **D** because they had no representatives in Parliament

Directions: Follow the steps to answer this question:
How did Enlightenment theories support the American bid for independence?

Step 1: Recall information: In the chart, briefly describe each theory or idea.

Theory	Main Idea
Divine Right of Kings	
Natural Rights	

Step 2: How did the theory of the divine right of kings support the British government's actions regarding the American colonies?

Step 3: Complete the topic sentence that follows. Then write two or three more sentences that support your topic sentence.

Locke's theory of natural rights set the stage for conflict between the colonists and the British government because

Questions at the end of the chapter help you review content and assess your understanding of the summary.

Critical-thinking questions are broken into manageable steps.

Use the Chapter Notetaking Study Guide to organize your section notes to answer the chapter focus question.

Chapter 2 Notetaking Study Guide

Now you are ready to answer the Chapter 2 Focus Question: **How did the growth of democratic ideals in the colonies lead to the American Revolution?**

► Complete the following chart to help you answer this question. Use the notes that you took for each section.

Thoughts Spark Action: Ideas that Led to the American Revolution

Religious Concepts

The Great Awakening
- was a religious movement that encouraged people to examine their lives and commit themselves to God.
- encouraged people to think that, if they could decide how to worship, they could also decide ________.
- was one of the first movements to involve people from ________.

Enlightenment Concepts

Thinkers tried to use reason to find natural laws that governed politics, society, and economics.

John Locke proposed that people have ________ that belong to them from birth. He argued that a ruler who does not protect the rights of the people should be ________.

Colonial Government

- By the 1770s, most educated colonists believed they had ________.
- The colonies were partially self-governing. Each colony had its own ________ to make laws. Each colony also had a ________, either appointed by the king or by the proprietor of the colony.
- In 1735, the ________ case established the principle of ________.

British Actions That Led to Colonial Anger

Stamp Act, ________, ________ Acts

Anger Led to Revolution

1774: The First Continental ________ met and agreed not to buy British goods.
1775: The Battles of ________ and ________ marked the start of the American Revolution.
1776: The Continental ________ adopted the ________ of ________. This document announced the creation of a new nation.

Refer to this page to answer the Unit 1 Focus Question on page 31.

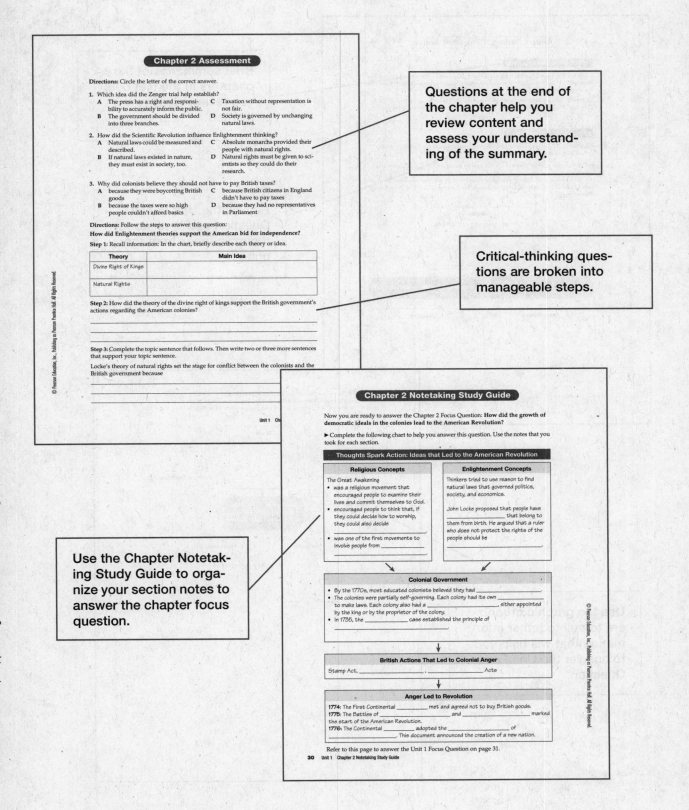

The Pulling It Together Activity helps you to look back on your reading and focus on the unit's big ideas.

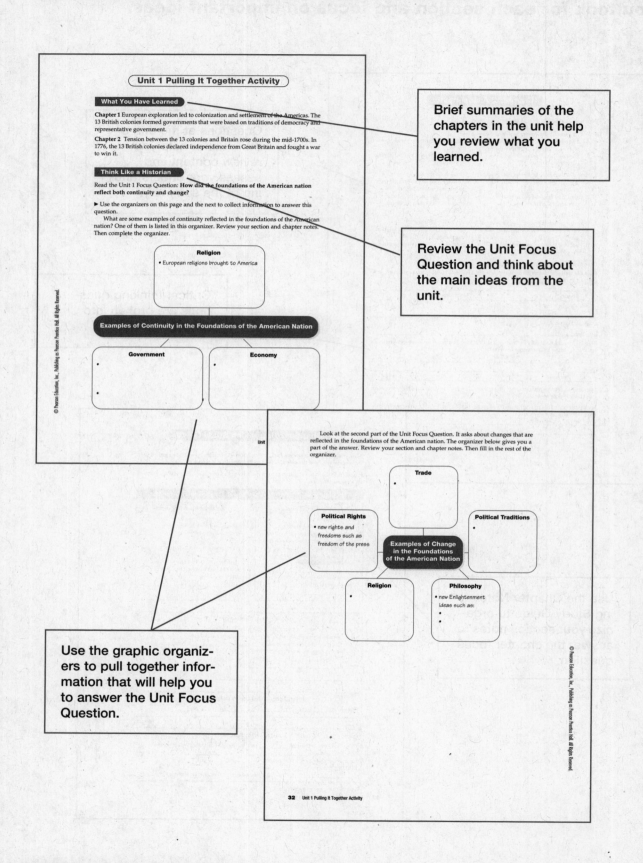

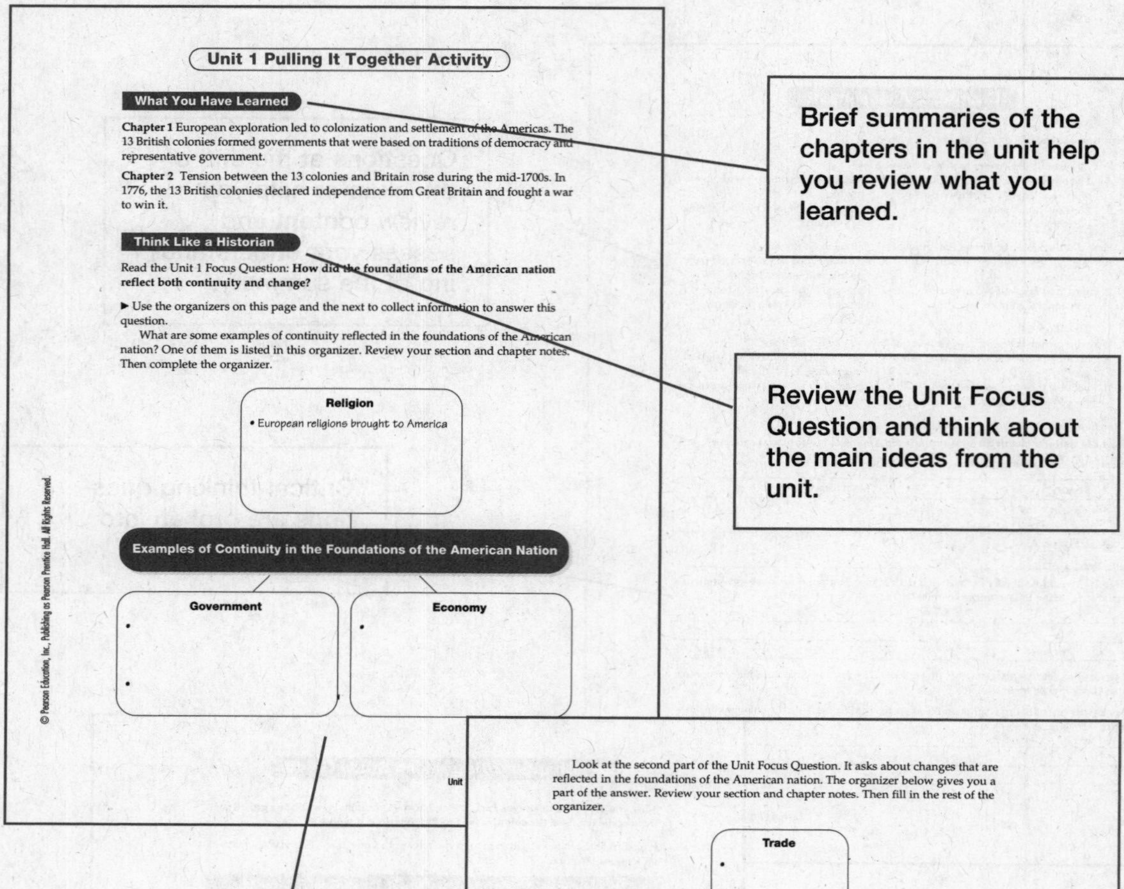
Unit 1 Pulling It Together Activity

What You Have Learned

Chapter 1 European exploration led to colonization and settlement of the Americas. The 13 British colonies formed governments that were based on traditions of democracy and representative government.

Chapter 2 Tension between the 13 colonies and Britain rose during the mid-1700s. In 1776, the 13 British colonies declared independence from Great Britain and fought a war to win it.

Think Like a Historian

Read the Unit 1 Focus Question: **How did the foundations of the American nation reflect both continuity and change?**

► Use the organizers on this page and the next to collect information to answer this question.

What are some examples of continuity reflected in the foundations of the American nation? One of them is listed in this organizer. Review your section and chapter notes. Then complete the organizer.

Look at the second part of the Unit Focus Question. It asks about changes that are reflected in the foundations of the American nation. The organizer below gives you a part of the answer. Review your section and chapter notes. Then fill in the rest of the organizer.

Brief summaries of the chapters in the unit help you review what you learned.

Review the Unit Focus Question and think about the main ideas from the unit.

Use the graphic organizers to pull together information that will help you to answer the Unit Focus Question.

Unit 1

Connecting with Past Learnings: The Foundations of American History

What You Will Learn

Chapter 1 European exploration led to colonization and settlement of the Americas. The 13 British colonies formed governments that were based on traditions of democracy and representative government.

Chapter 2 Tension between the 13 colonies and Britain rose during the mid-1700s. In 1776, the 13 British colonies declared independence from Great Britain and fought a war to win it.

Focus Your Learning As you study this unit and take notes, you will find the information to answer the questions below. Answering the Chapter Focus Questions will help build your answer to the Unit Focus Question.

Chapter 1 Focus Question
How did the American colonists establish their own way of life with strong roots in the past?
(page 2)

Chapter 2 Focus Question
How did the growth of democratic ideals in the colonies lead to the American Revolution?
(page 16)

Unit 1 Focus Question
How did the foundations of the American nation reflect both continuity and change?
(page 31)

Chapter Standards

History-Social Science 7.11.1, 7.11.2, 7.11.3, 8.1.4, 8.2.1

Chapter 1

Chapter 1 American Roots

(Beginnings to 1732)

What You Will Learn

Our modern American political system has its roots in ancient traditions. Judaism and Christianity molded American beliefs about justice and equality. Greek, Roman, and English traditions shaped our current system of government and law.

Chapter 1 Focus Question

As you read this chapter, keep this question in mind: **How did the American colonists establish their own way of life with strong roots in the past?**

Section 1

Roots of Democratic Government

Section 1 Focus Question

What are the roots of American government? To begin answering this question,

- Explore the moral values of the Judeo-Christian tradition.
- Learn about Greco-Roman systems of government.
- Find out how the English Parliament influenced American ideas about individual rights.

Section 1 Summary

Early American colonists brought with them beliefs about government and human rights. These ideas came from the Judeo-Christian tradition, from ancient Greece and Rome, and from the English political system.

The Judeo-Christian Tradition

Judaism and Christianity both developed in the ancient Middle East. The teachings of these religions are called the Judeo-Christian tradition. The Hebrews, now called the Jews, followed religious and moral laws called the Ten Commandments. These rules explain how people should treat each other and respect God. The Jews taught that everyone, even rulers, had to obey God's law.

Christianity is based on the teachings of a Jew named Jesus, who lived about 2,000 years ago. Jesus said that all people, rich and poor, were equal in the eyes of God. Over time, it became the dominant religion in Europe and later America. Judeo-Christian ideas of justice and equality influenced American society. ✓

Key Events

1215 Magna Carta places limits on the power of English monarchs.

1492 Christopher Columbus reaches the Caribbean, bringing Europe and the Americas into contact.

1620 Pilgrims sign the Mayflower Compact.

✓ Checkpoint

Name the place where Judaism and Christianity were founded.

___

The Greco-Roman Tradition

The Greeks lived in many city-states; Athens was the first to adopt **direct democracy**. In this system of government, an assembly of citizens makes decisions. Athenians believed citizens should perform their public duties. For example, a citizen might have to serve on a **jury**, a panel of citizens who pass judgments in a trial. But citizenship was limited. Slaves, women, and foreigners could not take part in government.

Greek ideas influenced the Roman civilization of Italy. The Romans created a **republic**, a form of government in which people pick representatives to govern in their name. Rome's republic eventually weakened and became an empire. The Roman Empire spread throughout Europe, carrying its laws and traditions with it. These included the ideas that everyone is equal before the law and that accused people are innocent until proven guilty. After 500 years the Roman Empire fell and many Greek and Roman ideas were forgotten. ✓

English Parliamentary Traditions

Long after the fall of Rome, England developed a system of government that would provide three major influences for American democracy. First, in 1215 King John signed the Magna Carta. This charter limited the king's power to tax, protected private property, and guaranteed the right to trial by jury. The Magna Carta established the idea that everyone had certain political rights. Second, nobles formed a council to advise the king called a Parliament (PAHR luh ment). They had the right to approve new taxes. Parliament developed into a two-house **legislature**, which is a group of people that has the power to make laws for its country. Third, in 1689 Parliament adopted the English Bill of Rights. A **bill of rights** is a written list of freedoms that a government promises to protect. For example, the English Bill of Rights protected **habeus corpus**. This is the principle that a person cannot be held in prison without being charged with a crime. Rulers were also banned from raising taxes or an army without Parliament's approval. ✓

Check Your Progress

1. How did the Judeo-Christian and Roman traditions promote ideas of equality?

____

____

____

2. What are three English political traditions that influenced American government?

____

____

____

✓ Checkpoint

List two forms of government that arose from the Greek and Roman traditions.

____

____

Vocabulary Builder

Magna Carta means "Great Charter" in Latin. Why do you think the English saw the Magna Carta as a "great" document?

____

____

____

✓ Checkpoint

Name two things the English Bill of Rights kept rulers from doing without Parliament's approval.

____

____

____

Section 1 Notetaking Study Guide

Question to Think About As you read Section 1 in your textbook and take notes, keep this question in mind: **What are the roots of American government?**

► Use these graphic organizers to record key information from the section. Some information has been filled in to get you started.

Ancient Traditions and Their Influence

Place	Religious or Political Tradition	Influential Idea
Middle East	Judaism	
		All people, rich or poor, are ______ in the eyes of God.
Greece	• Direct democracy	• Citizens have public duties, such as serving on ______.
Rome	• • Roman law	• People can elect ______ to rule them. •

What: Magna Carta

When:

Why it's important:
- first document to restrict English king's power
-
-
-

English Parliamentary Traditions

What: Parliament
When:
Why it's important:
- example of a two-house legislature
-
-

What: English Bill of Rights
When:
Why it's important:
Protected basic rights of citizens, such as:
-

Limited monarch's power to:
- raise taxes
-

Refer to this page to answer the Chapter 1 Focus Question on page 15.

Section 2

An Age of Exploration

Section 2 Focus Question

How did European exploration link the Americas to other parts of the world? To begin answering this question,

- Learn about the world in the 1400s.
- Follow European explorers in search of new trade routes.
- Journey with Columbus as he sails to the Americas.
- Discover the impact of the Columbian Exchange.

Section 2 Summary

Trade networks connected Europe, Asia, and Africa. Early American civilizations were isolated from contact with other continents. European explorers sought new trade routes to Asia to bring them wealth. In doing so they reached the Americas, causing great change as different peoples, plants, and animals mixed.

The World in the 1400s

The Americas were cut off from the rest of the world in the 1400s. The Americas were home to two powerful civilizations. In present-day Mexico, the Aztecs built a great empire and ruled millions of people. The Incas built a mighty empire in South America. Other peoples formed smaller societies with ways of life based on their local environments. For example, on the Great Plains groups of hunters followed herds of buffalo.

The rise of the religion of Islam in the Middle East in the 600s helped connect Africa and Asia through conquest and trade. The trade route stretching from China to the Middle East was called the Silk Road. The Chinese also briefly explored the South China Sea and the Indian Ocean.

In West Africa, the Muslim empire of Songhai was the chief trading power. Traders traveled across the Sahara, the world's largest desert. Trade also enriched East Africa. ✓

Europe Begins to Explore

In the early Middle Ages, most of Europe had been isolated. Then, about 1100, Europeans began a series of Crusades. These were religious wars intended to recapture the Holy Land of the Middle East from Muslim control. After 200 years of war, the Crusades failed. But the contact with the Middle East had increased European interest in trade. In the 1300s Europeans rediscovered many Greek and Roman ideas. Europe also made new advances in art, medicine, and science. The printing press helped spread these ideas. Historians call this period of expanding knowledge the Renaissance (REHN uh sahns). Europeans also gained new tools

Key Events

1215 Magna Carta places limits on the power of English monarchs.

1492 Christopher Columbus reaches the Caribbean, bringing Europe and the Americas into contact.

1620 Pilgrims sign the Mayflower Compact.

✓ Checkpoint

Name two great empires that arose in the Americas.

____

____

Vocabulary Builder

The word *renaissance* means "rebirth." Why do you think this period in European history was called a rebirth?

____

____

____

from Muslim sailors, such as the compass and the astrolabe. These helped sailors navigate on the ocean.

Strong rulers emerged in England, France, Spain, and Portugal. They wanted to increase their wealth by trading with the lands in Asia. But Muslim and Italian merchants controlled existing trade routes. If they wanted a share of the trade, these rulers would have to find a new route to Asia. Prince Henry of Portugal hired **cartographers**, or map makers, to make more accurate maps and sea charts. He also had new, faster ships called caravels built. In 1497 Vasco da Gama sailed around Africa to India, giving Portugal a new route to Asian riches. ✓

✓ Checkpoint

List two tools Europeans got from Muslim sailors.

____

____

Columbus Reaches the Americas

In 1492, the Italian-born sailor **Christopher Columbus** led a Spanish expedition west across the Atlantic Ocean. Columbus hoped to reach Asia, but his three ships actually landed on an island off the coast of North America. Thinking he was in the East Indies, Columbus called the native people he met Indians. Europeans later realized that Columbus had not reached Asia, but new lands. They called the new lands the Americas. Columbus made three more voyages to the Americas. He founded a **colony**, a group of people who settle in a new place but are ruled by the government of their homeland. Later, the Spanish conquered the Aztec and Inca empires. ✓

✓ Checkpoint

Where did Columbus think he had landed when he reached the Americas?

____

The Columbian Exchange

The voyages of Columbus led to an exchange of people, ideas, plants, and animals between Europe, Africa, Asia, and the Americas. This Columbian Exchange had good and bad effects. American crops such as corn, potatoes, tomatoes, and tobacco became popular in Europe. The Americas received new animals such as cattle, chickens, horses, and pigs. But huge numbers of Native Americans were killed by European diseases like smallpox and influenza. The Spanish also enslaved Native Americans and Africans to work on **plantations**, large farms with many workers. An estimated 10 million Africans were captured and brought to the Americas as part of this terrible slave trade. ✓

✓ Checkpoint

List three food crops that were brought to Europe as part of the Columbian Exchange.

____

____

____

Check Your Progress

1. How did trade encourage European exploration?

____

____

2. How did the Columbian Exchange contribute to the rise of the slave trade?

____

____

Section 2 Notetaking Study Guide

Question to Think About As you read Section 2 in your textbook and take notes, keep this focus question in mind: **How did European exploration link the Americas to the other parts of the world?**

► Use these charts to record key information from the section.

The Americas in the 1400s

Civilization	Where	Why It Was Important
Aztec		• a great empire that ruled millions of people from the ______________ to the ______________
Inca		• empire stretched for almost ____________ miles

Expansion and Trade

Term or Event	What It Was	Why It Was Important
Silk Road		
Spread of Islam across Southwest Asia, North Africa, into Europe		
	European attempts to recapture the Holy Land	
Renaissance		led to spread of knowledge and interest in new discoveries

Explorers

Name	Country	Achievement
Zheng He		Explored Indian Ocean and South China Sea
		Discovered a water route from Europe to Asia by sailing around the southern tip of Africa.
Columbus	Spain	

The Columbian Exchange

To Europe, Africa, and Asia	To the Americas
Crops such as: • tobacco • • •	• Animals: cattle, ______________, ______________, and ______________ • Diseases: ______________ and ______________ • Slaves from ______________

Refer to this page to answer the Chapter 1 Focus Question on page 15.

Section 3

Commerce and Colonies

Section 3 Focus Question

What chain of events led to the founding of the early colonies and their experiments with self-government? To begin answering this question,

- Find out about economic changes in Europe.
- See how Europeans began rivalries in North America.
- Learn about Virginia, England's first colony.
- Discover how the Pilgrims founded Plymouth colony.

Key Events

1215 Magna Carta places limits on the power of English monarchs.

1492 Christopher Columbus reaches the Caribbean, bringing Europe and the Americas into contact.

1620 Pilgrims sign the Mayflower Compact.

Section 3 Summary

Economic changes in Europe encouraged more exploration and trade, leading European nations to set up competing colonies in North America. England's first successful colonies in North America were Virginia and Plymouth.

Economic Changes in Europe

As Europe grew, trade became a key source of wealth. More trade meant a greater need for money to make exchanging goods easier. Banks loaned money to businesses, profiting by charging **interest**, a percentage of money paid back in addition to the original amount of the loan. Bold merchants developed new ways to increase their profits. They began cooperating to put their money into large projects. That way they could share the risks as well as the profits. This economic system of people putting money into businesses or projects to make a profit is called **capitalism**. Today, capitalism is the dominant economic system in the United States and around the world.

Capitalism encouraged exploration. By founding colonies, countries gained new sources of raw materials and places to sell their goods. This fit into the policy of **mercantilism** adopted by many European rulers. Mercantilism was an economic policy which held that a nation's wealth was measured by its supply of gold and silver. ✓

✓ Checkpoint

Name the basis of a country's wealth in a mercantile economy.

____

Colonizing North America

Spain's American colonies provided it with great wealth. This encouraged nations such as England, France, and the Netherlands to seek their own trade routes and colonies. Explorers such as John Cabot, Jacques Cartier, and Henry Hudson searched unsuccessfully for a **northwest passage**, or a water route past North America. But their voyages paved the way for new colonies. In the early 1600s, France founded New France in present-day Canada. By the 1700s the colony reached all the way from Quebec to Louisiana. The Dutch set up their New Netherland colony on

Manhattan Island on the Hudson River. The first English colonists settled on Roanoke Island, near what is now North Carolina, in 1585. But after a few years, this "Lost Colony" vanished. ✓

✓ Checkpoint

Name three explorers who searched for a northwest passage.

____

____

____

The Jamestown Colony

England's first successful American colony was founded in 1607 on the James River in Virginia. The Virginia Company set up this Jamestown Colony under the rights given to the Company by a royal **charter**, or official document that grants certain rights. The colony was established on swampy land, and settlers struggled to feed themselves. But Captain John Smith took command and put the colonists to work. Eventually, the Virginia colonists were able to make money by growing and exporting tobacco.

In 1619, the Virginia Company let male colonists vote for representatives to an assembly. Called the House of Burgesses, this group was the first **representative government** in the English colonies. This practice of voters electing representatives to make laws for them goes back to the Roman Republic. ✓

✓ Checkpoint

Name the work the Virginia colonists first did to make money.

____

____

The Plymouth Colony

England's second American colony was founded by a group of Protestants called the Pilgrims. The Pilgrims wanted the freedom to practice their religion without interference from the Church of England. In 1620 a group of Pilgrims and other settlers set sail for Virginia on board the *Mayflower*. Blown off course, they landed on the coast of what is now Massachusetts. The Pilgrims wanted to stay, but they had no charter for a colony so far north. So the 41 male colonists signed the Mayflower Compact, a set of rules to govern their colony.

The Pilgrims named their colony Plymouth. With the help of Native Americans, the colonists survived a harsh winter. They created a representative government with an elected council that made laws for the colony. These laws included rules on how to worship. This was not **religious freedom**, or the right of all individuals to follow their own religious beliefs. Over time, freedom of religion became a key principle of American democracy. ✓

Vocabulary Builder

The term *Pilgrim* was first used by William Bradford to describe the English Protestants who wanted to separate from the Church of England. The word *pilgrim*, which means "one who travels to foreign lands," can also be applied to this group.

✓ Checkpoint

What was the Mayflower Compact?

____

____

____

Check Your Progress

1. How did capitalism encourage colonization and exploration?

____

____

____

2. Give two examples of representative government in the English colonies.

____

____

____

Section 3 Notetaking Study Guide

Question to Think About As you read Section 3 in your textbook and take notes, keep this question in mind: **What chain of events led to the founding of the early colonies and their experiments with self-government?**

► Use this graphic organizer to record key details. Some information has been filled in to get you started.

Commerce and Colonies

Economic Changes in Europe

- increase in trade
- rise of ____________, an economic system in which people invest money in projects and businesses to make ___a profit___.
- rise of mercantilism, an economic policy that argues ____.

French And Dutch Colonies

- France, the Netherlands, and England all search unsuccessfully for ____________.
- France creates ___the colony of New France___ in what is now ____________. First settlements are in 1605 and 1608. The French eventually settle as far south as ____________.
- In 1626 the ____________ form the colony ____________ on Manhattan Island.

English Colonies

- The ____________ colony is founded in Virginia in 1585 but fails.
- The Jamestown colony is founded in ____________ in the year ____________ and succeeds after colonists begin to grow and export ____________.
- Government: Virginia creates the ____________, the first example of representative government in the English colonies.
- In 1620, the Pilgrims, who want freedom to ____________, found the ____________ after they are blown off course.
- Government: The Pilgrims sign ___Mayflower Compact___, agreeing to create a form of ____________ for their colony.

Refer to this page to answer the Chapter 1 Focus Question on page 15.

Section 4

The 13 English Colonies

Section 4 Focus Question

How did the thirteen colonies develop economies based on agriculture, commerce, and handmade goods? To begin answering this question,

- Learn about life in the New England colonies.
- Find out how the Middle Colonies were started.
- Learn about the economy and society of the Southern colonies.
- Discover how colonial trade worked.

Section 4 Summary

By 1732, England had 13 colonies in North America. These colonies were divided into three regions: New England, the Middle Colonies, and the Southern Colonies. Each region had a unique economy and society.

The New England Colonies

Massachusetts, Rhode Island, Connecticut, and New Hampshire made up the New England Colonies. English Protestants called Puritans founded Massachusetts. The Puritans were very strict about the practice of religion, and several settlers left to found their own colonies. Roger Williams founded Rhode Island, and Minister Thomas Hooker founded Connecticut. New Hampshire was founded by colonists looking for better farmland.

New England had a cold climate with rugged land and rocky soil. Farms were small and most people practiced **subsistence farming**, growing only enough to feed themselves. But fish and forests were abundant, allowing many colonists to make a living fishing or working in shipbuilding and trade. ✓

The Middle Colonies

The Middle Colonies—New York, New Jersey, Delaware, and Pennsylvania—lay between New England and Virginia. The English took over the Dutch colony of New Netherland in 1664 and renamed it New York. William Penn founded Pennsylvania in 1682. Penn was a Quaker, a member of a Protestant group that opposed war and supported equality and religious freedom. The colonies of New Jersey and Delaware split off from New York and Pennsylvania, respectively.

The Middle Colonies had good land and a mild climate. This led to bigger farms that produced **cash crops**, or crops grown to be sold for profit. The Middle Colonies also developed a variety of crafts and industries. ✓

Key Events

1215 Magna Carta places limits on the power of English monarchs.

1492 Christopher Columbus reaches the Caribbean, bringing Europe and the Americas into contact.

1620 Pilgrims sign the Mayflower Compact.

✓ Checkpoint

List the New England Colonies.

____

____

____

____

Vocabulary Builder

What is the difference between cash crops and subsistence-farming crops?

____

____

____

✓ Checkpoint

List the Middle Colonies.

____

____

____

____

The Southern Colonies

The Southern Colonies included Virginia, Maryland, North Carolina, South Carolina, and Georgia. Maryland was formed in 1634 as a colony for English Catholics. Maryland's assembly passed the Act of Toleration, which gave religious freedom to all Christians. The colony of Carolina was created by a group of proprietors in 1663 and was later split into North and South Carolina. James Oglethorpe founded Georgia as a place for **debtors**, people who could not pay their debts, to start a new life.

The South had a warm climate and huge plantations that grew cash crops like tobacco and rice. Enslaved Africans did most of the plantation work. Slaves had almost no rights. Farther inland, on the eastern side of the Appalachian Mountains, settlers cleared their own land and lived by subsistence farming. ✓

✓ Checkpoint

List the Southern Colonies.

____

____

____

____

____

Colonial Trade

American merchants in the colonies developed many trade routes. One route went up and down the Atlantic coast. A second route carried goods across the Atlantic to England. A third route, known as the triangular trade, linked the colonies to the Caribbean and Africa. New England slave ships carried captive Africans to the West Indies.

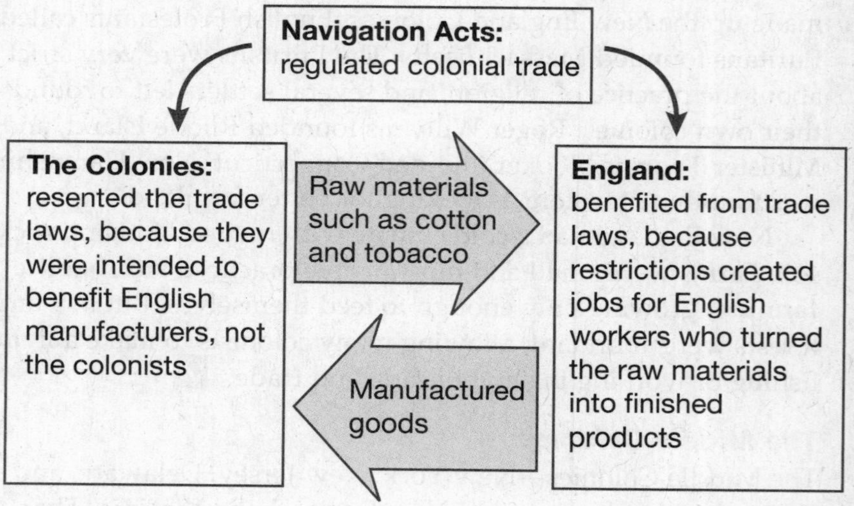

Navigation Acts:
regulated colonial trade
The Colonies:
resented the trade laws, because they were intended to benefit English manufacturers, not the colonists
Raw materials such as cotton and tobacco
Manufactured goods
England:
benefited from trade laws, because restrictions created jobs for English workers who turned the raw materials into finished products

✓

✓ Checkpoint

Name the trade that took place between Africa, the Colonies, and the Caribbean.

____

Check Your Progress

1. What types of farming were practiced in New England, the Middle Colonies, and the Southern Colonies?

____

____

____

2. What was the purpose of the Navigation Acts?

____

____

Section 4 Notetaking Study Guide

Question to Think About As you read Section 4 in your textbook and take notes, keep this question in mind: **How did the thirteen colonies develop economies based on agriculture, commerce, and handmade goods?**

▶ Use this chart to record key information from the section. Some information has been filled in to get you started.

The 13 English Colonies

Region	Colony	Reason for Founding or How Founded	Economy of Region
New England	Massachusetts		
		• better farmland •	• •
		• •	• • shipbuilding
		religious freedom	
Middle Colonies			• large farms: grew ________
	New Jersey	• •	• a variety of ________ ________
		• • religious and political freedom	
	Delaware		
Southern Colonies		• profit from land sale •	• plantation farming: produced ________; dependent on ________ ________
		• •	• small farms: engaged in
	North Carolina	• •	
		• •	
	Georgia	• •	

Refer to this page to answer the Chapter 1 Focus Question on page 15.

Chapter 1 Assessment

Directions: Circle the letter of the correct answer.

1. Which of the following systems of government come from the Greco-Roman tradition?
   - **A** monarchy and anarchy
   - **B** direct democracy and republic
   - **C** communism and socialism
   - **D** feudalism and Renaissance

2. Which of the following words refers to an economic system in which people put money into businesses or projects to make profits?
   - **A** capitalism
   - **B** republicanism
   - **C** mercantilism
   - **D** subsistence

3. What document did the Pilgrims sign in 1620?
   - **A** The Magna Carta
   - **B** The Mayflower Compact
   - **C** The English Bill of Rights
   - **D** The Act of Toleration

4. Which colonial region had an economy that depended on plantations, cash crops, and slave labor?
   - **A** New England
   - **B** The Middle Colonies
   - **C** The Southern Colonies
   - **D** New France

Directions: Follow the steps to complete this task:

Compare the governments of the first two English colonies in America.

Step 1: Recall information: Record the reasons why each colony was founded.

	Jamestown Colony	Plymouth Colony
Why founded		

Step 2: Compare how the foundings of the two colonies were alike and how they were different.

How They Were Alike	How They Were Different

Step 3: Complete the topic sentence that follows. Then write two or three more sentences that support your topic sentence.

The reasons why Jamestown and Plymouth were founded influenced each colony's government ____

____

____

____

Chapter 1 Notetaking Study Guide

Now you are ready to answer the Chapter 1 Focus Question: **How did the American colonists establish their own way of life with strong roots in the past?**

► Complete the following charts to help you answer this question.

Roots of Democratic Government

Judeo-Christian Tradition	Greco-Roman Tradition	English Parliamentary Tradition
• Judaism taught that even the most powerful ruler was subject to ______. • Christianity became the official religion of the ______. • taught that all people were ______	• A republic is ______ ______. • Juries are ______ ______.	• The Magna Carta was the first document to ______ ______. • Parliament is ______ ______. • The English Bill of Rights was ______ ______.

Commerce and Colonies

During the 1400s, Europe began to explore, encouraged by the growth of capitalism, which is ______.
Colonies were important to the theories of capitalism and ______ because they provided sources of ______ and a place to ______.

The Thirteen Colonies

	New England Colonies	Middle Colonies	Southern Colonies
Forms of government	Representative government, as colonists had agreed in the ______	The English took over the Dutch colony of ______.	Jamestown had a ______ ______.
Religious ties	A group of English Protestants called ______ founded the Massachusetts Bay Colony.	Pennsylvania became a model of ______.	Maryland was established as a ______ ______; assembly adopted the ______.
Economy	subsistence farming, ______, ______	______ farms, crafts, ______	______ farming, ______ labor

Refer to this page to answer the Unit 1 Focus Question on page 31.

Chapter Standards

History-Social Science 7.11.4, 7.11.5, 7.11.6, 8.1.1, 8.1.2, 8.1.3, 8.1.4, 8.3.7

Chapter 2

From Colonies to Nation (1680–1783)

What You Will Learn

American colonists developed traditions of self-government, freedom of religion, and freedom of the press.

Chapter 2 Focus Question

As you read through this chapter, keep this question in mind: **How did the growth of democratic ideals in the colonies lead to the American Revolution?**

Section 1

A Tradition of Liberty

Section 1 Focus Question

How did the traditions of liberty take hold in the colonies? To begin answering this question,

- Find out how the colonies became self-governing.
- Understand the significance of the Great Awakening.
- Learn about the importance of freedom of the press.

Key Events

1735	John Peter Zenger found not guilty of libel.
1776	Americans declare independence from Britain.
1783	American Revolution ends with the signing of the Treaty of Paris.

Section 1 Summary

Self-government in colonial America was strengthened by religious ideals and freedom of the press.

Self-Government in the Colonies

American colonists were subjects of the British monarch who were expected to obey English law. However, the distance separating Britain from North America made it hard for England to govern its colonies. As a result, the early English colonists set up forms of self-government. The Jamestown colonists, for example, set up the first colonial legislature. New Englanders developed the **town meeting**, a gathering in which residents meet once a year to make decisions for the community.

A more complex system was needed for governing an entire colony. Each colony had a governor, usually appointed by the king or the proprietor of the colony. Colonies also had their own legislatures to create and pass laws. Most legislatures were made up of two houses: an upper house and a lower house. ✓

Vocabulary Builder

A proprietor is an owner of a business or a colony. The word is closely related to the word *property*.

✓ Checkpoint

Name a form of self-government used in New England.

____

The Great Awakening

Religion had always played an important role in the 13 English colonies. However, by the 1700s the Puritan tradition was declining in New England. Still, churches were centers of faith and community life.

A passionate Christian movement swept through the colonies in the 1730s and 1740s. This period of religious revival is called the Great Awakening. It was a response to the belief that religion was becoming less important in colonial life.

Massachusetts preacher **Jonathan Edwards** called on people to commit themselves to God or risk being "sinners in the hands of an angry God." Other forceful preachers quickly spread the ideas of the Great Awakening throughout the colonies. One such speaker, the English minister George Whitefield, held outdoor meetings from Georgia to Massachusetts. The huge crowds who came to listen to his sermons heard him call on all sinners to reform.

The Great Awakening led to the rise of many new organized churches. This development led to increased tolerance of religious differences. The Great Awakening was also one of the first movements to involve people in many American colonies. It affected the way people viewed their political rights, because they realized that if they could decide how to worship God, they could also decide how to govern themselves. ✓

✓ Checkpoint

Name the Massachusetts preacher who was a major figure of the Great Awakening.

___

Freedom of the Press

In 1734, an important court case helped establish the right to a free press. **Freedom of the press** is the right of newspapers and other public media to publish articles believed to be accurate.

Printing presses had been established throughout the colonies, leading to the emergence of many publications. Newspapers, for example, began to appear in the early 1700s. Benjamin Franklin had established *Poor Richard's Almanac* during this period. Then in 1734, **John Peter Zenger**, publisher of the *Weekly Journal* in New York City, was arrested for printing articles that showed the governor in a bad light. Zenger was charged with **libel**, the publishing of statements that unjustly damage a person's reputation.

Zenger's trial was a sensation. His lawyers proved that the statements he published were true. Therefore, Zenger could not be convicted of libel. The case helped establish that a democracy depends on well-informed citizens, and that the press has a right and responsibility to inform the public of the truth. Today, freedom of the press is considered to be one of the most important American liberties. ✓

✓ Checkpoint

Why was John Peter Zenger arrested?

___

___

Check Your Progress

1. How did the Great Awakening influence people's political views?

___

___

2. What principle did the Zenger case establish?

___

___

Section 1 Notetaking Study Guide

Question to Think About As you read Section 1 in your textbook and take notes, keep this section focus question in mind: **How did the traditions of liberty take hold in the American Revolution?**

▶ Use this chart to record key information from the section. Some of the information has been filled in to get you started.

Moving Toward Liberty

Self-Government	Freedom of Religion	Freedom of the Press
Situation: Colonists subject to British rule, but everyday decisions in each town couldn't be addressed quickly enough by London. **Response:** Colonists developed the ________/________. Villagers gathered to ______ and ______ local issues.	**Situation:** The Great Awakening movement in 1730s and 1740s led to many new organized churches. **Response:** ________________	**Situation:** John Zenger printed articles showing the governor in a negative light. **Response:** Zenger was charged with ________ and put on trial.
Situation: A more complex system of government was needed for each colony as a whole. **Response:** Colonists created ____________ to make laws. Each colony set its own ____________ for electing representatives.	**Situation:** The Great Awakening showed people that they could decide for themselves how to worship God. **Response:** ________________	**Situation:** Zenger wins his case. **Response:** The principle was established that a ____________ depends on well-informed ____________, so the press has a right and ____________ to keep the public informed of the ____________. This right is known as ____________.

Refer to this page to answer the Chapter 2 Focus Question on page 30.

Section 2

Impact of the Enlightenment

Section 2 Focus Question

How did the Enlightenment affect people's ideas about government? To begin answering this question,

- Discover the roots of the Enlightenment.
- Learn how reason was applied to politics.
- Find out about the spread of Enlightenment ideas.

Section 2 Summary

The Enlightenment and the Scientific Revolution had a huge impact on the American colonies.

Roots of the Enlightenment

Starting in the late 1600s, a group of European thinkers came to believe that all problems could be solved by human reason. These thinkers called themselves **enlightened**, or free from the superstitions and ignorance of the Middle Ages. For this reason, this period of European history is called the Enlightenment.

During the Middle Ages, Christian leaders had taught that the individual was less important than the salvation of the soul. Renaissance thinkers emphasized the individual, using the ideas of ancient Greece and Rome to increase their understanding. Enlightenment focused on the reasoning power of the individual.

The most important influence on the Enlightenment was the Scientific Revolution. During the 1500s, European scientists used reason, observation, and experimentation to learn about the physical world.

Astronomers such as Copernicus and Galileo used careful observation and math to argue that the sun was at the center of the solar system. According to them, Earth revolved around the sun. Isaac Newton's later work supported the theory that everything in the physical world follows unchanging natural laws. All motion, Newton argued, could be measured and described mathematically. Such ideas had a great influence on the Enlightenment. Enlightenment thinkers tried to use reason to find natural laws that governed politics, society, and economics. ✓

Applying Reason to Politics

During the Enlightenment, almost every European country was ruled by an **absolute monarch**, a ruler with complete control over government and people. Monarchs claimed that they ruled by **divine right**, or the belief that the ruler's authority comes directly from God. Whatever rights people had were given to them by the monarch.

In 1690, the English philosopher **John Locke** proposed that people have certain **natural rights**, that is, rights that belong to

Key Events

1735	John Peter Zenger found not guilty of libel.
1776	Americans declare independence from Britain.
1783	American Revolution ends with the signing of the Treaty of Paris.

✓ Checkpoint

Name the most important influence on the Enlightenment.

____

Vocabulary Builder

To *violate* is to break or disregard. What is the noun form of this verb?

____

✓ Checkpoint

List the three natural rights according to John Locke.

____

____

____

✓ Checkpoint

Name two of Benjamin Franklin's inventions.

____

____

every human being from birth. These rights include life, liberty, and property. This view challenged the theory of divine right. According to Locke, rights did not come to the people from their king; their rights came directly from God. Locke further argued that people created governments to protect those rights. Finally, he concluded that if a monarch violates these rights, people are entitled to overthrow the monarch.

A French philosopher, the **Baron de Montesquieu** (MON tehs kyoo), also challenged the idea of divine right. In his 1748 book *The Spirit of the Laws*, Montesquieu argued that the powers of government should be clearly defined and limited. He favored **separation of powers**, or the division of the power of government into separate branches. He believed that separation of powers protected the rights of people because it kept any individual or group from gaining too much power. Montesquieu suggested that government should be divided into three branches: a legislative branch to make laws, an executive branch to enforce the laws, and a judicial branch to make judgments based on the laws. This division of power would become the basis of the modern United States government. ✓

Enlightenment Ideas Spread

The ideas of the Enlightenment spread throughout Europe and eventually reached the 13 English colonies in North America. By the 1770s, most educated colonists believed they had natural rights. This belief set the stage for conflict with the English government.

Among the colonists, **Benjamin Franklin** was the best example of the Enlightenment spirit. A successful printer in Philadelphia, Franklin studied literature, math, science, and philosophy. Among his accomplishments were several inventions, such as a lightning rod and bifocal glasses. The first lending library in the colonies was founded largely due to his efforts. Franklin supported Enlightenment ideas on human liberty, and he founded one of the first antislavery societies in the colonies. Later, he would become a leading voice in favor of independence from England. ✓

Check Your Progress

1. How did Montesquieu's idea of government influence the modern United States government?

____

____

____

2. What was the result of the spread of the belief in natural rights to the English colonies?

____

____

Section 2 Notetaking Study Guide

Question to Think About As you read Section 2 in your textbook and take notes, keep this section focus question in mind: **How did the Enlightenment affect people's ideas about government?**

▶ Use these charts to record key information from the section. Some of the information has been filled in to get you started.

Roots of the Enlightenment

1. The ______________ placed new emphasis on the individual. During the Scientific Revolution, what did scientists use to gain knowledge of the physical world? reason, observation, experiments
2. Astronomers __________ and __________ argued that the sun was at the center of the solar system.
3. What were Isaac Newton's discoveries?
   - gravity: ______________________________
   - physical world: ______________________________

↓

Political Thinking

1. John Locke's "natural rights": _____, _____, and _____
2. How did natural rights challenge the theory of divine right?
   - Rights did not come to the people from the _____, but directly from _____.
3. Locke concluded that if a monarch violates these rights, people are entitled to ______________________________.
4. Baron de Montesquieu
   - favored the ______________ of government.
   - suggested that government be divided into three branches: __________, __________, and _____.

↓

Enlightenment Ideas in the Colonies

1. Locke's ideas: Most educated colonists accepted the idea of natural rights.
2. Benjamin Franklin:
   - best example of ______________________________
   - supported Enlightenment ideas on ______________________________

Refer to this page to answer the Chapter 2 Focus Question on page 30.

Section 3
Declaring Independence

Key Events

1735 John Peter Zenger found not guilty of libel.

1776 Americans declare independence from Britain.

1783 American Revolution ends with the signing of the Treaty of Paris.

Section 3 Focus Question

How did *Common Sense* and the Declaration of Independence draw on British traditions and Enlightenment thinkers? To begin answering this question,

- Learn how taxation led to protest.
- Explore how protest led to revolution.
- Learn about the debate over independence.
- Analyze the Declaration of Independence.

Section 3 Summary

Conflict over taxation grew in the 1760s and 1770s, until at last war broke out between Britain and the colonies.

Taxation Leads to Protests

Tensions between Britain and the colonists grew after Britain passed the Stamp Act of 1765. Colonial newspapers, legal documents, and many other printed materials had to be stamped to show a tax was paid.

Most colonists strongly objected to the Stamp Act. Their objections were based on British Parliamentary traditions. Since the colonists did not elect representatives to the British Parliament, many felt Parliament had no right to tax them. Opponents of the Stamp Act took up the slogan, "No taxation without representation." Many colonists boycotted British goods. As a result, the Stamp Act was repealed in 1766.

Some angry colonists began calling themselves Patriots. One night in 1770, a fight led British soldiers to fire into a group of colonists armed with clubs. Five colonists were killed in what colonists called "the Boston Massacre." ✓

From Protest to Revolution

By 1773, many colonists were unhappy about British control of the colonial tea trade. In the incident known as the Boston Tea Party, Patriots raided British merchant ships and dumped 342 chests of tea overboard. In response, Parliament passed the "Intolerable Acts." One act closed Boston's port to most shipping. Another took away many of Massachusetts' rights to self-rule. In response, colonists held the first Continental Congress, at which representatives from all the colonies except Georgia agreed not to buy British goods.

In Massachusetts, Patriots formed groups of young soldiers ready to assemble quickly. They were known as **minutemen**. On April 18, 1775, about 700 British soldiers met a group of minutemen in the battles of Lexington and Concord. The British suffered a costly defeat, and the American Revolution began. ✓

✓ Checkpoint

List two products affected by the Stamp Act.

____

____

Vocabulary Builder

Based on context clues, define the word *intolerable*.

____

____

✓ Checkpoint

Name one of the provisions of the "Intolerable Acts."

____

Debate Over Independence

In January 1776, **Thomas Paine** published a best-selling pamphlet called *Common Sense*. In forceful, everyday language, Paine made the case for independence. He argued that King George III was "an enemy to liberty." Paine concluded that "common sense" led to one conclusion: separation. Paine's logic and powerful words swayed more colonists to support independence.

Slowly, delegates to the Continental Congress accepted the idea of separation. Thomas Jefferson drafted a document that outlined the reasons for breaking with Britain. Congress changed some words but kept his most important ideas. On July 4, 1776, the Congress adopted the Declaration of Independence. ✓

The Declaration of Independence

In the Declaration of Independence, Thomas Jefferson carefully explained why the Americans wanted independence.

Declaration of Independence

	Purpose	Foundation
Preamble: ***Introduction***	explains goals of the Declaration	Enlightenment: Natural laws govern society; these laws come to people directly from God.
Natural Rights: ***First section***	states general ideas about society and government	Locke: Governments are created to protect people's rights; people have a right to reject a government that fails to do so.
Grievances (formal complaints): ***Second section***	provides a list of complaints against King George	Magna Carta: Trial by jury is a basic right; the King must not impose taxes without the consent of the people.
Conclusion	announces creation of a new, independent nation	Many colonists supported separation from Britain.

✓

Check Your Progress

1. How did Parliament react to the Boston Tea Party?

___

2. How did Thomas Paine contribute to the cause of independence?

___

___

✓ Checkpoint

Name the pamphlet that convinced many colonists to support independence.

___

✓ Checkpoint

Which part of the Declaration of Independence explains the document's goals?

___

Section 3 Notetaking Study Guide

Question to Think About As you read Section 3 in your textbook and take notes, keep this question in mind: **How did *Common Sense* and the Declaration of Independence draw on British traditions and Enlightenment thinkers?**

► Use this chart to record key information from the section. Some of the information has been filled in to get you started.

American Anger Leads to Independence	
1765	Britain passed the ____________, which put a tax on ____________, legal documents, and other items. Since colonists did not elect ____________ to Parliament, they took up the slogan, "No ____________ without ____________." Colonists began to ____________ British goods. Finally Parliament canceled the ____________.
1770	British troops fired on a crowd of colonists, killing five. This was called the ____________. Patriots formed "____________ of ____________" to inform one another of local events.
1773	A group of Patriots raided British ____________ in Boston harbor, and they destroyed chests of tea. This became known as the ____________. In response, ____________ passed harsh new laws to punish Massachusetts. Patriots called these the ____________.
1774	Colonists organized the ____________, which included representatives of all the colonies except Georgia. They met in ____________ and agreed not to buy British goods.
1775	British troops marched from Boston to ____________, where they were confronted by several dozen ____________. Shooting broke out. The British moved on to ____________, where fighting continued. The British took heavy losses. Fighting soon spread.
January 1776	Thomas ____________ published a pamphlet called ____________. It convinced many colonists to support ____________.
June 1776	A ____________ was formed to write a document outlining the reasons for separating from Britain. Most of the writing was done by ____________.
July 1776	The Continental ____________ adopted the ____________ of ____________.

Refer to this page to answer the Chapter 2 Focus Question on page 30.

Declaration of Independence Notetaking Study Guide

Question to Think About As you read the Declaration of Independence in your textbook and take notes, keep this question in mind: **How does the Declaration of Independence support the colonists' claim to independence?**

► Use this chart to record key information from the Declaration of Independence. Some of the information has been filled in to get you started.

The Declaration of Independence		
Part 1: Preamble	Purpose: to state why the Declaration of Independence was written	What it says the document will do: explain the reasons that impel the colonists to separate from Great Britain
Part 2: Declaration of Natural Rights	What it says about: Men: • ________ • have the right to ______, ______, and the ______ Role of government: ________ ________ Role of people when their government doesn't protect their rights: ________ ________	
Part 3: List of Grievances	Purpose: ________ ________ ________ ________ ________	Main Ideas: 1. The British government allows colonists no say in determining ______. 2. King George's actions show little or no ______ ______
Part 4: Resolution of Independence	Purpose: ________ ________ ________ ________	Powers of free and independent states: • wage war and make peace • ________ • ________

Section 4
A New Nation

Key Events

1735	John Peter Zenger found not guilty of libel.
1776	Americans declare independence from Britain.
1783	American Revolution ends with the signing of the Treaty of Paris.

Section 4 Focus Question

How did Americans win their independence? To begin answering this question,

- Learn about the fighting in the Middle Colonies.
- Discover why Saratoga was a turning point.
- Explore the long road to victory.
- Learn about the aftermath of the Revolution.

Section 4 Summary

When the Revolutionary War began, many people felt the Americans had no chance of victory. But when the fighting ended, Americans had created a new nation.

Fighting in the Middle Colonies

Not all colonists wanted independence from Britain. **Loyalists**, or people who remained loyal to Britain, believed that the safety and economic success of the colonies depended on their connection with Britain. They also felt that Britain was too powerful to be defeated. Perhaps a third of colonists were Loyalists. Another third were Patriots, and the rest were uncommitted.

By March 1776, the British had abandoned Boston. Fighting shifted to the Middle Colonies.

The Continental Army was poorly trained and disorganized. It was made up of volunteers who often left their ranks to help out back home. Congress was slow in supplying money for the war.

Meanwhile, the British army and navy were made up of paid professionals with the latest equipment. The British had support from many Native Americans. The British also hired German **mercenaries**, or soldiers who fight because they are paid to, not because they believe in the cause.

The British defeated Washington's army in August 1776; New York City and Long Island were lost. Washington and the Continentals retreated to New Jersey, then into Pennsylvania. The Americans seemed almost beaten.

On the night of December 25, 1776, Washington's army crossed the icy Delaware River back into New Jersey. They marched through a snowstorm to surprise and capture a group of German mercenaries at Trenton. The Continental Army won another victory at Princeton, New Jersey, a few weeks later. These victories boosted Patriot spirits. ✓

Saratoga: A Turning Point

In late summer 1777, the British army set out to attack Albany, New York, from the south, west, and north. Victory would give

Vocabulary Builder

The definition of *mercenary*, the noun, is given in the text. *Mercenary* can also be an adjective. It means greedy, or only interested in money.

✓ Checkpoint

List two problems the Continental Army faced.

____

____

____

____

the British control of the Hudson River. If this happened, Washington's forces would be cut off from New England. They would not be able to get the soldiers and supplies they needed.

The British plan, however, went terribly wrong. On its way to Albany, the western British army was blocked by Patriot forces. The British southern army captured Philadelphia and decided to spend the winter there. That left only the British northern army to fight the Continental Army. At the Battle of Saratoga, the British were outnumbered when hundreds of local militia turned out to help the Continental soldiers. Cut off from retreat by the colonial forces, the British surrendered on October 17, 1777.

The victory at Saratoga was a turning point in the Revolution. It was proof enough of American chances of winning the war to bring France in as an American ally in February 1778. This **alliance**, or agreement between two countries to aid and support each other, was crucially important to the American war effort. Spain also went to war against Britain. ☑

✓ Checkpoint

Name the British unit that fought at Saratoga.

____

Long Road to Victory

Washington's army, camped at Valley Forge, Pennsylvania, suffered through the cold winter of 1777–1778. The Americans lacked food and equipment, but word of their difficulties led many Patriots to send help. By the fall of 1781, the Continental Army had recaptured most of South Carolina. Now the advantage was on the American side. British General Cornwallis moved north to Virginia and set up a base at Yorktown, on the coast, so he could get supplies by sea. However, Washington quickly surrounded Cornwallis on land. At the same time, the French navy cut off his escape by sea. Cornwallis and his army were forced to surrender. ☑

✓ Checkpoint

Why were the British unable to escape from Yorktown by sea?

____

____

Aftermath of the Revolution

The loss of Cornwallis' army made Parliament realize that the Americans could be defeated only at great cost. In 1782, the British and Americans negotiated a treaty to end the war and recognize American independence.

The ideals of the American Revolution inspired people around the world, including the citizens of France. In 1789, the French Revolution began. The American Revolution also inspired many Latin American peoples under Spanish rule. ☑

✓ Checkpoint

Name the European country strongly affected by the American Revolution.

____

Check Your Progress

1. What two early victories in New Jersey boosted the Americans' spirits?

____

2. Why did the French join the American war effort?

____

____

Section 4 Notetaking Study Guide

Question to Think About As you read Section 4 in your textbook and take notes, keep this section focus question in mind: **How did Americans win their independence?**

► Use this graphic organizer to record key information from the section. Some of the information has been filled in to get you started.

The War for Independence

START HERE

1. Loyalists were colonists who __________ __________. It is estimated that one __________ of colonists were Loyalists.

2. The soldiers of the Continental Army were __________ and disorganized. Many felt free to __________. The British army and __________ were well-equipped professionals. Britain also hired German __________.

3. The Continental Army suffered a major defeat on __________, New York, in August 1776. Washington retreated into __________ __________, then into __________. Then Washington scored two victories at the battles of __________ and __________, both in New Jersey.

4. __________ was a turning point in the Revolution. In this battle, only one of three British forces fought. British General __________ was __________. He was forced to surrender. This battle convinced France that __________ __________ __________. It led France to enter into an __________ with the United States.

5. At the Battle of __________, a British army was trapped by land and sea.

6. The Treaty of Paris ended the war and __________. The ideals of the American Revolution helped inspire revolutions in __________ and __________.

Refer to this page to answer the Chapter 2 Focus Question on page 30.

Chapter 2 Assessment

Directions: Circle the letter of the correct answer.

1. Which idea did the Zenger trial help establish?

- **A** The press has a right and responsibility to accurately inform the public.
- **B** The government should be divided into three branches.
- **C** Taxation without representation is not fair.
- **D** Society is governed by unchanging natural laws.

2. How did the Scientific Revolution influence Enlightenment thinking?

- **A** Natural laws could be measured and described.
- **B** If natural laws existed in nature, they must exist in society, too.
- **C** Absolute monarchs provided their people with natural rights.
- **D** Natural rights must be given to scientists so they could do their research.

3. Why did colonists believe they should not have to pay British taxes?

- **A** because they were boycotting British goods
- **B** because the taxes were so high people couldn't afford basics
- **C** because British citizens in England didn't have to pay taxes
- **D** because they had no representatives in Parliament

Directions: Follow the steps to answer this question:

How did Enlightenment theories support the American bid for independence?

Step 1: Recall information: In the chart, briefly describe each theory or idea.

Theory	Main Idea
Divine Right of Kings	
Natural Rights	

Step 2: How did the theory of the divine right of kings support the British government's actions regarding the American colonies?

____

____

____

Step 3: Complete the topic sentence that follows. Then write two or three more sentences that support your topic sentence.

Locke's theory of natural rights set the stage for conflict between the colonists and the British government because ______________________

____

____

____

Chapter 2 Notetaking Study Guide

Now you are ready to answer the Chapter 2 Focus Question: **How did the growth of democratic ideals in the colonies lead to the American Revolution?**

▶ Complete the following chart to help you answer this question. Use the notes that you took for each section.

Thoughts Spark Action: Ideas that Led to the American Revolution

Religious Concepts

The Great Awakening

- was a religious movement that encouraged people to examine their lives and commit themselves to God.
- encouraged people to think that, if they could decide how to worship, they could also decide ________________.
- was one of the first movements to involve people from ________________ ________________.

Enlightenment Concepts

Thinkers tried to use reason to find natural laws that governed politics, society, and economics.

John Locke proposed that people have ________________ that belong to them from birth. He argued that a ruler who does not protect the rights of the people should be ________________.

Colonial Government

- By the 1770s, most educated colonists believed they had ________________.
- The colonies were partially self-governing. Each colony had its own ________________ to make laws. Each colony also had a ________________, either appointed by the king or by the proprietor of the colony.
- In 1735, the ________________ case established the principle of ________________.

British Actions That Led to Colonial Anger

Stamp Act, ________________, ________________ Acts

Anger Led to Revolution

1774: The First Continental ____________ met and agreed not to buy British goods.
1775: The Battles of ________________ and ________________ marked the start of the American Revolution.
1776: The Continental ____________ adopted the ________________ of ________________. This document announced the creation of a new nation.

Refer to this page to answer the Unit 1 Focus Question on page 31.

Unit 1 Pulling It Together Activity

What You Have Learned

Chapter 1 European exploration led to colonization and settlement of the Americas. The 13 British colonies formed governments that were based on traditions of democracy and representative government.

Chapter 2 Tension between the 13 colonies and Britain rose during the mid-1700s. In 1776, the 13 British colonies declared independence from Great Britain and fought a war to win it.

Think Like a Historian

Read the Unit 1 Focus Question: **How did the foundations of the American nation reflect both continuity and change?**

▶ Use the organizers on this page and the next to collect information to answer this question.

What are some examples of continuity reflected in the foundations of the American nation? One of them is listed in this organizer. Review your section and chapter notes. Then complete the organizer.

Religion

- European religions brought to America

Examples of Continuity in the Foundations of the American Nation

Government

-
-

Economy

-

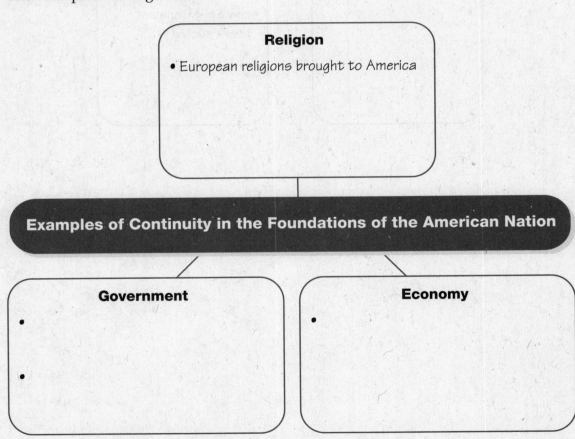

Look at the second part of the Unit Focus Question. It asks about changes that are reflected in the foundations of the American nation. The organizer below gives you a part of the answer. Review your section and chapter notes. Then fill in the rest of the organizer.

Examples of Change in the Foundations of the American Nation

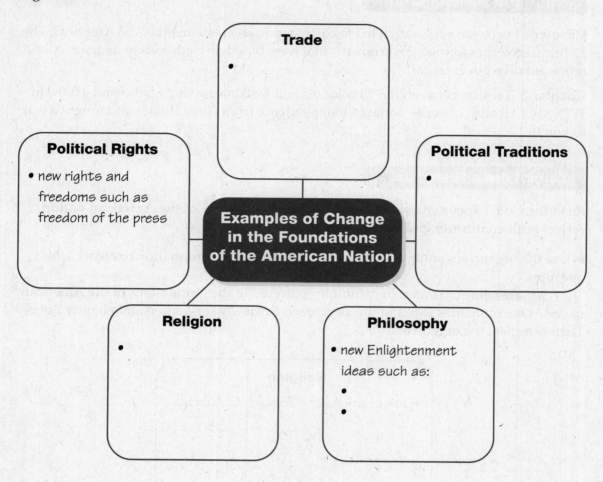

Trade
-

Political Rights
- new rights and freedoms such as freedom of the press

Political Traditions
-

Religion
-

Philosophy
- new Enlightenment ideas such as:
  -
  -

Unit 2

The Constitution of the United States

What You Will Learn

Chapter 3 Delegates from each state met in Philadelphia in 1787 to revise the Articles of Confederation. The delegates decided that the nation needed a stronger federal government.

Citizenship Handbook To be an active citizen, it is important to understand the ideas behind the U.S. Constitution.

Focus Your Learning As you study this unit and take notes, you will find the information to answer the questions below. Answering the Chapter Focus Questions will help build your answer to the Unit Focus Question.

Chapter 3 Focus Question
How did the U.S. Constitution overcome the weaknesses of the Articles of Confederation and provide for the organization of the new government?
(page 34)

Citizenship Handbook Focus Question
How did the Constitution create a strong government with roots in history that allowed for change and met the needs of the people?
(page 47)

Unit 2 Focus Question
What are the roles and responsibilities of governments and citizens?
(page 61)

Chapter Standards

History-Social Science 8.2.2, 8.2.3, 8.2.4, 8.2.6, 8.3.1, 8.3.2, 8.3.5

Chapter 3

Creating the Constitution (1776–1790)

What You Will Learn

Weaknesses in the Articles of Confederation led to the drafting of a new constitution for the nation. After much debate, the states approved the Constitution, but many insisted that a bill of rights be added.

Chapter 3 Focus Question

As you read the section in this chapter, keep this question in mind: **How did the U.S. Constitution overcome the weaknesses of the Articles of Confederation and provide for the organization of the new government?**

Section 1

Governing a New Nation

Section 1 Focus Question

What were major successes and failures of the government under the Articles of Confederation? To begin answering this question,

- Learn about the new state constitutions.
- Learn about the Articles of Confederation.
- Find out about laws for settling new lands in the west.
- Understand the problems of the Articles of Confederation.

Section 1 Summary

Americans created new state and national governments based on the principles of the American Revolution. Problems under the Articles of Confederation led to calls for a stronger national government.

Government by the States

Many of the former colonies wrote new state constitutions. A **constitution** is a document stating the rules under which government will operate. Most states minimized the power of state governors because colonial governors had abused their power. Instead, most power was given to the state legislature, the lawmaking body elected by the people.

The new state constitutions allowed more people to vote. In most states, white men 21 years or older could vote if they owned some property, but women and African Americans were not allowed to vote. Virginia was the first state to have a bill of rights, which is a list of essential freedoms that the government is required to respect. ✓

Key Events

1776	Many new American states write constitutions.
1787	Constitutional Convention creates a new plan of government.
1791	After three fourths of states approve it, the Bill of Rights goes into effect.

✓ Checkpoint

List one characteristic of the new state governments.

____

____

____

The Articles of Confederation

The Continental Congress created the Articles of Confederation in 1777. This plan created a new national government for the United States with restricted powers.

The national government had a single branch, a one-house legislature called Congress, which had the power to pass laws, deal with foreign nations and Native Americans, make war and peace, coin or borrow money, and run a post office. All states were equal, and most power remained in the hands of the states. ✓

Settling the Western Lands

The Land Ordinance of 1785 created a way for national lands to be sold to the public. It divided public western lands into square townships of six miles on each side. This would result in a grid of squares. Within each township there would also be a grid, one mile on each side. Within each township, one section was set aside to support schools. This reflected the belief of the nation's leaders that democracy depended on education.

A law called the Northwest Ordinance of 1787 applied to the territory north of the Ohio River. It guaranteed basic rights to settlers, outlawed slavery, and established a process for creating new states in the territory. ✓

Growing Problems

Under the Articles of Confederation, the United States won its independence, negotiated a peace treaty with Britain, and created rules for settling new territories. There were also problems: trade rivalries and taxation between states hurt the economy, the national government was too weak to stop public unrest, and it had little money because it could not collect taxes.

During the mid-1780s, economic hard times in Massachusetts caused many farmers to lose their land because they could not pay their taxes. In Shays' Rebellion, a group of Massachusetts farmers rose up against the state in protest. The rebellion failed, but it led to calls for a stronger national government. ✓

Check Your Progress

1. Why were the state and national governments' powers limited?

____

____

2. List two problems with the national government under the Articles of Confederation.

____

____

____

✓ Checkpoint

List two powers of the national government created by the Articles of Confederation.

____

____

✓ Checkpoint

Name two laws that related to the settling of Western lands.

____

____

✓ Checkpoint

List two successes of the national government created by the Articles of Confederation.

____

____

____

Section 1 Notetaking Study Guide

Question to Think About As you read Section 1 in your textbook and take notes, keep this section focus question in mind: **What were major successes and failures of the government under the Articles of Confederation?**

► Use these charts to record key information from the section. Some of the information has been filled in to get you started.

Government by the States

Problems the Colonists had with Colonial Government		Main Characteristics of the State Governments
Colonial governors: most colonists were unhappy with the governors appointed by the British crown	Changed in new constitutions →	**State governors:** had ____________ power
Parliament: Parliament, which was part of the central government, exerted power over the elected ____________ legislatures.		**Voting:** ____________ people were allowed to vote
		Individual rights: protected in several states' ____________ of ____________

National Government Under the Articles of Confederation

Main Characteristics

- No executive or ____________ branch of government
- One legislative branch, called ____________, with each state having one vote
- ____________ out of 13 states had to approve laws
- Legislative power limited to:
  -
  -
  -
  -
  -

Strengths

- Won ____________ from Britain and negotiated peace treaty
- The ____________ and the ____________ established rules for settling new lands and creating new states.

Weaknesses

- No authority to regulate ____________ or collect ____________
- Could not protect land from foreign occupation
- Could not stop public unrest as shown in ____________.

Refer to this page to answer the Chapter 3 Focus Question on page 44.

Section 2

The Constitutional Convention

Section 2 Focus Question

What role did compromise play in the creation of the U.S. Constitution? To begin answering this question,

- Learn how the Constitutional Convention began.
- Read about the proposals in the Virginia Plan.
- Find out about the terms of the Great Compromise.
- Learn how slavery issues influenced the Constitution.
- Discover the source of the new Constitution's authority.

Section 2 Summary

By its end, the Constitutional Convention of 1787 had replaced the Articles of Confederation. The new U.S. Constitution created a stronger, more complex national government based on the authority of the people, not the states.

The Constitutional Convention Begins

The Constitutional Convention met in Philadelphia in 1787. At the start, the delegates agreed to hold discussions in secret so that there would be less public pressure. The convention's initial purpose was to revise the Articles of Confederation, but soon its members agreed that revising the Articles was not enough. The delegates representing twelve states needed to organize an entirely new framework of government. George Washington was quickly voted president of the convention. ✓

The Virginia Plan

James Madison wrote the Virginia Plan, which proposed a strong central government with three branches instead of one. The **judicial branch** would consist of a system of courts to settle disputes involving national issues, and an executive branch would carry out the laws. It was agreed that the executive branch would have one chief executive, or president.

Congress would remain the legislative branch. However, the Virginia Plan sought to change Congress. It added a second house and made it so each state would be represented in the two houses based on its population. The more people a state had, the more seats it would have in each house. This idea drew support from big states like Virginia, Pennsylvania, and Massachusetts. ✓

The Great Compromise

States with small populations opposed the changes in the legislative branch and offered their own plan called the New Jersey Plan. It called for a single house of Congress where all the states would have equal representation.

Key Events

1776	Many new American states write constitutions.
1787	Constitutional Convention creates a new plan of government.
1791	After three fourths of states approve it, the Bill of Rights goes into effect.

✓ Checkpoint

Name the location of the Constitutional Convention of 1787.

____

✓ Checkpoint

List the three branches of government proposed in the Virginia Plan.

____

____

____

✓ Checkpoint

List the two houses of Congress that the Great Compromise proposed.

✓ Checkpoint

Name two main issues about slavery that divided the northern and southern states during the Constitutional Convention.

✓ Checkpoint

Name the author of the Preamble to the U.S. Constitution.

The Great Compromise settled the disagreement between the large and small states. A **compromise** is an agreement in which each side gives up part of what it wants. To please the large states, the House of Representatives was developed. Each state's representation in the House would be based on population, and its members would serve two-year terms. In the Senate, which was formed to please the small states, each state would have two senators serving six-year terms.

The Great Compromise was a vital step in creating a new Constitution. Now, small-state delegates were willing to support a strong central government. ✓

Debates Over Slavery

Slavery also divided the convention. The southern states, where there were more slaves, wanted slaves to count toward representation in the House. Northerners argued that slaves, who were not allowed to vote, should not be counted. It was agreed that each slave would count as three fifths of a person. This was called the Three-Fifths Compromise.

The Three-Fifths Compromise was a gain for the South, which got more seats in the House. Northern delegates reluctantly agreed in order to keep the South in the Union.

A second dispute arose when northern delegates called for a total ban on the buying and selling of slaves. A compromise was reached whereby the import of slaves from other countries could be banned in 20 years, while there would be no restrictions on the slave trade within the United States. ✓

A New Constitution

After many more weeks of debate, the delegates agreed on all the terms. A "Committee of Style" wrote the Constitution's final wording. **Gouverneur Morris** was largely responsible for writing the Preamble, or introduction. The Preamble highlights a difference between the Constitution and the Articles of Confederation. The Articles were a pact between separate states. By opening with "We the People of the United States," the Constitution made it clear that its authority came from the people, not the states. ✓

Check Your Progress

1. What was the initial purpose of the Constitutional Convention of 1787?

2. What was important about the first words of the Preamble to the new U.S. Constitution?

Section 2 Notetaking Study Guide

Question to Think About As you read Section 2 in your textbook and take notes, keep this section focus question in mind: **What role did compromise play in the creation of the U.S. Constitution?**

► Use these organizers to record key information from the section. Some of the information has been filled in to get you started.

The Constitutional Convention

Issue: How to encourage debate during the convention without public pressure
Solution: Convention delegates voted to hold discussions in secret.

↓

Issue: How to create a stronger national government with more powers than under the Articles of Confederation
Solution Provided by the Virginia Plan: Create a government with ______________ branches, and separate ______________ into two houses. James Madison authored the plan.

↓

Issue: How many people should lead the executive branch
Solution Reached After a Vote: ______________

↓

Issue: How to elect representatives to the two houses of the legislative branch
Solution Proposed by the Virginia Plan: Elect representatives to both houses according to ______________. **Solution Proposed by the New Jersey Plan:** Give each state ______________ vote(s), regardless of its population. **Solution Reached by the Great Compromise:** House of ______________ would be based on ______________, and states would be represented equally in the ______________. ______________ suggested The Great Compromise.

↓

Issue: How to show that the Constitution derived its authority from the people
Solution: Add a preamble that says, "We the ______________..." Gouverneur Morris wrote the Preamble.

Refer to this page to answer the Chapter 3 Focus Question on page 44.

Section 3

Debating the Constitution

Key Events

1776	Many new American states write constitutions.
1787	Constitutional Convention creates a new plan of government.
1791	After three fourths of states approve it, the Bill of Rights goes into effect.

Section 3 Focus Question

How did those in favor of the Constitution achieve its ratification? To begin answering this question,

- Read about the arguments for and against the Constitution.
- Learn about the debate over ratification of the Constitution.
- Find out why the Bill of Rights was added to the Constitution.

Section 3 Summary

After the 1787 Convention, the Constitution was sent to the states for approval. Its opponents and supporters debated energetically, and after the Bill of Rights was added, all the states approved the Constitution.

Federalists Versus Antifederalists

The Federalists wanted a strong federal, or national, government. Three important federalist leaders, **Alexander Hamilton, John Jay,** and James Madison, wrote a series of 85 newspaper essays called the *Federalist Papers* in support of the Constitution.

At the heart of the Federalist position was the need for a stronger central government. The Federalists argued that in order for the Union to last, the national government had to have powers denied it under the Articles of Confederation, including the power to enforce laws.

The opponents of the Constitution were known as Antifederalists. Many Antifederalists, such as **George Mason** and Patrick Henry, agreed that the Articles of Confederation were not strong enough. However, they felt that the Constitutional Convention had gone too far.

Antifederalist Arguments Against the Constitution	
1	The Constitution weakened the state governments by giving too much power to the national government. Antifederalists feared that a too strong central government would wipe out state power and individual freedom.
2	The Constitution also did not include a bill of rights to protect basic freedoms.
3	The president could become like a king by being repeatedly reelected.

✓

Vocabulary Builder

Federal means "formed by a union of states, in which each gives up power to a central authority." How does this relate to the goal of the Federalists?

____

____

____

✓ Checkpoint

Name the Federalists' main argument in favor of the Constitution.

____

____

The Ratification Debate

The Constitution was submitted to the states, and each state called a convention to decide whether to **ratify**, or approve, the Constitution. At least nine states had to ratify the Constitution, or it would not go into effect. Delaware acted first. Its convention approved the Constitution in December 1787. Pennsylvania, New Jersey, Georgia, and Connecticut followed close behind.

The Federalists' strong efforts in Massachusetts led to approval in that state despite opposition in rural areas from which Shays' Rebellion had drawn its strength. By then, Maryland and South Carolina had ratified, which made a total of eight state ratifications. Then in June 1788, New Hampshire became the ninth state to ratify the Constitution, meaning it could now go into effect. The other states eventually approved the Constitution, with Rhode Island being the last of the original 13 states to do so in May 1790. ✓

✓ Checkpoint

Name the first and last states to ratify the Constitution.

First: ______________________

Last: ______________________

The Bill of Rights

After nine states had ratified the Constitution, Congress took steps to prepare for a presidential election. George Washington was elected the first President, with John Adams as Vice President.

During the debate on the Constitution, many states had insisted that a bill of rights be added. This became one of the first tasks of the new Congress that met in March 1789.

In 1789, Congress passed a series of amendments, or changes to a document. By December 1791, three fourths of the states had ratified 10 amendments. These amendments are known as the Bill of Rights.

The Bill of Rights protects citizens against governmental abuses of power. The First Amendment protects freedom of religion, speech, and the press. Recalling the importance of colonial militias, the Second Amendment deals with the right to bear arms. The Third Amendment bars Congress from forcing citizens to keep troops in their homes, as Britain had done. The Fourth Amendment protects citizens from unreasonable searches of their homes or seizure of their property. The Fifth through Eighth Amendments mainly protect those accused of crimes. The last two amendments restricted the powers of the national government to those granted in the Constitution. ✓

✓ Checkpoint

List three freedoms the First Amendment protects.

____

____

____

Check Your Progress

1. Why did the Antifederalists object to the Constitution?

____

____

2. What role does the Bill of Rights play?

____

____

Section 3 Notetaking Study Guide

Question to Think About As you read Section 3 in your textbook and take notes, keep this section focus question in mind: **How did those in favor of the Constitution achieve its ratification?**

► Use these charts to record key information from the section. Some of the information has been filled in to get you started.

Federalists Versus Antifederalists

Federalists

Leaders: 1. John Jay, 2. ______________, 3. ______________

Position on the new Constitution: ______________

Main argument for position: need for a __________ central government

Antifederalists

Leaders: 1. Patrick Henry, 2. ______________

Position on the new Constitution: ______________

Arguments for position:

1. ______________________________
2. ______________________________
3. The President could become like a king by being repeatedly reelected.

The Ratification Debate

- Approval needed from __________ states before the Constitution could go into effect.
- Importance of Massachusetts: Antifederalists hoped it would reject the Constitution because opposition was strong where Shays' Rebellion had occurred. It was approved after a major campaign by the Federalists.
- Importance of Virginia: Virginia was __________ and __________. If it rejected the Constitution, ______________ and other states might do so, too.

The Bill of Rights

Many states believed that a bill of rights was essential to protect basic liberties and to protect against abuses by the __________.

- First Amendment: guarantees freedom of __________, __________, and __________.
- Second Amendment: deals with the right to ______________.
- Third Amendment: bars Congress from ______________.
- Fourth Amendment: protects citizens from ______________ or ______________.
- Fifth through Eighth Amendments: protect citizens who are ______________ ______________.
- Ninth and Tenth Amendments: limit the powers of the ______________ to those granted in the ______________.

Refer to this page to answer the Chapter 3 Focus Question on page 44.

Chapter 3 Assessment

Directions: Circle the letter of the correct answer.

1. Who had the most political power under the Articles of Confederation?

A the state governments
B the President
C the Continental Congress
D the Supreme Court

2. What was a result of the Great Compromise during the Constitutional Convention?

A the immediate end of the slave trade
B adding the Bill of Rights to the Constitution
C the organization of a national government with only one branch
D the creation of a legislative branch with two houses

3. One reason that some of the Antifederalists opposed the Constitution was

A they believed they had a better plan for the national government.
B they believed it gave too much power to the states.
C they believed the Constitution should include a bill of rights.
D they believed slavery should be allowed north of the Ohio River.

Directions: Follow the steps to answer the following question:

What do the successes and failures of the government under the Articles of Confederation tell you about it?

Step 1: Recall information: List two successes and two failures of the government under the Articles of Confederation.

Successes	Failures
1. 2.	1. 2.

Step 2: Compare: What do the successes of the government tell you about it? What do the failures of the government tell you about it?

What the Successes Tell You	What the Failures Tell You

Step 3: Complete the topic sentence that follows. Then write two or three more sentences that discuss the strengths and weaknesses of the Articles of Confederation.

Under the Articles of Confederation, the United States ______________________

____

____

____

____

____

____

____

Chapter 3 Notetaking Study Guide

Now you are ready to answer the Chapter 3 Focus Question: **How did the U.S. Constitution overcome the weaknesses of the Articles of Confederation and provide for the organization of the new government?**

► Complete the following charts to help you answer this question. Use the notes that you took for each section.

Articles of Confederation	
Form of government	• single branch: a one-house legislature called Congress • each state had ________ vote(s) • ______ states had to agree before a law could go into effect
Limited government	• limited ____________ government; most power held by the ____________ • ____________ could not enforce laws

Constitutional Convention of 1787	
Virginia Plan	• strong central government • three branches of government: • • • • legislature divided into ____________ houses • representation based on ____________ • Small states objected to the plan because the more ____________ a state had, the more ____________ it would have.
New Jersey Plan	• ____________ house(s) in Congress • ____________ representation for each state • expanded powers of Congress to ____________ and ____________
The Great Compromise	Two houses of Congress • lower house: ____________ • representation based on ____________ • upper house: ____________ • each state had ________ seats
The Three-Fifths Compromise	• Southerners said that enslaved people should be counted in calculating how many ____________ a state should have in Congress. Northerners objected because enslaved people were not allowed to ____________. • As a compromise each enslaved person was counted as three fifths of a ________ .

Refer to this page to answer the Unit 2 Focus Question on page 61.

Constitution Notetaking Study Guide

Question to Think About As you read the Constitution in your textbook and take notes, keep this question in mind: **How do the amendments affect life in the United States today?**

► Use the charts on this page and the next to record key information about amendments to the U.S. Constitution. Some of the information has been filled in to get you started.

AMENDMENTS 11–18 TO THE U.S. CONSTITUTION				
Amendment	**Year Ratified**	**Subject**	**Does the amendment allow...**	**Yes or No**
Eleventh	1795	suits against states	a citizen of one state to sue the government of another state in federal court?	no
Twelfth			electors to cast one ballot for President and Vice President?	
Thirteenth			slavery to exist in the United States?	
Fourteenth			states to make laws that limit the rights of citizens?	
Fifteenth			the federal government or states to limit the right to vote based on race?	
Sixteenth			Congress to tax people on their income?	
Seventeenth			state legislatures to choose senators?	
Eighteenth			people to make, sell, or transport alcohol?	

► Complete this chart to record information about the last nine amendments to the U.S. Constitution.

AMENDMENTS 19–27 TO THE U.S. CONSTITUTION				
Amendment	**Year Ratified**	**Subject(s)**	**Does the amendment allow...**	**Yes or No**
Nineteenth	1920	women's suffrage	women to vote in state and federal elections?	yes
Twentieth			the Vice-President-elect to become President if the President-elect dies before taking office?	
Twenty-first			people to make, sell, or transport alcohol?	
Twenty-second			a person to serve as President for more than two terms?	
Twenty-third			the people living in the District of Columbia to vote for President?	
Twenty-fourth			U.S. citizens to be required to pay a tax before voting in federal elections?	
Twenty-fifth			the Vice President to take over the duties of President if the President declares that he or she is unable to carry them out?	
Twenty-sixth			citizens eighteen or older to vote?	
Twenty-seventh			members of Congress to receive right away a pay increase they voted for themselves?	

Refer to these charts to answer the Unit 2 Focus Question on page 61.

Citizenship Handbook

What You Will Learn

The U.S. Constitution is the supreme law of the United States. It determines the structure of the federal government. Government also operates at the state and local levels.

Citizenship Handbook Focus Question

As you read this handbook, keep this question in mind: **How did the Constitution create a strong government with roots in history that allowed for change and met the needs of the people?**

Summary 1

Summary 1 Focus Questions

- What were the ideas behind the Constitution?
- What is the structure of the Constitution?
- What are the basic ideas underlying the U.S. Constitution?

Summary

In drafting the Constitution, the Framers used ideas and principles from a variety of historical documents and important thinkers of Europe.

Ideas Behind the Constitution

The delegates to the Constitutional Convention were influenced by past experiments with democracy and natural rights. American leaders looked to the ancient Roman Republic as a model. A **republic** is a government in which citizens rule themselves through elected representatives.

The following principles from the Magna Carta and the English Bill of Rights influenced the U.S. Constitution:

- Citizens have rights, which the government must protect.
- Even the head of the government must obey the law.
- Taxes cannot be raised without the consent of the people.
- Elections should be held frequently.
- People accused of crimes have the right to trial by jury and the right of **habeas corpus**, meaning no person may be held in prison without being charged with a specific crime.
- People have the right to **private property**, or property owned by an individual.

Enlightenment thinkers John Locke and Baron de Montesquieu were also key influences. Locke declared that every person has a natural right to life, liberty, and property. Montesquieu

Chapter Standards

History-Social Science 7.11.5, 8.1.4, 8.2.1, 8.2.5, 8.2.6, 8.2.7, 8.3.6, 8.3.7

Vocabulary Builder

Republic comes from two Latin words: *res*, which means "interest," and *publicus*, which means "public." How does a republic represent the public interest?

____

____

____

____

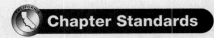

suggested the concept of separation of powers. **Separation of powers** states that the powers of government must be clearly defined and divided into legislative, executive, and judicial branches.

The Pilgrims drafted the first document of self-government in North America, the Mayflower Compact. Each of the 13 colonies' charters identified the power and limits of government by the king of England. In writing the Constitution, the Framers sought to prevent the abuses listed by Thomas Jefferson against George III in the Declaration of Independence. ✓

✓ Checkpoint

Name two documents from British history that influenced the U.S. Constitution.

___

___

Structure of the Constitution

The Preamble, or opening statement, of the Constitution outlines the goals of the document. Seven sections called the Articles make up the main body of the Constitution. The first three Articles describe the branches of government: legislative, executive, and judicial. Article IV requires states to honor one another's laws and sets up a system for admitting new states. Article V provides a process for amending the Constitution. Article VI declares the Constitution as the "supreme law of the land." Article VII sets up the procedure for the states to ratify the Constitution. In more than 200 years, only 27 changes have been made to the Constitution. ✓

Vocabulary Builder

Preamble comes from Latin roots meaning "walking in front of."

✓ Checkpoint

List two issues dealt with in Article IV of the Constitution.

___

___

___

___

Principles of the Constitution

The Constitution rests on seven basic principles.

- **Popular sovereignty** asserts that the people are the main source of the government's authority.
- **Limited government** means the government only has powers given by the Constitution.
- Separation of powers divides the federal government into three branches. Each branch has its own duties.
- **Checks and balances** is a system by which each branch of government has the power to limit the action of the other two. Like the separation of powers, this is designed to prevent the abuse of power.
- **Federalism** is the division of power between the federal government and the states.
- Republicanism provides for a government in which people elect representatives to carry out their will.
- The principle of individual rights means the Constitution protects rights such as freedom of speech and the right to trial by jury. ✓

✓ Checkpoint

List three of the basic principles embodied in the Constitution.

___

___

___

Check Your Progress

1. What was Montesquieu's idea of the separation of powers?

___

___

2. What is described in the first three Articles of the Constitution?

___

Constitution Notetaking Study Guide

Keep in mind the Summary 1 Focus Questions as you read about the Constitution in your textbook and take notes.

▶ Use these charts to help you record key Constitution facts. Some information has been filled in to get you started.

Ideas Behind the Constitution

Ideas from Rome and England

The Example of Rome: The government of early Rome was a republic in which citizens ruled through ______________. However, this form of government collapsed and was replaced with a ______________.

Documents from England: The ______________ and the English ______________ placed limits on the power of rulers and protected the ______________ of citizens.

Ideas from the Enlightenment

John Locke:

1.

2.

3. People have a right to rebel if a ruler violates the people's natural rights.

Baron de Montesquieu:

Goal of separation of powers: ______________

Articles of the Constitution

Article	Subject of the Article
Article I	
Article II	establishes the powers of and limits on the President
Article III	
Article IV	
Article V	
Article VI	
Article VII	

Seven Principles of the Constitution

Principle	Meaning
Popular sovereignty	
Limited government	
Separation of powers	
Checks and balances	
Federalism	
Republicanism	
Individual Rights	

Refer to this page to answer the Citizenship Handbook Focus Question on page 60.

Summary 2

Summary 2 Focus Question

What are the powers of each branch of government?

Summary

The federal government consists of three branches, each of which has its own unique powers and responsibilities.

How the Federal Government Works: The Legislative Branch

Article I of the Constitution sets up the Congress to make the nation's laws. Congress consists of two bodies: the Senate and the House of Representatives.

The Senate is based on equal representation and includes two senators from each state. Senators serve six-year terms. The Vice President serves as the president of the Senate.

The House of Representatives is the larger of the two bodies. Representation in the House is based on a state's population. People elect their representatives for two-year terms. The leader of the House, called the Speaker, regulates debates and agendas in the House.

Congress's most important power is the power to make the nation's laws. A law starts as a bill, most of which can be introduced in either the House or the Senate. Congress can also collect taxes, coin money, establish post offices, fix standard weights and measures, and declare war.

Much of the work in Congress is done through committees. Each committee deals with a specific topic, such as defense, education, or science. ✓

How the Federal Government Works: The Executive Branch

Article II of the Constitution sets up the executive branch to carry out laws and to run the affairs of the national government. The President is the head of the executive branch, which also includes the Vice President and the Cabinet. The people in the many departments and agencies are also part of the executive branch. The Framers of the Constitution intended Congress to be the most powerful branch of government. Therefore, while the Constitution is very specific about the powers of the legislature, it offers few details about the powers of the President. Beginning with George Washington, Presidents have taken the actions they thought were necessary to meet the nation's changing needs. Today, the President can veto bills, propose laws, grant pardons, appoint high officials, negotiate treaties, and serve as commander in chief of the armed forces.

The President serves a four-year term and cannot serve more than two terms. The President is elected through a system called

Vocabulary Builder

Read the bracketed text. Based on context clues, write a definition of *agenda*.

____

____

✓ Checkpoint

Name the two bodies of the legislative branch.

____

____

the electoral college. Americans do not directly elect the President; rather, they vote for a group of electors. The number of electors depends on each state's number of senators and representatives. In most states, the presidential candidate with the majority of votes receives all of the electoral votes. The candidate who receives the most electoral votes becomes President. ✓

How the Federal Government Works: The Judicial Branch

The Constitution also establishes a Supreme Court and authorizes Congress to establish any other courts that are needed. The system of federal courts was set up under the Judiciary Act of 1789.

Most federal court cases begin in district courts, where evidence is presented and a judge or a jury decides the facts of a case. If a party disagrees with the decision of the judge or jury, it may appeal. An **appeal** asks that the decision be reviewed by a higher court. A judge in an appellate court or court of appeals reviews the decision to determine if the lower court interpreted and applied the law correctly.

Court cases can be filed under federal or state jurisdiction. A **jurisdiction** is the power to hear and decide cases. Most cases are tried under state jurisdiction because they involve state laws. A case may be placed under federal jurisdiction if:

- The United States is either suing another party or being sued by another party.
- The case is based on the Constitution or on a federal law.
- The case involves disputes between different states.

The Supreme Court is at the top of the judicial branch, and it consists of a chief justice and eight associate justices. The President nominates the judges, and Congress must approve the appointments. The Supreme Court is the final court of appeals. Decisions rest on a majority of at least five of the justices.

There is no court of appeals beyond the Supreme Court. However, the Supreme Court may sometimes reverse its own past decisions.

The most important power of the Supreme Court is the power to decide what the Constitution means. The Court can declare whether acts of the President or laws passed by Congress are unconstitutional. **Unconstitutional** means that an act or law is not allowed by the Constitution. ✓

Check Your Progress

1. What and who makes up the executive branch?

____

____

2. Describe the process by which a justice is added to the Supreme Court.

____

____

✓ Checkpoint

Name the system by which the President is elected.

____

✓ Checkpoint

List the two things that the Supreme Court can declare unconstitutional.

____

____

Branches of Government Notetaking Study Guide

Keep in mind the Summary 2 Focus Question as you read about the structure of the U.S. government in your textbook and take notes.

► Use these charts to help you record key facts about the branches of government. Some information has been filled in to get you started.

The Legislative Branch

The Senate	House of Representatives
Number of members for each state: two per state Length of term: ______ President of the Senate: ______	Number of members for each state: based on population Current number of members: ______ Representatives elected by: ______ Length of term: ______

Powers of Congress:
1. make nation's laws, 2. collect ______, 3. coin ______, 4. establish post offices, 5. fix standard ______ and ______, 6. declare ______

The Executive Branch

Duties: Carry out the ______ and run the affairs of ______
Head executive: ______
Other members: Vice President, Cabinet, ______, ______
Length of President's term: ______, but no more than two terms
System by which President is elected: ______

The Judicial Branch

Lower Courts
1. In district courts, ______ is presented during trials, and a ______ or a ______ decides the facts of the case.
2. A party that disagrees with a decision may ______ to a higher court.
3. Appellate court judges review the decisions of district courts to ______.
4. Jurisdiction is ______.

The Supreme Court
Court consists of: ______
Justices appointed by: ______
Appointments must be approved by: ______
Length of Justices' service: ______
Main job: ______
Number of cases heard per year: ______
Most important power: ______
What the court can declare as unconstitutional: ______.

Refer to this page to answer the Citizenship Handbook Focus Question on page 60.

Summary 3

Summary 3 Focus Question

How can the Constitution be amended to meet changing needs?

Summary

The Founders created a Constitution that allowed for change. The first ten changes made to the Constitution concerned the rights of the American people.

Amending the Constitution

Some of the Framers were dissatisfied with the Constitution because the final document did not address the rights of the American people. The Framers fixed the omission by adding the Bill of Rights, the first ten amendments to the Constitution. Such an addition was possible because the Constitution included Article V, which laid out the method of amending the Constitution. **Amending** is another word for changing the Constitution.

The Constitution can be changed in one of four ways. There are two ways of proposing an amendment. First, Congress can propose an amendment. Second, members of a national convention can formally propose an amendment.

An amendment can be ratified or approved through the actions of the state legislature, or it can also be ratified through the actions of state conventions. Conventions are special meetings that are called to address a specific issue.

The first ten amendments, also known as The Bill of Rights, are the part of the Constitution that addresses the freedoms guaranteed to all citizens.

The Bill of Rights

Amendment	Subject Addressed
First	freedom of religion, speech, and the press; right of petition and assembly
Second	right to bear arms
Third	government cannot force people to quarter troops in their homes
Fourth	protects against unreasonable search and seizure
Fifth	rights of people accused of crimes
Sixth	right to trial by jury in criminal cases
Seventh	right to trial by jury in civil cases
Eighth	forbids excessive bail and cruel or unusual punishment
Ninth	people's rights are not limited to those listed in the Constitution
Tenth	states or people have all powers not denied or given to federal government by the Constitution

✓

Vocabulary Builder

Omission is a noun meaning "something left out." Based on this definition, what do you think the word *omit* means?

____

____

✓ Checkpoint

What are the first ten amendments called?

____

The First Amendment

The colonial experience inspired the First Amendment to the Constitution. Pilgrims, Puritans, Quakers, and Catholics had all come to North America in the 1600s because they wanted to practice their religion freely. However, some religious leaders, such as Thomas Hooker, Roger Williams, and Anne Hutchinson, were driven out of their New England towns after disputes with their community leaders over religious issues. The Constitution's Framers sought to end such church-versus-state disputes by drafting the First Amendment. Thus, the First Amendment affirms freedom of religion as a basic right. Americans are free to follow any religion or no religion at all. It is their choice.

The freedom-of-religion part of the First Amendment had been inspired by the Virginia Statute on Religious Freedom, which was written by Thomas Jefferson. Jefferson later spoke of a "wall of separation between Church and State." However, not everyone agrees on how religion and government should be separated. Some people believe that the First Amendment means that religion should play no role in government. Others argue that the Amendment merely says that Congress cannot establish an official, state-supported church or make laws that interfere with freedom of worship.

The First Amendment also protects the right of Americans to speak without fear of punishment. In addition, the amendment protects the press from government censorship. **Censorship** is the power to revise, change, or prevent the publication of news. Undemocratic governments often shut down newspapers and jail people who criticize the government. These governments must silence dissent to stay in power.

The founders remembered that King George III and Parliament had ignored colonists' petitions protesting the Stamp Act. Such experiences had a powerful effect on the leaders who wrote the Bill of Rights. The First Amendment thus guarantees the right of Americans to assemble in peaceful protest and protects Americans' right to petition the government for a change in policy. ✓

Vocabulary Builder

If *consent* is the opposite of *dissent*, what does *dissent* mean?

____

____

✓ Checkpoint

List the five freedoms covered by the First Amendment.

____

____

____

____

____

Check Your Progress

1. Explain the two ways by which an amendment to the U. S. Constitution can be ratified.

____

____

2. What colonial experience led American leaders to specifically protect the right of citizens to follow any religion or no religion?

____

____

____

Amending the Constitution Notetaking Study Guide

Keep in mind the Summary 3 Focus Question as you read about changing the Constitution in your textbook and take notes.

► Use these charts to help you record key facts. Some information has been filled in to get you started.

Amendment Process	
Proposing Amendments 1. 2. National convention formally proposes an amendment.	Ratifying Amendments 1. 2.

The Bill of Rights	
Amendment	**Rights and Protections**
First Amendment	• Protects freedom of religion, freedom of ______, and freedom of the ______ • Also protects the right of petition and peaceful ______
Second Amendment	Right to ______
Third Amendment	Protects against the ______ of ______ in people's homes
Fourth Amendment	Protects against unreasonable ______ and ______
Fifth Amendment	Protects the rights of people accused of ______
Sixth Amendment	Right to a ______ by ______ in criminal cases
Seventh Amendment	Right to a ______ by ______ in ______ cases
Eighth Amendment	Forbids ______ and cruel or unusual ______
Ninth Amendment	People's ______ are not limited to ______
Tenth Amendment	States or people have all ______ not denied or ______ by the Constitution

Refer to this page to answer the Citizenship Handbook Focus Question on page 60.

Summary 4

Summary 4 Focus Questions

- What are the powers of state and local governments?
- What are the rights and responsibilities of citizens?

Summary

Not only do state and local governments have many important responsibilities, but individual citizens have many important responsibilities as well.

State and Local Government

Under the principle of federalism, the Constitution divides powers between the federal government and the governments of the states. In general, the federal government deals with national issues.The states concern themselves with local needs.

State governments resemble the federal government in many ways. Each state has its own constitution that can be amended, and it has the same three branches of government. Each state has a legislature, a governor who serves as the chief executive, and a judiciary. There are some differences between federal and state governments. Nebraska, for instance, is the only state in the Union with a one-house legislature.

The Constitution lays out many of the powers given to the states. State governments have the power to create corporate law, regulate trade within the state, maintain public schools, and establish local governments. States also make laws about marriage and divorce, conduct elections, and provide for public safety. States and the federal government also share some powers. They both provide for the public welfare, administer criminal justice, charter banks, raise taxes, and borrow money.

The Constitution identifies the powers of the federal and state government, but it says nothing about local government, which consists of smaller units such as counties, cities, and towns.

Like federal and state governments, local governments have budgets. Local budgets are generally spent on education. Cities, towns, and school districts hire teachers, buy books, and maintain school buildings. Although local governments control the school system, they are required by law to meet the state's education standards.

Local governments play a more direct role in people's everyday lives than federal or state governments do. For instance, local governments hire people who interact with citizens on a regular basis. These include firefighters, police officers, and garbage collectors. Local governments also maintain local roads and hospitals, provide public services, run libraries, oversee parks and recreational facilities, and inspect the safety of buildings. ✓

✓ Checkpoint

Name three units of local government.

____

____

____

Rights and Responsibilities of Citizenship

A **citizen** is someone who is entitled to all the rights and privileges of a nation. To be a citizen of the United States, a person must be born in the United States, have a parent who is a United States citizen, be naturalized, or be 18 years old or younger when his or her parents are naturalized. **Naturalization** is the official legal process of becoming a citizen. To be naturalized, a person must live in the United States for at least five years. The person must then apply for citizenship, take a citizenship exam, undergo interviews, and finally take the citizenship oath before a judge. In this oath, the person swears to "support and defend the Constitution and laws of the United States."

A naturalized citizen enjoys every right of a natural-born citizen except one. Only natural-born citizens may serve as President or Vice President.

Many of American citizens' rights are spelled out in the Bill of Rights. But the Ninth Amendment states that citizens' rights are not limited to those specifically listed in the Constitution. Over the years, federal and state laws have identified rights that were not mentioned in the Constitution. For example, the Constitution does not mention education. But today, laws in every state guarantee that children have the right to an education.

The law holds citizens to certain responsibilities. For example, every citizen must obey the law and pay taxes or face legal punishment. Good citizens meet other responsibilities as well. These are not required by law, but they are important. These responsibilities include learning about important issues and voting in federal, state, and local elections.

Some people participate in the political process through interest groups. An **interest group** is an organization that represents the concerns of a particular group. These groups work to influence lawmakers. Examples of interest groups are the National Rifle Association and the Sierra Club.

Young people, too, can get involved in the political process. For example, students in one community in California organized to get assistance paying for public transportation. Using their First Amendment rights, they collected signatures on petitions and held peaceful public rallies. Finally, local transportation officials came up with a plan to solve the problem. ✓

Vocabulary Builder

Political comes from the Greek word *polis*, meaning "city." The word *police* shares the same root.

✓ Checkpoint

Name two examples of interest groups.

____

____

Check Your Progress

1. Which level or levels of government are responsible for education?

____

2. Which amendment states that citizens have rights not mentioned in the Constitution?

____

Governments and Citizens Notetaking Study Guide

Keep in mind the Summary 4 Focus Questions as you read about the powers of state and local governments and the responsibilities of citizens in your textbook and take notes.

► Use these charts to help you record key facts. Some information has been filled in to get you started.

State Government	
Each state has its own constitution. State governments made up of: • executive (headed by ________) • •	Powers of State Government: • create corporate law • • • • • •

Local Government
Includes county, ________, and ________ Most of local budgets are spent on ________. Local governments hire ________, ________, and ________. Local governments maintain ________ and ________ and provide public services.

Citizenship
• A ________ is entitled to all the rights and privileges of a particular nation. • To be a citizen of the United States, a person must be one of the following: 1. 2. 3. • ________ is the official legal process of becoming a citizen. Steps in process: 1. 2. 3. 4. 5. • Some responsibilities of citizens are required by ________. • Other responsibilities are not required by law. These include serving the community, staying well informed, ________ in elections, and helping to create a just ________.

Refer to this page to answer the Citizenship Handbook Focus Question on page 60.

Citizenship Handbook Assessment

Directions: Circle the letter of the correct answer.

1. The electoral college is the system used to determine who becomes
- **A** chief justice.
- **B** representative.
- **C** President.
- **D** senator.

2. In what way are state governments like the federal government?
- **A** Both levels of government are divided into three branches.
- **B** Both levels of government maintain schools.
- **C** All states have two-house legislatures, as does the federal government.
- **D** Both levels of government have the power to coin money.

3. Which of the following principles of the U.S. Constitution introduces the idea that government authority comes from the people?
- **A** limited government
- **B** republicanism
- **C** checks and balances
- **D** popular sovereignty

Directions: Follow the steps to answer this question.

How does the structure of the federal government reflect the Framers' belief that power should rest in the hands of citizens?

Step 1: Recall details about each branch of the federal government.

	Branch		
	Executive	**Legislative**	**Judicial**
Highest office or level		Congress	
How officeholders are selected	nationwide election through electoral college system		

Step 2: Compare: In which of the three branches are the top officeholders most directly selected by voters?

____

Step 3: Complete the topic sentence that follows. Then write two or three more sentences that support your topic sentences.

The Framers of the Constitution felt that power should rest in the hands of the citizens because ____

____

____

____

Citizenship Handbook Notetaking Study Guide

Now you are ready to answer the Citizenship Handbook Focus Question: **How did the Constitution create a strong government with roots in history that allowed for change and met the needs of the people?**

► Complete the following chart to help you answer this question. Use the notes that you took for each section.

The Foundation of Strong Government

Ideas Behind the Constitution

American leaders looked to Rome as an example of a ____________, or government in which citizens rule themselves through elected ____________.

The ______________ and the English ______________ placed limits on the ruler and protected the rights of citizens.

The ideas of the European Enlightenment thinkers ______________ and ______________ were very influential.

Structure of the Constitution

The ____________, or opening statement, of the Constitution outlines six main goals.	The first three Articles describe the branches of government: ____________, ____________ and ____________.

The Constitution rests on seven basic principles: popular sovereignty, ____________, ____________, ____________, ____________, federalism, and ____________.

Amendments to the Constitution

An amendment can be ratified or approved by three fourths of ______________ or ______________.

The first ten amendments are known as ______________.

They address ______________.

The ______________ states that Americans are entitled to many rights, not just those spelled out in the Constitution.

State and Local Government

Like the federal government, each state has a ____________ and three ______________.

Some of the many duties of state government include regulating ____________ within the state, making laws about ____________ and divorce, conducting ____________, and providing for public ____________.

____________ government plays the most direct role in people's lives.

Refer to this page to answer the Unit 2 Focus Question on page 61.

Unit 2 Pulling It Together Activity

What You Have Learned

Chapter 3 Delegates from each state met in Philadelphia in 1787 to revise the Articles of Confederation. The delegates decided that the nation needed a stronger federal government.

Citizenship Handbook To be an active citizen, it is important to understand the ideas behind the U.S. Constitution.

Think Like a Historian

Read the Unit 2 Focus Question: **What are the roles and responsibilities of governments and citizens?**

► Use the organizers on this page and the next to collect information to answer this question.

What are the responsibilities of citizens? Some of them are listed in this organizer. Review your section and chapter notes. Then complete the organizer.

From the Bill of Rights

- freedom of religion, speech, and the press
- trial by jury and equal treatment before the law
-
-

Rights Added Later

- equal education
- right to vote for:
  -
  -
  -

Rights and Responsibilities of Citizens

Civic Responsibilities

- voting
-
-

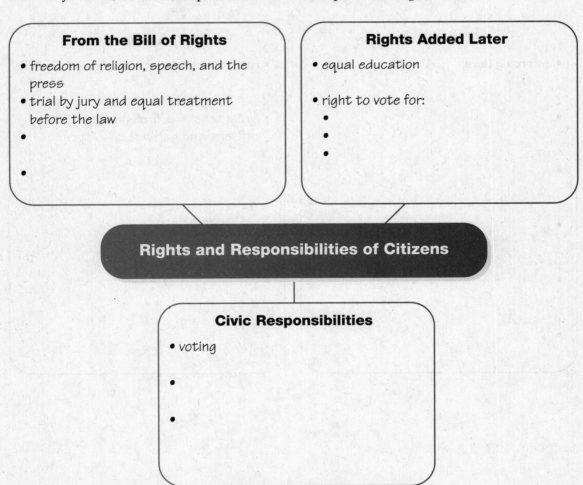

Look at the other part of the Unit Focus Question. It asks about responsibilities of government. The organizer below gives you a part of the answer. Review your section and chapter notes. Then fill in the rest of the organizer.

Responsibilities of Government

Federal

- *making treaties, war, and peace*
-
-
-
-

State

- *enforcing laws*
-
-
-
-
-

Local

- *running schools and libraries*
- *hiring teachers, firefighters, police officers, and garbage collectors*
-
-
-
-

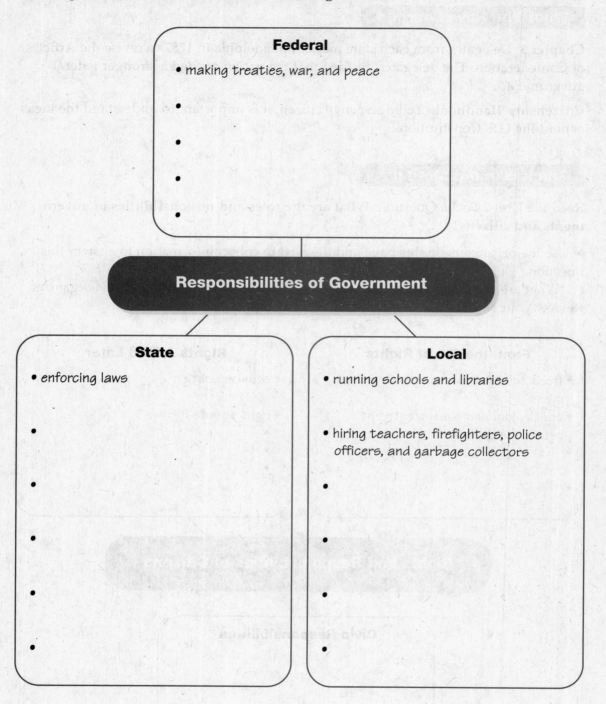

Unit 3

The New Republic

What You Will Learn

Chapter 4 As the nation's first President, George Washington established the U.S. government's authority in domestic as well as foreign affairs. Political divisions and strife with France rocked John Adams's presidency.

Chapter 5 The Louisiana Purchase of 1803 doubled the size of the United States. At the same time, the United States struggled to remain neutral in its foreign policy. British support of Native Americans led to the War of 1812.

Chapter 6 During the early 1800s, the federal government increased its authority. At the same time, the Monroe Doctrine expanded U.S. influence in Latin America. More people earned the right to vote during Andrew Jackson's presidency, yet Jackson forced Native Americans in the South to move west.

Focus Your Learning As you study this unit and take notes, you will find the information to answer the questions below. Answering the Chapter Focus Questions will help build your answer to the Unit Focus Question.

Chapter 4 Focus Question
How did Americans respond to internal and external challenges?
(page 64)

Unit 3 Focus Question
What problems might a new nation face?
(page 109)

Chapter 5 Focus Question
How did Jefferson and Madison deal with unresolved problems?
(page 78)

Chapter 6 Focus Question
How did the nation reflect a growing sense of national pride and identity?
(page 92)

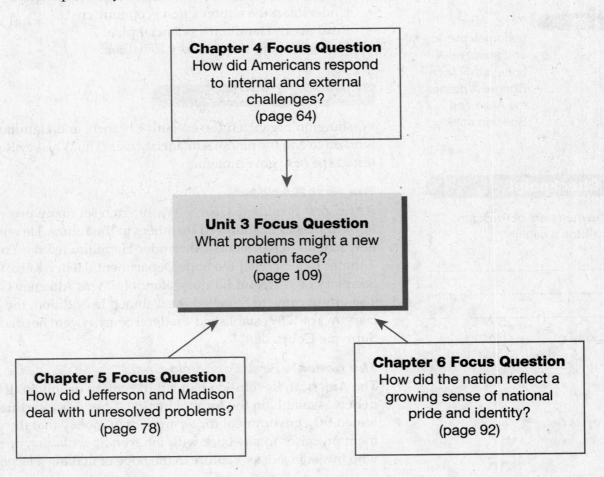

Chapter Standards

History-Social Science 8.1.3, 8.3.4, 8.3.5, 8.3.7, 8.4.1, 8.4.2, 8.5.3

Key Events

1789	Washington organizes new government departments and appoints heads.
1795	Senate approves Jay's Treaty with Britain.
1798	"XYZ Affair" becomes public and sours relations with France. Congress passes the Alien and Sedition acts.

✓ Checkpoint

List the members of President Washington's cabinet.

____

____

____

____

Chapter 4

First Steps (1789–1800)

What You Will Learn

The new federal government dealt with challenges at home and abroad. During John Adams's presidency, disagreements increased between the parties.

Chapter 4 Focus Question

As you read this chapter, keep this question in mind: **How did Americans respond to internal and external challenges?**

Section 1

Launching a New Nation

Section 1 Focus Question

How did President Washington set the course for the new nation? To begin answering this question,

- Learn about the first President, George Washington.
- Understand the nation's first economic crisis.
- Read about Hamilton's financial plan.
- Find out about the Whiskey Rebellion.

Section 1 Summary

Washington organized the executive branch, and Hamilton worked to end the nation's financial crisis. The Whiskey Rebellion tested the new government.

The First President

As the first President, George Washington set many **precedents**, or examples to be followed by others in the future. He created new federal departments. Alexander Hamilton led the Treasury, Thomas Jefferson led the State Department, Henry Knox was Secretary of War, and Edmund Randolph was Attorney General. The group came to be called the Cabinet. In addition, the Judiciary Act of 1789 established a federal court system headed by the Supreme Court. ✓

The Nation's First Economic Crisis

The American Revolution had left the nation deeply in debt. The debt was mainly in the form of bonds. A **bond** is a certificate issued by a government for an amount of money that the government promises to pay back with interest. **Speculators**, or people who invest in a risky venture in the hope of making a large profit, bought many bonds. Because they bought the bonds for less than they were worth, it did not seem fair to pay speculators in full, especially since the original bondholders had lost money. The government also questioned whether or not it should pay back state debts. ✓

Hamilton's Financial Plan

It fell to Alexander Hamilton, the new secretary of the treasury, to come up with a plan to solve the financial crisis. The first part of his plan was for the government to pay back all federal and state debts. However, many southern states did not want the federal government to pay state debts because they had paid theirs on their own. The South eventually agreed to this part of Hamilton's plan, and in return, the government would build its capital in the South.

The second part of the plan was to charter a national bank for depositing government funds. Members of Washington's cabinet fought over whether the government had the right to do this. Jefferson argued that a national bank was **unconstitutional**—contrary to what is permitted by the Constitution. He called for a "strict" interpretation, or reading, of the Constitution. According to this view, the government's power was limited to what the Constitution specifically says. Hamilton, on the other hand, called for a "loose" interpretation. He believed that the Constitution gave Congress the power to do things not directly permitted, as long as they were "necessary and proper." A national bank was created, but constitutional interpretation continues to provoke disagreement.

Southerners also opposed the last part of Hamilton's plan, a national **tariff**, or a tax on imported goods. The tariff benefited Northern industries because it protected them from lower priced foreign goods. Since Southerners had little industry, the tariff only hurt them by raising prices. Congress did not pass the tariff. ✓

The Whiskey Rebellion

Congress imposed a tax on all whiskey made and sold in the country, but many farmers who made whiskey opposed this tax. Some Pennsylvania farmers started a violent protest. Washington sent federal troops to Pennsylvania, showing that armed rebellion would not be accepted. ✓

Check Your Progress

1. What two crises occurred during the early part of President George Washington's administration?

____

____

2. What were the three parts to Hamilton's financial plan?

____

____

✓ Checkpoint

After the American Revolution, the nation's debt was mostly in what form?

____

Vocabulary Builder

Provoke comes from the Latin verb *provocare*, which means "to call out." What is being "called out" in the underlined sentence?

____

✓ Checkpoint

Name the two types of constitutional interpretation used during the debate about the national bank.

____

____

✓ Checkpoint

What caused the Whiskey Rebellion?

____

Section 1 Notetaking Study Guide

Question to Think About As you read Section 1 in your textbook, keep this question in mind: **How did President Washington set the course for the new nation?**

▶ Use this chart to record key information from the section.

Launching a New Nation

The first job of the President and Congress: to put a working government in place

Executive Branch

- Congress passed laws to set up three executive departments: ________ ________
- The President appointed a secretary to head each department. He also appointed an ________ to advise him on legal matters.
- This group of people became known as the ________.

Judicial Branch

- The Constitution called for a judiciary, or a court system.
- The ________ provided for a Supreme Court of 6 justices, ___ circuit courts, and 13 ________ courts.
- Main job of federal courts: ________ ________

Hamilton's Financial Plan

The American Revolution had left the national government and states deeply in debt, which was mainly in the form of ______.

Part 1: Paying the Debt

- Hamilton wanted the United States to honor its ______.
- Many southerners opposed the plan to repay ______ debts.
- The agreement: ______ ______ ______ ______

Part 2: ________

- The debate over the bank focused on the powers of the ________ under the ________.
- Some had a ______ interpretation of the Constitution. Others had a ______ interpretation.
- The bank was ______.

Part 3: High Tariff

- Hamilton wanted a high tariff to ______ for the federal government and to protect U.S. manufacturers from ________.
- Southerners argued the tariff would help the ______ but ______ the South.
- Congress ______ it.

The Whiskey Rebellion

- To raise money, Congress ________ all whiskey made and sold in the United States.
- It led to an ____________ that tested the ________ of the new government.
- Washington sent the ________ as a sign that armed revolt was unacceptable.

Refer to this page to answer the Chapter 4 Focus Question on page 77.

Section 2

The Birth of Political Parties

Section 2 Focus Question

How did two political parties emerge? To begin answering this question,

- Learn why political parties emerged.
- Read about the differences between Republicans and Federalists.
- Find out about the election of 1796.

Section 2 Summary

The Framers did not expect political parties to develop. But differences over issues led to the creation of parties. After the 1796 election, tensions increased between the parties.

Political Parties Emerge

The Framers of the Constitution did not expect political parties to form in the United States. Rather, they thought that government leaders would rise above personal or local interests and work together for the sake of the whole nation. They proved to be wrong.

In those days, people spoke of *factions* rather than *political parties*. A **faction** was an organized political group, and the word was not complimentary. **James Madison** thought factions were selfish groups that ignored the well-being of the whole nation. In the *Federalist Papers*, he wrote that an effective national government would prevent the growth of factions. President Washington feared the effects of factions and tried to discourage their growth. Despite his efforts, by the early 1790s, political parties began to form. ✓

Republicans Against Federalists

The two parties that formed were called the Republicans and the Federalists. The Republicans developed out of Democratic-Republican clubs that accused the federal government of growing too strong. They wanted to keep most power at the state or local level. The Federalists took their name from the people who had supported the adoption of the Constitution. They believed that the United States needed a strong federal government to hold the country together.

At the time that both parties were organizing, the Federalists had an advantage. This was because President Washington usually supported **Alexander Hamilton** and his policies rather than **Thomas Jefferson** and his policies. Finally, in 1793, Jefferson resigned as secretary of state because he was unhappy with the federal government's support of Federalist policies.

Key Events

1789 Washington organizes new government departments and appoints heads.

1795 Senate approves Jay's Treaty with Britain.

1798 "XYZ Affair" becomes public and sours relations with France. Congress passes the Alien and Sedition acts.

✓ Checkpoint

Name the term that people used instead of the term *political parties*.

____

Republicans	Federalists
• **Main Supporters:** southern planters and northern artisans and farmers • **Main Leaders:** Thomas Jefferson and James Madison • Supported strong state government • Opposed a national bank • Opposed a tariff on imported goods • Strictly interpreted the Constitution • Supported France because it had recently overthrown its king	• **Main Supporters:** merchants, other property owners, and workers in trade and manufacturing • **Main Leader:** Alexander Hamilton • Supported a strong national government • Supported a national bank • Supported a tariff on imported goods • Supported Britain's monarchy • Loosely interpreted the Constitution

✓

✓ Checkpoint

List the main supporters of the Republicans and Federalists.

Republicans: ____________________

____

Federalists: ____________________

____

____

The Election of 1796

George Washington announced he would not run for a third term as President. His action set an important precedent. Not until Franklin Roosevelt ran for and won a third term in 1940 would any President seek more than two terms. In 1951, the Twenty-second Amendment limited the President to two terms.

Today, the President and Vice President run together on the same ticket. However, at the time of the 1796 election, the President and the Vice President were not elected as a ticket. The candidate with the most votes became President, and the candidate who came in second place was elected Vice President. In the 1796 election, a Federalist, **John Adams**, became President, but a Republican candidate, Thomas Jefferson, was elected Vice President. Not surprisingly, this led to serious tensions during the next four years. ✓

Vocabulary Builder

A *precedent* is an action or decision that is used as an example for a later one.

✓ Checkpoint

Name the person elected president in 1796.

____

Check Your Progress

1. Why did the Framers of the Constitution not expect political parties?

____

____

____

2. What were the two political parties' positions on the power of the national government?

____

____

____

Section 2 Notetaking Study Guide

Question to Think About As you read Section 2 in your textbook and take notes, keep this question in mind: **How did two political parties emerge?**

▶ Use these charts to record key information from the section. Some information has been filled in to get you started.

The Birth of Political Parties
At first, political parties did not exist because people felt a leader should represent ________________________. President Washington tried to discourage the growth of political parties, which were originally called __________________.

The Two Parties

	Federalists	Republicans
Origin	Took name from early supporters of the Constitution	Democratic-Republican clubs
Leaders	•	• James Madison •
Supporters	• merchants • •	• •
Position on state vs. federal power	•	•
Positions on other issues	Favored: • • • • close ties with ________	Favored: • • close ties with ________ Opposed: • •
Presidential candidate in 1796	•	•

Results of the 1796 Election
President: ______________ Vice President: ______________

Refer to this page to answer the Chapter 4 Focus Question on page 77.

Section 3

Troubles at Home and Abroad

Key Events

1789 Washington organizes new government departments and appoints heads.

1795 Senate approves Jay's Treaty with Britain.

1798 "XYZ Affair" becomes public and sours relations with France. Congress passes the Alien and Sedition acts.

Section 3 Focus Question

How did the actions of Britain and France affect the United States? To begin answering this question,

- Find out about conflicts in the Northwest Territory.
- Learn about the French Revolution and its effect on the United States.
- Read about President Washington's retirement.

Section 3 Summary

President Washington faced conflict with Native Americans and foreign threats to American shipping. He advised Americans to avoid political divisions and involvement in European affairs.

Conflicts in the Northwest Territory

The Northwest Territory was the land north and west of the Ohio River to the Mississippi River. The United States acquired the territory from Britain as part of the terms of the Treaty of Paris that ended the American Revolution.

Under the treaty, Britain had pledged to withdraw its forts from the region within "a reasonable time." Ten years later, however, the forts were still there. The British were also supplying Native American groups in the region with guns and ammunition. The British hoped that this would limit American settlement in the Northwest Territory.

Many American leaders believed that the country's future depended on settling its western lands, and during the 1780s, many American settlers migrated into the Northwest Territory. Native Americans, worried about holding onto their lands, joined together to oppose American settlement.

By 1790, the federal government had bought much of the Native Americans' lands south of the Ohio River. However, Native Americans in the Northwest Territory refused to sell and attacked settlers. In 1790, Washington sent troops to the Northwest Territory. Three battles occurred between American troops and Native Americans led by Little Turtle of the Miami Nation and Blue Jacket of the Shawnees. The Native Americans won the first two battles. The second battle was the worst defeat U.S. troops ever suffered in a battle with Native Americans.

In 1794, Washington sent General **Anthony Wayne** to lead the troops. He defeated the Native Americans at the Battle of Fallen Timbers. That battle broke the Native American hold on the Northwest. In the 1795 Treaty of Greenville, Native Americans surrendered most of their lands in the part of the Northwest Territory that is now Ohio. ✓

✓ Checkpoint

Name the battle and the treaty that ended conflict between settlers and Native Americans in the Northwest Territory.

____

____

The French Revolution

When the French Revolution began in 1789, Americans supported the effort of the French people to overthrow their king. By 1793, however, growing violence in France was becoming controversial in the United States, and it led Federalists to oppose the revolution. Republicans continued to support it, arguing that some violence could be expected in a fight for freedom.

By 1793, Britain and France were at war. Republicans supported France and Federalists supported Britain. President Washington issued a proclamation that said the United States would remain **neutral**, not favoring either side of the dispute. However, the United States would trade with both sides. Neither France nor Britain agreed with the U.S. position. Both countries started seizing American ships, fearing that trade with the United States would benefit the enemy. Britain made matters worse by the **impressment** of sailors on American ships, which meant seizing the sailors and forcing them to serve in the British navy.

Washington sent **John Jay** to negotiate a treaty with Britain. In 1795 Jay returned with a treaty. The United States agreed to pay debts owed to British merchants. Britain agreed to pay for the ships it had seized and to withdraw its troops from the Northwest Territory. But it refused to stop impressing sailors. It also refused to recognize a U.S. right to trade with France.

Republicans opposed Jay's Treaty, arguing that it gave away too much and got too little. But the Federalist-controlled Senate approved it to keep peace with Britain. ✓

Washington Retires From Public Life

Washington published his Farewell Address at the end of his second term. He advised Americans to avoid political divisions at home. He feared that violent divisions might tear the nation apart. Washington also emphasized his belief that the United States must stay out of European affairs. Washington's main accomplishments were establishing a federal government, ending the country's economic crisis, forcing the British to leave the Northwest Territory, and keeping the country out of war. ✓

Check Your Progress

1. What role did Britain play in conflicts in the Northwest Territory?

____

____

____

2. How did public support in the United States for the French Revolution change over time?

____

____

____

Vocabulary Builder

Reread the underlined sentence. If to proclaim something means to announce it, what is a *proclamation*?

____

✓ Checkpoint

What led the Federalists to oppose the French Revolution?

____

____

✓ Checkpoint

List the two things that Washington recommended in his Farewell Address.

____

____

Section 3 Notetaking Study Guide

Question to Think About As you read Section 3 in your textbook and take notes, keep this question in mind: **How did the actions of Britain and France affect the United States?**

► Use this chart to record key information from the section. Some information has been filled in to get you started.

I. Conflicts in the Northwest Territory

Conflict with Britain	• A decade after the ______________, British troops still occupied <u>forts</u> in the Northwest Territory. • The British were also supplying Native Americans with ______________ and ______________ to help limit American ______________.
Conflict with Native Americans	• Americans tried to ______________ Native Americans to sell their lands in the Northwest Territory. • Native Americans sold some land but ______________ to sell other lands. • After an American victory at the ______________, the leaders of defeated Native American nations gave up most of their land in the 1795 ______________.

II. The French Revolution

- At first, Americans ______________ the revolutionaries.
- Reasons the French Revolution became controversial
  1. Violence peaked in a period called the ______________. ______________ denounced the violence, but ______________ said some violence should be expected.
  2. Both <u>Britain</u> and ______________, which were at war, began stopping American ships and ______________ their cargoes. The British made matters worse by the ______________ of the ships' sailors.
- Terms of Jay's Treaty

  What the Americans agreed to: ______________

  What the British agreed to: ______________

  ____

  What the British did not agree to: ______________

  ____

III. Washington Retires

Farewell Address Advice	• •
Washington's accomplishments	• established federal government • • •

Refer to this page to answer the Chapter 4 Focus Question on page 77.

Section 4

The Presidency of John Adams

Section 4 Focus Question

How did problems with France intensify the split between the Federalists and Republicans? To begin answering this question,

- Find out about America's troubles with France.
- Discover the impact of the Alien and Sedition acts.
- Learn about the idea of states' rights.

Section 4 Summary

Events in Europe intensified the split between Federalists and Republicans. Tensions increased further with the passage of the Alien and Sedition acts.

Troubles With France

The decision of the United States to remain neutral during the war between France and Britain angered France because it had been an ally during the American Revolution. Also, the signing of Jay's Treaty with Britain made it appear as if the United States favored Britain over France. As a result, France refused to meet with an American diplomat and continued to seize American ships.

In 1797, Adams sent three diplomats to France. Agents of the French foreign minister demanded a bribe from the American diplomats, but the Americans refused to pay one. Many Americans, especially Federalists, were outraged when they learned of the so-called XYZ Affair. (XYZ refers to the three French agents whose real names were kept secret.)

The XYZ Affair led to an undeclared naval war with France. Adams and the Congress increased the size of the army and rebuilt the navy. In addition, Adams created a new department of the navy.

Adams, who opposed war, sent another group of diplomats to France. In 1800, a treaty was signed. France agreed to stop seizing American ships, and the United States avoided a full-scale war with France. The treaty angered many of Adams's fellow Federalists who wanted war with France. ✓

The Alien and Sedition Acts

The undeclared war with France increased distrust between the Federalists and Republicans. Federalists feared that European immigrants would spread dangerous ideas inspired by the French Revolution to America. They also feared that the new immigrants would favor the pro-French Republican Party when they became citizens.

The Federalist-controlled Congress decided to pass several laws. They had two main goals. First, they wanted to slow the

Key Events

1789	Washington organizes new government departments and appoints heads.
1795	Senate approves Jay's Treaty with Britain.
1798	"XYZ Affair" becomes public and sours relations with France. Congress passes the Alien and Sedition acts.

✓ Checkpoint

To what did the XYZ Affair lead?

____

process of becoming a citizen. Second, they wanted to stop immigrants and Republicans from spreading ideas that threatened Federalist control of the federal government.

The Alien Act increased the length of time from 5 to 14 years that it took for an **alien**, or outsider or someone from another country, to become a citizen. It also allowed the President to jail or deport aliens he considered dangerous.

The Sedition Act targeted Republicans. **Sedition** is an activity aimed at overthrowing a government. The act made saying or writing anything insulting or false about the government a crime punishable by jail or a fine. The Sedition Act placed the harshest limits on free speech in America's history. During 1798 and 1799, ten people were convicted under the act. Most were Republican editors and printers. ☑

✓ Checkpoint

Name the act that targeted Republicans.

____

States' Rights

Republicans denounced the Alien and Sedition acts. They declared that the Sedition Act violated free speech protections under the First Amendment of the Constitution. However, it had not yet been clearly established that the Supreme Court had the power to strike down a law as unconstitutional. To overturn this law, therefore, the Republicans worked through state legislatures.

James Madison and Thomas Jefferson wrote resolutions for the Virginia and Kentucky legislatures, respectively. They stated that the Alien and Sedition acts were unconstitutional and that states had the right to declare federal laws unconstitutional.

The Virginia and Kentucky resolutions had little short-term impact. No other states supported them. By 1802 the Alien and Sedition acts had expired, and Congress restored the waiting period for citizenship to five years.

Vocabulary Builder

The word *resolution* has different meanings depending on its context. Which definition is most like that in the bracketed text?

A. A statement of a group's opinion

B. The solving of a problem

The resolutions were far more important over the long run because they established the principles of states' rights and nullification. **States' rights** is the idea that the union binding "these United States" is an agreement between the states and that they therefore can overrule federal law. Nullification is the related idea that states have the power to **nullify**, or deprive of legal force, a federal law. The ideas increased in importance when the southern states began defending slavery. ☑

✓ Checkpoint

Name the two men who wrote resolutions for Virginia and Kentucky.

____

____

Check Your Progress

1. What was John Adams's response to problems with France after the XYZ Affair?

____

____

2. What two principles did the Virginia and Kentucky resolutions help to establish?

____

____

Section 4 Notetaking Study Guide

Questions to Think About As you read Section 4 in your textbook and take notes, keep this question in mind: **How did problems with France intensify the split between the Federalists and Republicans?**

► Use this chart to record key information from the section. Some information has been filled in to get you started.

The Presidency of John Adams

Troubles With France

- France was angry that the United States remained ____________ in the war between France and Britain. The French also felt that Jay's Treaty favored Britain.
- France ____________ an American diplomat and continued to seize ____________.
- XYZ Affair
  - French officials demanded a ____________ from three American ____________.
  - Many Americans, especially ____________, were outraged.
- American anger over the XYZ Affair led to an ____________. Adams increased the size of the ____________ and established a ____________ ____________.
- In 1800, France and the United States signed a treaty. France agreed to ____________, and the United States ____________ ____________.
- The treaty angered many ____________, which ____________ President Adams's political power.

The Alien and Sedition Acts

- Reasons Federalists opposed European immigration
  -
  -
- The Alien Act increased the time it took for an alien to ____________ ____________. It also allowed the President to jail or ____________ an alien he considered dangerous.
- The Sedition Act made it a crime to ____________ about the government. This was a limit on ____________.

States' Rights

- The legislatures of ____________ and ____________ passed resolutions stating that the Alien and Sedition acts were unconstitutional and that states had the right to ____________.
- The long-term effect was to establish the principles of states' rights and ____________, or the idea that states have the power to deprive a federal law of legal force.

Refer to this page to answer the Chapter 4 Focus Question on page 77.

Chapter 4 Assessment

Directions: Circle the letter of the correct answer.

1. Which was a crisis faced by President George Washington?
   - **A** Shays' Rebellion
   - **B** repaying war debt
   - **C** fighting a war with France
   - **D** Boston Tea Party

2. Which best describes the Republican Party?
   - **A** It supported Britain over France.
   - **B** Its leader was Alexander Hamilton.
   - **C** It opposed a national bank.
   - **D** Its supporters were merchants.

3. Which did George Washington support in his Farewell Address?
   - **A** avoiding political divisions at home
   - **B** adding a bill of rights to the Constitution
   - **C** supporting the French Revolution
   - **D** passing the Alien and Sedition Acts

4. Which was a result of the Virginia and Kentucky resolutions?
   - **A** idea of nullification
   - **B** freedom of religion
   - **C** individual rights
   - **D** Three-fifths Compromise

Directions: Follow the steps to answer this question:
How did the advice Washington gave in his Farewell Address reflect or not reflect his accomplishments as President?

Step 1: Recall information: In the chart, list Washington's advice and accomplishments.

Washington's Advice	Washington's Accomplishments
1.	1.
	2.
2.	3.
	4.

Step 2: Identify similarities and differences between his advice and accomplishments.

____

____

____

Step 3: Complete the topic sentence that follows. Then write two or three sentences explaining how Washington's accomplishments did or did not reflect his advice.

Washington's accomplishments as President ______________________

____

____

____

Chapter 4 Notetaking Study Guide

Now you are ready to answer the Chapter 4 Focus Question: **How did Americans respond to internal and external challenges?**

► Complete the following chart to help you answer this question. Use the notes that you took for each section.

Challenges Facing the New Government	
Internal Challenges	**External Challenges**
Organizing the Government • Congress passed laws to set up three departments in the executive branch: ______, ______, and ______ • Judicial branch: Judiciary Act of 1789	***The French Revolution*** • Federalist reaction: denounced the violence of the revolution • Republican reaction: ______
The Nation's First Economic Crisis • Problem: ______ • Solution: Alexander Hamilton proposed a ______ plan. Congress agreed to 1. ______ 2. ______	**France and Britain at War** • U.S. position: ______ • Effect of position: ______
The Whiskey Rebellion • To raise money, Congress imposed a ______ that led to a revolt. • Washington sent in the militia, which confirmed ______.	**Troubles with Britain** Jay's Treaty: • Americans agreed to: ______ • British agreed to: ______ • British did not agree to: ______
Political Disagreements • Two parties formed: ______, ______.	
Conflicts in the Northwest Territory • Reasons U.S. upset with Britain: ______ • Source of conflict with Native Americans: ______ Terms of the Treaty of Greenville: ______	**Troubles with France** • Jay's Treaty and XYZ Affair led to an ______ • U.S. agreement with France: ______ **Alien and Sedition Acts** Increasing tensions with France prompted the Federalist-led government to pass laws that made it harder to gain ______ and restricted ______.

Refer to this page to answer the Unit 3 Focus Question on page 109.

Chapter Standards

History-Social Science 8.4.1, 8.4.2, 8.5.1, 8.5.3, 8.8.2, 8.8.4

Chapter 5

The Era of Thomas Jefferson (1800–1815)

What You Will Learn

During Thomas Jefferson's presidency, the United States acquired a vast expanse of western territory. Conflicts with the British and Native Americans soon led to the War of 1812.

Chapter 5 Focus Question

As you read the sections in this chapter, keep this question in mind: **How did Jefferson and Madison deal with unresolved problems?**

Key Events

1803	The United States purchases Louisiana from France.
1811	Americans defeat Native Americans at Battle of Tippecanoe.
1812	United States declares war on Britain.

Section 1

Jefferson Takes Office

Section 1 Focus Question

How did Jefferson chart a new course for the government? To begin answering this question,

- Learn about the Republican victory in the election of 1800.
- Find out about Jefferson's new course for government.
- Learn about judicial review.

Section 1 Summary

After a bitter campaign, Thomas Jefferson took office as President. Jefferson tried to reduce the power of the federal government over states and citizens. Meanwhile, judicial review increased the Supreme Court's power.

Republicans Take Charge

The presidential campaign of 1800 was a bitter contest between the Federalists and the Republicans. The Federalists threatened a civil war if Jefferson won the election. **Thomas Jefferson**, the Republican candidate, received 73 electoral votes, defeating John Adams, the Federalist candidate. According to the Constitution, the person who received the next highest total of electoral votes would become Vice President. However, **Aaron Burr**, Jefferson's running mate, also received 73 votes. It was up to the House of Representatives to break the tie. After six days of deadlock, the House chose Jefferson. To avoid this situation in the future, the Twelfth Amendment to the Constitution established separate votes for President and Vice President.

Beginning with his inauguration, Jefferson established simpler customs that he believed were appropriate for a republic. For example, he walked to his inauguration rather than ride in a carriage. Equally important, Jefferson used his inaugural address to bring the country together. ✓

Jefferson Charts a New Course

The new President saw his election as a chance to introduce new ideas. He thought of it as the "Revolution of 1800." Jefferson's first goal was to reduce the federal government's power over states and citizens. He believed in an idea known as **laissez faire**, which means that the government should not interfere with the economy.

Jefferson's Main Policy Changes
• Reduced the number of people in government • Cut military spending • Eliminated federal taxes in the country, except tariffs • Released those jailed under the Sedition Act

Jefferson did not reverse all Federalist policies, however. For example, he believed that the nation should keep repaying its debt, and he did not fire most Federalist officeholders. ✓

The Supreme Court and Judicial Review

During his last hours in office, Adams appointed several judges. The Republicans argued that the appointments were an attempt to maintain Federalist power. When Jefferson took office, he ordered James Madison, his secretary of state, to stop work on the appointments. William Marbury, one of Adams's appointees, sued Madison to receive his commission. In his lawsuit, Marbury cited the Judiciary Act of 1789, which gave the Supreme Court the power to review cases brought against a federal official.

The outcome of the case, called *Marbury* v. *Madison*, changed the relationship of the three branches of government. In an opinion written by Chief Justice **John Marshall**, the Court declared the Judiciary Act was unconstitutional. Marshall stated that the Court's powers came from the Constitution. Therefore, Congress did not have the right to give the Court power in the Judiciary Act. This ruling established **judicial review**, or the authority of the Supreme Court to strike down unconstitutional laws. ✓

Check Your Progress

1. How did the election of 1800 affect future elections?

____

____

2. What power does judicial review give the Supreme Court?

____

____

✓ Checkpoint

Name the body that decided the election of 1800.

____

✓ Checkpoint

List a Federalist policy that Jefferson kept.

____

Vocabulary Builder

Reread the bracketed paragraph. The text says Marbury was one of Adams's appointees. Using context clues in the paragraph, write a definition of *appointee* on the lines below.

____

____

✓ Checkpoint

Name the justice who wrote the Supreme Court's decision in *Marbury* v. *Madison*.

____

Section 1 Notetaking Study Guide

Question to Think About As you read Section 1 in your textbook and take notes, keep this section focus question in mind: **How did Jefferson chart a new course for the government?**

► Use these charts to record key information from the section. Some information has been filled in to get you started.

The Election of 1800

- **The presidential candidates**
  1. Federalist: John Adams
  2. Republican: Thomas Jefferson
- The tie between ____________ and ____________ occurred because ____
- Deadlock resolved by ____________________________
- Amendment passed as a result of the tie: ____________________
- Amendment established ____

Jefferson Charts a New Course

- Jefferson's first goal as president: ________________________
- The reforms Jefferson made to meet his goal:
  -
  -
  -
  -
- Federalist policies Jefferson did not reverse:
  -
  -

The Supreme Court and Judicial Review

- In ____________ v. ____________, the Supreme Court ruled the ________________________ unconstitutional because ____
- This decision established ____________________, or the authority of the Supreme Court to strike down ________________________ laws.

Refer to this page to answer the Chapter 5 Focus Question on page 91.

Section 2

The Louisiana Purchase and Lewis and Clark

Section 2 Focus Question

What was the importance of the purchase and exploration of the Louisiana Territory? To begin answering this question,

- Learn about the nation's westward expansion.
- Find out about the Louisiana Purchase.
- Learn about Lewis and Clark's western expedition.

Section 2 Summary

Westward expansion sped up after the United States won its independence. The Louisiana Purchase almost doubled the size of the United States, and the Lewis and Clark expedition provided Americans with new knowledge of the West.

The Nation Looks West

By 1800, more than one million settlers lived between the Appalachian Mountains and the Mississippi River. Most settlers were farmers. Because there were few roads to the West, they shipped their crops down the Mississippi to the port at New Orleans. From there, the goods were shipped to markets in the East.

Spain, which controlled the Mississippi and New Orleans, had several times threatened to close the port to American ships. To prevent this from happening, the United States negotiated the Pinckney Treaty with Spain in 1795, which guaranteed Americans the right to ship goods down the Mississippi to New Orleans.

In 1801, Jefferson discovered that Spain had secretly transferred New Orleans and the rest of its Louisiana territory to France. Jefferson feared that Napoleon Bonaparte, the French leader, intended to expand France's control in America. ✓

The Louisiana Purchase

In 1802, before the transfer of Louisiana to France took place, Spain withdrew the right of Americans to ship their goods through New Orleans. Westerners demanded that Jefferson go to war to win back their rights.

Instead Jefferson sent James Monroe to Paris to offer to buy the city of New Orleans and a territory to the east called West Florida from the French. Monroe was assisted by Robert Livingston, the American minister in Paris.

Around this time, a revolution had driven the French from their Caribbean colony of Haiti. Without this base, France would have trouble defending Louisiana in a war. At the same time, tensions between France and Britain were rising, and war loomed. Napoleon needed money to support the war effort. As a result, France offered to sell not only New Orleans, but the entire

Key Events

1803	The United States purchases Louisiana from France.
1811	Americans defeat Native Americans at Battle of Tippecanoe.
1812	United States declares war on Britain.

✓ Checkpoint

Describe the route by which Western farm products traveled to markets in the East.

____

____

____

____

Louisiana Territory to the United States. The territory stretched from the Gulf of Mexico to Canada and from the Mississippi River to the Rocky Mountains.

Jefferson was delighted with the deal, which almost doubled the size of the country and gave the United States control of the Mississippi. However, the Constitution did not give the President the power to buy land from a foreign country. In the end, Jefferson decided that the power the Constitution gave the President to make treaties allowed him to buy Louisiana. The Senate approved the treaty, and Congress quickly voted to pay for the land. ✓

✓ Checkpoint

List the four boundaries of Louisiana Territory.

____

____

____

____

Lewis and Clark Explore the West

Even before the United States had bought Louisiana, Jefferson called on Congress to finance a western **expedition,** or long and carefully organized journey. Army officers **Meriwether Lewis** and **William Clark** were to lead the expedition.

Vocabulary Builder

An early definition of *expedition* was "helping forward or accomplishing." How can this definition still explain the word *expedition*?

____

____

____

Lewis and Clark's mission had three goals. First, they were to report on the geography, plants, animals, and other natural features of the region. Second, they were to make contact with Native Americans. Third, they were to find out if a waterway connected the Mississippi River to the Pacific Ocean.

Lewis and Clark left St. Louis in the spring of 1804 with about 40 men. In October, a Native American woman named Sacagawea joined the expedition as a translator. The following August, they reached the Continental Divide of the Rocky Mountains. A **continental divide** is the place on a continent that separates river systems flowing in opposite directions. On the western side of the Rockies, they reached the Columbia River, which carried them to the Pacific Ocean. They spent the winter at the point where the Columbia River meets the Pacific before beginning their half-year-long return journey in March 1806. With them, they brought a new awareness of a rich and beautiful part of the continent.

Zebulon Pike led another expedition through the southern part of the Louisiana Territory from 1805 to 1807. His return route took him into Spanish New Mexico, where he and his men were arrested as spies. After several months, they were released. As the Spanish had feared, Pike's reports about the Spanish borderlands created great American interest in the region. ✓

✓ Checkpoint

Name the Native American woman who served as a translator for Lewis and Clark.

____

Check Your Progress

1. Why was the Louisiana Purchase important?

____

____

2. What was one purpose of the Lewis and Clark expedition?

____

____

Section 2 Notetaking Study Guide

Question to Think About As you read Section 2 in your textbook and take notes, keep this section focus question in mind: **What was the importance of the purchase and exploration of the Louisiana Territory?**

▶ Use these charts to record key information from the section. Some information has been filled in to get you started.

Westward Expansion and the Louisiana Purchase
Importance of access to the Mississippi River: *few roads; farmers depended on the river to move their farm products to the east*
Importance of Pinckney's Treaty:
Jefferson's fear about the transfer of Louisiana to France:

The Louisiana Purchase
Jefferson's proposed deal:
Situation in France at the time: • •
France's offer:
Jefferson's dilemma:
Resolution to the dilemma:

Exploring the West
Reasons for Lewis and Clark's expedition: • • •
• **Route to Pacific:** • **Result:**
• **Route of Pike's Expedition:** • **Result:**

Refer to this page to answer the Chapter 5 Focus Question on page 91.

Section 3

A Time of Conflict

Key Events

1803	The United States purchases Louisiana from France.
1811	Americans defeat Native Americans at Battle of Tippecanoe.
1812	United States declares war on Britain.

Section 3 Focus Question

How did Jefferson respond to threats to the security of the nation? To begin answering this question,

- Learn about the defeat of the Barbary States.
- Find out about the threats to American neutrality.
- Read about the trade embargo Jefferson imposed.
- Explore the efforts of Tecumseh and the Prophet to preserve Native American lands and ways of life.

Section 3 Summary

Jefferson faced numerous threats to the nation's security and economy, including piracy, seizure of American ships by Britain and France, and unrest among Native Americans.

Defeating the Barbary States

Trade with Europe was critical to the U.S. economy. After the American Revolution, pirates began attacking American ships in the Mediterranean Sea. The pirates came from four North African countries known as the Barbary States. They were Morocco, Algiers, Tunisia, and Tripoli. European nations paid the Barbary States **tribute**, or money paid by one country to another in return for protection. In exchange, pirates left their ships alone.

For a time the United States also paid tribute, but Jefferson put an end to that practice and sent warships to the Mediterranean to protect American merchant ships. At first these military patrols went badly. For example, the warship *Philadelphia* ran aground near the Tripoli coast, and its crew was captured. However, the next year, a small force of American marines marched 600 miles across the Sahara to capture Tripoli. This victory inspired confidence in the ability of the United States to deal forcefully with threats from foreign powers. ✓

✓ Checkpoint

List the four Barbary States.

____

____

____

____

American Neutrality Is Challenged

By 1803 Britain and France were once again at war. The United States, which remained neutral, continued trading with both countries. Britain and France began seizing American ships carrying trade goods to the other country. This was an attempt to weaken one other by cutting off the other's foreign trade. In addition, Britain impressed, or forced, thousands of American sailors to serve in the British navy. ✓

✓ Checkpoint

Name the countries that challenged the United States' neutrality.

____

____

Jefferson Responds With an Embargo

Jefferson tried to force Britain and France to respect American neutrality by issuing an **embargo**. This is a government order that forbids foreign trade. In 1807 Congress passed the Embargo Act.

Jefferson predicted that France and Britain would soon stop attacking American ships.

However, Jefferson did not foresee the result of the embargo. The big loser proved to be the American economy. Declining exports caused crop prices to fall and tens of thousands of Americans to lose their jobs. The embargo was especially unpopular in New England, where merchants depended heavily on foreign trade. To evade the embargo, thousands of Americans turned to **smuggling**, or the act of illegally importing or exporting goods.

Congress finally repealed the Embargo Act in 1809. It then passed a law that reopened trade with all countries except Britain and France. The law stated that trade with Britain and France would resume when they started respecting America's trading rights as a neutral nation. ✓

✓ Checkpoint

List two effects of the Embargo Act on the United States' economy.

____

____

Tecumseh and the Prophet

After the Battle of Fallen Timbers, tens of thousands of settlers moved westward. Ohio became a state in 1803, and settlers moved into Indiana Territory and beyond.

The tide of settlement had a terrible impact on Native Americans. Westward expansion exposed Native Americans to disease, threatened their hunting grounds, and drove away game. The Native American population declined, as did the power of their traditional leaders.

Two Shawnee brothers, **Tecumseh** and Tenskwatawa, or the Prophet, began urging Native American resistance. They called on Native Americans to preserve their traditional ways.

American officials were concerned by Tecumseh's activities. While Tecumseh was gone, **William Henry Harrison**, the governor of the Indiana Territory, led an attack on Shawnee villages on the Tippecanoe River. Harrison's troops defeated the Native Americans. The Battle of Tippecanoe marked the high point of Native American resistance to settlement. Still, Tecumseh and his warriors continued their struggle for several more years. ✓

✓ Checkpoint

Name the two Native American leaders who fought back against American settlement in the West.

____

____

Check Your Progress

1. What were the main threats to American trade?

____

____

2. How did westward expansion affect Native Americans?

____

____

Section 3 Notetaking Study Guide

Question to Think About As you read Section 3 in your textbook and take notes, keep this section focus question in mind: **How did Jefferson respond to threats to the security of the nation?**

► Use this organizer to record key information from the section. Some information has been filled in to get you started.

Barbary Pirates

- Why they were a threat: stole property and enslaved sailors
- Some nations responded by ______
- How Jefferson responded: ______

Challenges Faced by the United States

American Neutrality Challenged

- Causes: War between Britain and France leads to restrictions on U.S. trade
- Actions taken by Britain and France: ______
- U.S. response: ______
- Results of embargo:
  - ______
  - ______
  - ______
- Congress repealed Embargo Act in 1809.

Native American Unrest

- Cause of unrest: rapid westward settlement
- Effects on Native Americans
  - exposed to new deadly diseases
  - ______
  - ______
  - ______
- Tecumseh and Tenskwatawa urged Native Americans to:
  - ______
  - ______
- U.S. response to unrest: ______

Refer to this page to answer the Chapter 5 Focus Question on page 91.

Section 4
The War of 1812

Section 4 Focus Question

What were the causes and effects of the War of 1812? To begin answering this question,

- Find out why the United States moved toward war with Britain.
- Learn about the early days of the war.
- Read about the war in the West and South.
- Learn about the final battles of the war.

Section 4 Summary

The War of 1812 started badly for the United States. However, America's eventual victory increased American nationalism.

The Move Toward War

When James Madison became President in 1809, Americans were angry with the British for supplying arms to Native Americans and impressing American sailors. To most Americans, the country's honor was at stake. They felt a new sense of **nationalism**, or pride in one's country.

In 1810, Henry Clay of Kentucky and John C. Calhoun of South Carolina became leaders in the House of Representatives. The two men and their supporters were called **war hawks** because they were eager for war with Britain. Opposition to war was strongest in New England, where many believed war would harm American trade.

Relations with Britain worsened in the spring of 1812 when the British told the United States they would continue impressing sailors. Meanwhile, Native Americans in the Northwest began new attacks on frontier settlements. In June, Congress declared war on Britain. ✓

Early Days of the War

Britain was still at war in Europe at the time, but it was not willing to meet American demands in order to avoid war. When the war began, Americans were confident they would win. However, because of military cuts under Jefferson, the United States military was not prepared for war.

At the beginning of the war, Britain set up a blockade of the American coast. A **blockade** is the action of shutting a port or road to prevent people or supplies from coming into an area or leaving it. By the end of the war, the British were able to close off all American ports.

One early naval success for the United States was the USS *Constitution's* defeat of the British warship the *Guerrière*. ✓

Key Events

1803	The United States purchases Louisiana from France.
1811	Americans defeat Native Americans at Battle of Tippecanoe.
1812	United States declares war on Britain.

✓ Checkpoint

Name the region in the United States where opposition to the war with Britain was strongest.

____

✓ Checkpoint

Name an action the British took at the beginning of the war.

____

✓ Checkpoint

List two commanders who led American forces to victory.

The War in the West and South

In the West, the Americans and British fought for control of the Great Lakes and the Mississippi River. The British captured American General William Hull's troops after they tried to invade Canada. American forces under **Oliver Hazard Perry**, however, scored an important victory against the British on Lake Erie. William Henry Harrison and his troops defeated the British at the Battle of the Thames. In the South, Creek warriors attacked several American settlements. **Andrew Jackson** led American troops to victory against the Creeks in the Battle of Horseshoe Bend. ✓

Vocabulary Builder

The word *negotiate* comes from the Latin word for "to carry on business." What do you think the word *negotiating* means in the context of the underlined sentence?

Final Battles

After the British defeated Napoleon in 1814, they sent more troops to fight against the United States. In August, British troops attacked Washington, D.C., burning down several government buildings, including the White House. The British moved on Baltimore, where they attacked Fort McHenry. British warships bombarded the fort throughout the night of September 13, 1814. At dawn, however, the Americans still held the fort. An American, Francis Scott Key, witnessed the battle and wrote the poem, "The Star-Spangled Banner." Set to music, it later became the national anthem of the United States.

Britain began to tire of the war, so the two sides began negotiating a peace treaty. On Christmas Eve 1814, the United States and Britain signed the Treaty of Ghent, ending the war. It took several weeks for the news to reach the United States, and during this time, the two sides fought one last battle. In January 1815, American forces under General Andrew Jackson defeated the British at the Battle of New Orleans.

Meanwhile opponents of the war met in Hartford, Connecticut, in December 1814. Some delegates suggested that New England **secede**, or withdraw, from the United States. However, the convention quickly ended when news of the treaty arrived.

✓ Checkpoint

Name the battle that occurred after the peace treaty was signed.

To some Americans, the War of 1812 was the "Second War of Independence." Once and for all, the United States had secured its independence from Britain, and European nations would now have to treat the young republic with respect. ✓

Check Your Progress

1. What British actions led to the War of 1812?

2. Why was the United States unprepared for war?

Section 4 Notetaking Study Guide

Question to Think About As you read Section 4 in your textbook and take notes, keep this question in mind: **What were the causes and effects of the War of 1812?**

► Use these charts to record key information. Some information has been filled in to get you started.

The Move Toward War
The President during the War of 1812 was James Madison.
The two main reasons Americans wanted to go to war with Britain were ____________ and ____________.
Supporters of the war were called ____________.
New Englanders opposed the war because ____________.

Early Days of the War
The war did not come at a good time for Britain because ____________ ____________.
Near the start of the war, the British Navy ____________.
The U.S. warship that won an early battle was the ____________.

The War in the West and South
U.S. General William Hull invaded ____________, and then ____________. Then British General Isaac Brock ____________.
The U.S. naval commander ____________ won an important battle on Lake Erie. U.S. General William Henry Harrison won the Battle of ____________ where ____________ was killed.
____________ defeated the Creeks in the Battle of ____________.

Final Battles
In 1814, the British could send more troops to fight the war the United States because ____________.
During an attack on the nation's ____________ in 1814, British troops burned ____________.
During the British attack on ____________ in Baltimore, Francis Scott Key wrote the words to ____________.
The Treaty of ____________ ended the War of 1812.
Before news of the war's end reached the U.S., ____________ led the U.S. to victory in the Battle of ____________.
Federalists met at the ____________ where some suggested New England ____________ from the U.S.

Refer to this page to answer the Chapter 5 Focus Question on page 91.

Chapter 5 Assessment

Directions: Circle the letter of the correct answer.

1. Which was a goal of President Thomas Jefferson?
   - **A** declare war on Britain
   - **B** add a Bill of Rights to the Constitution
   - **C** reduce the size of the federal government
   - **D** reduce the powers of state governments

2. Who was the Treaty of Ghent between?
   - **A** Thomas Jefferson and James Madison
   - **B** William Marbury and John Marshall
   - **C** the United States and France
   - **D** the United States and Britain

3. What was an effect of the Embargo Act?
   - **A** increased unemployment in America
   - **B** higher prices for American crops
   - **C** war between Britain and France
   - **D** war with Native Americans

Directions: Follow the steps to answer this question:

How might the United States be different if the Louisiana Purchase had not occurred?

Step 1: Recall information: In the chart, list three benefits of the Louisiana Purchase for the United States.

Benefits of the Louisiana Purchase in 1803
•
•
•

Step 2: Now imagine what two ways the United States would be different today if it had been denied those benefits.

Differences in the United States Without Those Benefits
•
•

Step 3: Complete the topic sentence that follows. Then write two or three more sentences that support your topic sentence.

Without the Louisiana Purchase, the United States____________________

____

____

____

____

Chapter 5 Notetaking Study Guide

Now you are ready to answer the Chapter 5 Focus Question: **How did Jefferson and Madison deal with unresolved problems?**

► Complete the following organizer to help you answer this question. Use the notes that you took for each section.

Unresolved Problems

Challenges Facing Jefferson		Jefferson's Responses
Size and power of the federal government	→	• reduced number of federal employees • • •
Access to the Mississippi River and land for American settlers	→	• •
Pirates attacking American ships	→	• •
Impressment and seizure of American sailors and ships	→	•

Challenges Facing Madison		Madison's Response
• British continue to arm Native Americans in Northwest •	→	• United States declared war on Britain.

Refer to this page to answer the Unit 5 Focus Question on page 109.

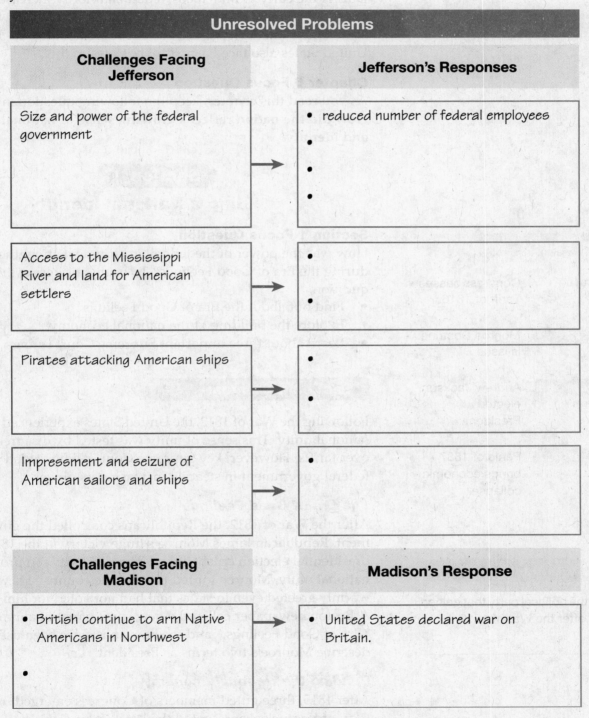

Chapter 6

A Changing Nation (1815–1840)

What You Will Learn

During the early to mid-1800s, federal authority increased, and the status of the United States among other nations grew. At the same time, American politics became more democratic. The United States also faced a crisis over states' rights.

Chapter 6 Focus Question

As you read this chapter, keep the following question in mind: **How did the nation reflect a growing sense of national pride and identity?**

Chapter Standards

History-Social Science 8.4.2, 8.4.3, 8.5.2, 8.6.2, 8.8.1

Key Events

1816	Congress passes Tariff of 1816.
1823	Monroe Doctrine is issued.
1828	Andrew Jackson elected President.
1837	Panic of 1837 brings economic collapse.

Section 1

Building a National Identity

Section 1 Focus Question

How was the power of the federal government strengthened during the Era of Good Feelings? To begin answering this question,

- Find out about the Era of Good Feelings.
- Explore the building of the national economy.
- Learn about three important Supreme Court rulings.

Section 1 Summary

Following the War of 1812, the United States experienced a rise in national unity. This sense of unity was tested by disagreements over tariffs. However, key Supreme Court rulings aided the federal government in steadily increasing its power.

The Era of Good Feelings

After the War of 1812, the Republicans controlled the government. Republican James Monroe's huge victory in the 1816 presidential election crushed the Federalist Party. To promote national unity, Monroe toured parts of the country. He was warmly greeted even in states that had not voted for him in 1816. A Boston newspaper called the new spirit of national unity the "Era of Good Feelings," and the name has since been used to describe Monroe's two terms as President. ✓

✓ Checkpoint

Name the political party that gained power after the War of 1812.

____

Building the National Economy

After 1815, three gifted members of Congress emerged. **Henry Clay** of Kentucky represented the West. **John C. Calhoun** of South Carolina spoke for southern interests. **Daniel Webster** of Massachusetts was a leading politician for the Northeast.

The economy was one topic of debate for these men. When the first Bank of the United States closed in 1811, the U.S. economy suffered. In 1816, Congress approved a new **charter**—a legal document giving certain rights to a person or company—for a second Bank of the United States. This federal bank stabilized the money supply and helped business, but it did not solve all the nation's economic problems. After the War of 1812, British companies began to sell manufactured goods below market price in America, a practice known as **dumping**. This drove many New England companies out of business. Congress responded by passing the Tariff of 1816, which taxed foreign goods like cloth, iron, leather goods, and paper. Congress passed even higher tariffs in 1818 and 1824. Such protective tariffs were popular in the North, where they protected local factories. But in the South, people resented the high tariffs that made goods more expensive.

Henry Clay defended high tariffs in a plan he called the American System. He said the money from tariffs could pay to build infrastructure, such as bridges, canals, and roads. Clay argued that this would help all regions. Southerners rejected the American System and continued to oppose the tariffs. ✓

Three Important Supreme Court Rulings

Between 1819 and 1824, the Supreme Court issued three major rulings that affected the economy and the power of the federal government. In *Dartmouth College* v. *Woodward* (1819), the Court protected private contracts. A **contract** is an agreement between two or more parties that can be enforced by law. This ruling promoted **capitalism**, an economic system in which private businesses compete in a free market. In *McCulloch* v. *Maryland* (1819), the Court ruled that a state cannot pass a law that violates a federal law. In addition, the Court said states had no power to interfere with federal institutions. This protected the second Bank of the United States from being taxed by the state of Maryland. In *Gibbons* v. *Ogden* (1824), the Court blocked New York State from giving a steamboat company the sole right to carry passengers on the Hudson River. Because the trip involved trade between two or more states, it was considered **interstate commerce**. Only Congress can regulate such trade. The *McCulloch* v. *Maryland* and *Gibbons* v. *Ogden* rulings both increased the power of the federal government when dealing with the states. ✓

Check Your Progress

1. Why did Congress pass protective tariffs?

____

____

2. How did the Supreme Court's rulings increase the power of the federal government?

____

____

Vocabulary Builder

The word *infrastructure* means "foundation" or "basic framework." How do structures like roads and bridges serve as a foundation or framework for the nation?

____

____

✓ Checkpoint

Name three key members of Congress and the regions they represented.

Member: ______________

Region: ______________

Member: ______________

Region: ______________

Member: ______________

Region: ______________

✓ Checkpoint

Name the Supreme Court ruling that said states cannot pass laws that violate federal laws.

____

Section 1 Notetaking Study Guide

Question to Think About As you read Section 1 in your textbook and take notes, keep this section focus question in mind: **How was the power of the federal government strengthened during the Era of Good Feelings?**

► Use these charts to record key information from the section.

Important Political Figures During the Era of Good Feelings	
Henry Clay	Congressman from ________ who represented ________ interests; proposed the ________
John C. Calhoun	Congressman from ________ who represented ________ interests; emphasized ________
	Congressman from ________ who represented northern interests; supported ________

Important Economic Issues

Topic	Why It Was Needed	What It Did
Second Bank of United States	________ made too many loans and issued too much money.	Loaned money and controlled the ________
Tariff of 1816	________ manufacturers were ________, which hurt American businesses.	________ on foreign goods, pleasing ________ and upsetting ________

Key Supreme Court Cases

Case	Supreme Court Ruling
________ v. ________ (____)	**Question:** Can Maryland tax a state branch of the ________? **Decision:** States cannot ________ federal institutions or violate ________.
________ v. Woodward (1819)	**Question:** Can New Hampshire change the charter of ________? **Decision:** The charter was a private contract protected by the ________.
Gibbons v. Ogden (1824)	**Question:** Can ________ grant a steamship company a ________ on the Hudson River ferry? **Decision:** The ferry trip involved ________, which only ________ can ________.

Refer to this page to answer the Chapter 6 Focus Question on page 108.

Section 2

Dealing With Other Nations

Section 2 Focus Question

How did U.S. foreign affairs reflect new national confidence? To begin answering this question,

- Learn about U.S. relations with Spain.
- Find out how Spanish colonies won independence.
- Learn about the Monroe Doctrine.
- Examine U.S. relations with Canada.

Section 2 Summary

After the War of 1812, the United States settled border disputes with Spain and Britain involving Florida and Canada. Many Latin American colonies declared independence. The Monroe Doctrine aimed to prevent European powers from interfering with these nations or other U.S. interests in the Americas.

Relations With Spain

The Spanish territory of Florida was a source of conflict between the United States and Spain. The Spanish could not stop enslaved African Americans who had escaped from plantations in Georgia and Alabama from crossing into Florida. Many of these former slaves joined the Seminole Nation. The Seminoles in turn often crossed the border to raid American settlements. In 1817, the U.S. government sent Andrew Jackson to recapture escaped slaves. Jackson destroyed Seminole villages and then captured two Spanish towns. Spain realized that it could not defend Florida from the United States, so it decided to give up the territory. Spain **ceded**, or gave up, Florida to the United States in the Adams-Onís Treaty of 1819. ✓

Spanish Colonies Win Independence

Spain's control of its other American colonies was also fading. The people of Latin America were inspired by the American and French revolutions to seek independence. In 1810, **Father Miguel Hidalgo** (ee DAHL goh) led an unsuccessful rebellion against Spanish rule in Mexico. But in 1820, there was another revolution, forcing Spain to grant Mexico independence in 1821. Mexico overthrew its emperor and became a republic in 1823.

In South America, **Simón Bolívar** (see MOHN boh LEE vahr) led several struggles for independence. Known as the Liberator, Bolívar defeated the Spanish in 1819 and formed the Republic of Great Colombia. This included what are now Colombia, Ecuador, Panama, and Venezuela. The people of Central America soon followed by declaring their independence from Spain in 1821. They formed the United Provinces of Central America two years later. By 1825, most of Latin America had thrown off European rule. ✓

Key Events

1816	Congress passes Tariff of 1816.
1823	Monroe Doctrine is issued.
1828	Andrew Jackson elected President.
1837	Panic of 1837 brings economic collapse.

✓ Checkpoint

Name the reason Spain was willing to cede Florida to the United States.

____

____

Vocabulary Builder

To *liberate* means "to set free." Why do you think Simón Bolívar was called the Liberator?

____

____

____

✓ Checkpoint

Name two events that inspired Latin American independence movements.

____

____

The Monroe Doctrine

In 1822, the United States recognized the independence of Mexico and six other former colonies in Latin America. But European powers like France and Russia wanted to help Spain regain its colonies. Great Britain and the United States opposed this idea. In 1823, Britain suggested that America and Britain act jointly. They would announce that they would protect the freedom of Latin America. President **James Monroe** approved, but Secretary of State **John Quincy Adams** argued that the United States would look like Britain's junior partner if the two cooperated.

In a message to Congress in 1823, the President stated what is now called the Monroe Doctrine. The United States would not allow European nations to create American colonies or to interfere with the free nations of Latin America. Any attempt to do so would be considered "dangerous to our peace and safety." In truth, the United States was not strong enough to block European action. Only the British navy could do that. As U.S. power grew, however, the Monroe Doctrine boosted the influence of the United States in the region. ✓

✓ Checkpoint

Name the region covered by the Monroe Doctrine.

____

Relations With Canada

Britain faced its own challenges in Canada. In 1791, this British colony was divided into Upper and Lower Canada. After each part rebelled in 1837, Britain rejoined the colony in 1841 under the Act of Union. This act gave the Canadian people greater **self-government**—the right of people to rule themselves independently. Britain, however, still had ultimate control.

Canadian relations with the United States were strained. Tensions were particularly high during the War of 1812 when U.S. forces tried to invade Canada. However, relations improved as Britain and the United States settled several border disputes involving Canada from 1818 to 1846. Eventually, the United States and Canada established excellent relations. These relations remain strong even today. ✓

✓ Checkpoint

Name the act that reunited Canada in 1841.

____

Check Your Progress

1. What are two reasons the United States was upset about relations with Spanish Florida?

____

____

____

2. Why did Secretary of State Adams not want the United States to work with Great Britain on the Monroe Doctrine?

____

____

Section 2 Notetaking Study Guide

Question to Think About As you read Section 2 in your textbook and take notes, keep this section focus question in mind: **How did U.S. foreign affairs reflect new national confidence?**

▶ Use these organizers to record key information from the section. Some information has been filled in to get you started.

Latin American Independence

Region	Country/countries to gain independence	When
North America	Mexico: First a ________, then a ________	
	People in this region declared their independence from Spain and formed the ________________.	1821
South America	________________ made up of today's nations of Colombia, Ecuador, Panama, and Venezuela	
	Brazil announced its independence from ________.	

U.S.-Foreign Relations

Relations With Spain →

Sources of U.S. Conflict With Spain:
- Escaped slaves ________________.
- Seminoles in Florida raided ________________.
- The United States seized ________.
- Spain ceded ________ to the United States in ________.

Relations With Canada →

- How Canada was divided before 1841: Upper and Lower Canada
- What the Act of Union was:
- Importance of the Act of Union:
- Why tensions were high during the War of 1812:

Monroe Doctrine →

- What it stated:
- When issued:
- Factors that led up to its statement:

Refer to this page to answer the Chapter 6 Focus Question on page 108.

Key Events

1816	Congress passes Tariff of 1816.
1823	Monroe Doctrine is issued.
1828	Andrew Jackson elected President.
1837	Panic of 1837 brings economic collapse.

✓ Checkpoint

List two reasons Jackson was deeply loved by millions of Americans.

____

____

Section 3

The Age of Jackson

Section 3 Focus Question

How did the people gain more power during the Age of Jackson? To begin answering this question,

- Find out about the conflict between Adams and Jackson.
- Learn about a new era in politics.
- Discover how Jackson became President.

Section 3 Summary

The period from the mid-1820s to the end of the 1830s is called the Age of Jackson, after President **Andrew Jackson**. Jackson had a huge impact on American politics. His administration allowed everyday Americans to play a greater role in government.

Adams and Jackson in Conflict

Born in a log cabin, Andrew Jackson began his life with very little. However, Jackson's toughness and determination helped him become wealthy. Jackson stood for the idea that ordinary people should participate, or take part, in American political life. As a general and later as President, Andrew Jackson was deeply loved by millions of ordinary Americans who respected his humble beginnings and firm leadership.

In the presidential election of 1824, Jackson won the most popular and electoral votes, but not a majority. According to the Constitution, the House of Representatives would have to decide the election. Candidate and Speaker of the House Henry Clay told his supporters to vote for John Quincy Adams. When Adams was elected and made Clay his secretary of state, Jackson was outraged. His supporters claimed that Clay and Adams had made a "corrupt bargain." These rumors burdened Adams as President. He had ambitious plans for the nation, but he lacked the political skill to push his programs through Congress. Adams never won Americans' trust, and as a result, he served only one term. ✓

A New Era in Politics

Jackson's defeat was the beginning of a new era in politics. By 1824, **suffrage**—the right to vote—had been granted to almost all adult white males, not just those who owned property. However, suffrage was still restricted. Women and enslaved African Americans could not participate in government. States also were changing how they chose presidential electors. Previously, state legislatures chose them. Now, that right went to the voters. In 1824, the voters in 18 out of 24 states chose their electors.

Greater voting rights were part of a larger spread of democratic ideas. Jackson and his supporters believed that ordinary people should vote and hold public office. Jackson did not trust government and banks, which he felt favored the rich. Jackson and his supporters strongly opposed special privileges for those of high social status.

During the 1824 election, the Republican Party split. Jackson's supporters called themselves Democrats. Supporters of Adams called themselves National Republicans. After his defeat in 1824, Jackson won the 1828 presidential election over Adams. Later he won the 1832 election over Nationalist Republican candidate Henry Clay.

In 1836, the new Whig Party replaced the Republicans. The Democrats and Whigs would be the two major parties in U.S. politics until 1852. The new parties adopted a new way of choosing their presidential candidates. The two parties began to hold **nominating conventions**, or large meetings of party delegates who choose party candidates. Previously, a party's members of Congress held a **caucus**—a meeting of members of a political party. ✓

Jackson Becomes President

Three times as many people voted in the election of 1828 as had voted in 1824. Most of these new voters supported Jackson, who easily defeated Adams. The election revealed growing sectional and class divisions among American voters. Jackson did best in the West and South and had strong support from farmers, small business people, and workers nationwide. Adams was most popular in his home region of New England.

Jackson's supporters called the election a victory for the "common man." Some supporters called Jackson the "People's President." Tens of thousands of ordinary people came to the Capitol to attend Jackson's inauguration. Once in office, Jackson replaced some government officials with his own supporters. Although this was not a new practice, Jackson openly defended what he was doing. He claimed that bringing in new people furthered democracy. This practice of rewarding government jobs to supporters of a party that wins an election became known as the **spoils system.** ✓

Check Your Progress

1. What was different about the voting rights enjoyed by citizens in 1824 compared to earlier elections?

____

____

____

____

2. How did political parties change the way they chose candidates after 1836?

____

____

✓ Checkpoint

Name two political parties that formed during the Age of Jackson.

____

____

Vocabulary Builder

There is an old military saying, "to the victors belong the spoils." *Spoil* is another word for loot or prize. Why do you think the name *spoils system* was given to Jackson's practice of putting his supporters in office?

____

____

✓ Checkpoint

How many more people voted in the 1828 election than in the 1824 election?

____

Section 3 Notetaking Study Guide

Question to Think About As you read Section 3 in your textbook and take notes, keep this section focus question in mind: **How did people gain more power during the Age of Jackson?**

▶ Use these charts to record key information from the section. Some information has been filled in to get you started.

Important Events During the Age of Jackson

Year	Event
1824	**Presidential Election** • Who ran: ______ • Who won the electoral vote: Jackson • Problem with results: ______ • How election was decided: by a vote in the House of Representatives • Who was ultimately elected: ______
1824–1828	**John Quincy Adams's Presidency** • Burdened by charges of a ______ • Had ______ plans but accomplished ______ • Lacked the ______ skills to push his programs through ______
1828	**Presidential Election** • Who ran: ______ • Who won: ______ • Revealed growing ______ and ______ divisions
1832	**Presidential Election** • Who ran: ______ • Who won: ______

Key Political Changes During the Age of Jackson

What Changed	How It Changed	What It Replaced
Suffrage	Almost all adult white males were allowed to vote and hold office.	Most states had required men to own property before they could vote.
Choosing the electoral college		
Choosing political candidates		
Ideas about who should participate in political life		Only those with money and power should vote and run for office.

Refer to this page to answer the Chapter 6 Focus Question on page 108.

Section 4
Indian Removal

Section 4 Focus Question

Why did Jackson use force to remove Indians from the Southeast? To begin answering this question,

- Learn about the Native Americans of the Southeast.
- Explore the conflict over land.
- Follow the Trail of Tears.

Section 4 Summary

As the population of white settlers in the Southeast grew, conflicts arose with Native Americans in the region. President Andrew Jackson decided to forcibly remove thousands of Native Americans and relocate them to the West.

Native Americans of the Southeast

In 1828, more than 10,000 Native Americans lived east of the Mississippi. These nations included the Cherokee, Chickasaw, Choctaw, and Creek. The groups lived in various parts of Alabama, Mississippi, Georgia, North Carolina, and Tennessee. The Seminoles, who lived in Florida, had an unusual origin. They were a combination of Creeks who had moved into Florida in the late 1700s, Florida Native Americans, and escaped African American slaves. Many of the southeastern Native Americans were farmers or lived in towns.

The Cherokees in particular adopted some white customs. Many Cherokees became Christians. They also had businesses, small industries, schools, and even a newspaper written in English and Cherokee. The alphabet for the Cherokee language was created by a leader named **Sequoyah** (sih KWOY uh). In 1827, the Cherokee set up a government based on a written constitution. They claimed status as a separate nation. ✓

Conflict Over Land

To many government leaders and white farmers, Native Americans stood in the way of westward expansion. Furthermore, Native Americans lived on fertile land. White farmers wanted that land for growing cotton.

Policies to move Native Americans from their lands dated from the presidency of Thomas Jefferson. Jefferson thought that the only way to prevent conflict and protect Native American culture was to send the Native Americans west. After the War of 1812, the federal government signed treaties with several Native American groups in the Old Northwest. Groups agreed to give up their land and move west of the Mississippi River. The pressure to move increased on the Native Americans who remained in the Southeast.

Key Events

1816	Congress passes Tariff of 1816.
1823	Monroe Doctrine is issued.
1828	Andrew Jackson elected President.
1837	Panic of 1837 brings economic collapse.

✓ Checkpoint

List two white customs adopted by the Cherokees.

____

____

Vocabulary Builder

The "Old Northwest" is the name for land around the Great Lakes that was once the northwestern part of the United States. Why do you think we do not call the Southeast the "Old Southeast"?

____

____

In 1825 and 1827, the state of Georgia passed a law that forced the Creeks to give up most of their land. Then in 1828, Georgia tried to get the Cherokees to leave the state, but they refused to move, choosing instead to sue the state of Georgia. Both cases eventually made their way to the Supreme Court. The first case, *Cherokee Nation* v. *Georgia*, reached the Supreme Court in 1831. The decision in this suit went against the Cherokees. However, in the second case, *Worcester* v. *Georgia* (1832), the Court declared that Georgia's laws "can have no force" within Cherokee land. In his ruling, John Marshall pointed to treaties that the United States had signed guaranteeing certain territory to Native Americans. These treaties meant Georgia could not take away Cherokee territory. President Andrew Jackson, who wanted to move Native Americans to the West, refused to support the Court's decision. Instead, Jackson chose to enforce the Indian Removal Act of 1830. This law gave him the power to offer Native Americans land west of the Mississippi for their land in the East. ✓

✓ Checkpoint

Name the law that allowed President Jackson to move Native American groups to the West.

____

On the Trail of Tears

Believing they had no choice, most Native American leaders signed treaties agreeing to move to Indian Territory in the west. Today, most of that area is in the state of Oklahoma. The Choctaws signed the first treaty in 1830, and they moved between 1831 and 1833. However, the federal government did not give the Choctaw enough food and supplies for the long trip. As a result, many people died in the cold winter weather. The Cherokees held out a few years longer. Finally, President Martin Van Buren forced the Cherokees to move in the winter of 1838–1839 while being guarded by 7,000 soldiers. Once again, there were not enough supplies. Some 4,000 of the 15,000 Cherokees who began the journey died along the route that became known as the Trail of Tears.

The Seminoles refused to move, choosing instead to fight a war against removal. In the 1840s, most Seminoles were eventually removed to Indian Territory. In their new homes, Native Americans struggled to rebuild their lives under very difficult conditions. ✓

✓ Checkpoint

What was the Trail of Tears?

____

____

____

Check Your Progress

1. What did the Supreme Court rule in *Worcester* v. *Georgia*?

____

____

____

2. What happened to most of the Native American groups in the Southeast?

____

____

Section 4 Notetaking Study Guide

Question to Think About As you read Section 4 in your textbook and take notes, keep this section focus question in mind: **Why did Jackson use force to remove Indians from the Southeast?**

► Use these organizers to record key information from the section. Some information has been filled in to get you started.

Time Line of Indian Removal

Date	Events
After 1812	Indian groups in the Old Northwest give up their land and move to Indian Territory.
1825, 1827	Georgia passes law that forces the Creeks to give up their land.
1827	The Cherokees form an independent government with a ________________________.
1828	The Cherokees refuse Georgia's order to leave, suing the state instead.
1832	The Supreme Court rules in *Worcester* v. *Georgia* that ________________________.
1831–1833	The U.S. government forces the Choctaws to leave the Southeast and settle in ________________________.
1838–1839	The U.S. government forces the Cherokees to leave the Southeast for Indian Territory. Thousands die on the journey known as ________________________.
1840s	Many of the ____________ are forced to leave after fighting U.S. forces to resist removal to Indian Territory.

Cause and Effect: Indian Removal

Cause: Conflict Over Land

- Why government wanted Native American land: ____________________
- Why white settlers wanted Native American land: ____________________
- Native American groups living in the Southeast:
  1.
  2.
  3.
  4.
  5.

→

Effect: Indian Removal

- Policies to move Native Americans from their land dated from the time of Thomas Jefferson
- What the Indian Removal Act of 1830 did: ____________________
- Believing they had no choice, most Native Americans signed treaties agreeing to ____________________
- What happened on the Trail of Tears: ____________________

Refer to this page to answer the Chapter 6 Focus Question on page 108.

Section 5
Finance and States' Rights

Key Events

1816	Congress passes Tariff of 1816.
1823	Monroe Doctrine is issued.
1828	Andrew Jackson elected President.
1837	Panic of 1837 brings economic collapse.

Section 5 Focus Question

How did old issues take a new shape in the conflict over a national bank and tariffs? To begin answering this question,

- Learn about the Bank War.
- Explore the struggle over states' rights.
- Examine the Nullification Crisis.
- Find out about the end of the Jackson Era.

Section 5 Summary

Jackson faced two major political conflicts during his presidency. One involved the second Bank of the United States. The other dealt with the thorny issue of states' rights.

The Bank War

The second Bank of the United States earned strong support from business people. The Bank loaned money to many businesses and was a safe place for the federal government to keep its money. The money it issued formed a stable currency. But Andrew Jackson and many other Americans believed that the Bank favored the rich and hurt everyday people. For example, the Bank sometimes limited the amount of money that state banks could lend. In the South and West, the Bank was blamed for the economic crisis of 1819, which cost many people their farms.

In 1832, Nicholas Biddle, the Bank's president, got Congress to renew the Bank's charter. Jackson vetoed this bill, promising to defeat Biddle. Most voters stood behind Jackson, who won the election by a large margin. As a result, the Bank ceased to exist when its charter ran out in 1836. ✓

✓ Checkpoint

Name the two men who opposed each other during the Bank War.

____

____

The Struggle Over States' Rights

Since the founding of the United States, Americans had debated how to divide power between the federal government and the states. The Constitution gives the federal government many significant powers, but at the same time, the Tenth Amendment states that powers not specifically given to the federal government are reserved to the states or the people. Over the years, the issue of balancing federal and state power had come up repeatedly. During Jackson's presidency, arguments over this issue caused a serious crisis. ✓

✓ Checkpoint

Name the Constitutional amendment that reserves certain powers to the states and people.

____

The Nullification Crisis

The issue of states' rights was raised again in 1828 when Congress passed a new tariff on manufactured goods. This tariff helped northern businesses but hurt southerners, who were forced to pay more for goods. Southerners felt the law was unfair, and to many, the tariff issue was part of a larger problem. Slavery was unpopular outside the South. If the federal government could enforce what southerners considered an unjust law, could it also use its power to ban slavery? Vice President John C. Calhoun argued that the states had the right of **nullification**—an action by a state that cancels a federal law to which the state objects.

Arguments For Nullification	Arguments Against Nullification
• The Union was formed by an agreement between the states. • States kept the right to nullify federal laws that the people of the state considered unfair.	• The Union had been formed by the American people, not the states. • The supreme power in the land lay with the American people, not the states.

When Congress passed another high tariff in 1832, South Carolina voted to nullify the tariffs. State leaders also threatened to secede, or leave the Union. Jackson asked Congress to allow the federal government to collect its tariff by force if necessary. But he also supported a compromise bill that would lower the tariffs. In 1832, Congress passed both laws. South Carolina accepted the new tariff, ending the crisis. ✓

The End of the Jackson Era

Martin Van Buren, Jackson's Vice President, won the presidency in 1836. Just as he took office, the U.S. economy faced the Panic of 1837. British mills began buying less cotton, which caused cotton prices to fall. Cotton growers could not repay their bank loans, which caused hundreds of banks to fail. Van Buren's presidency was ruined.

In 1840, the Whig candidate, **William Henry Harrison**, easily beat Van Buren. The Whigs had learned how to reach ordinary voters by using parades and other forms of entertainment in their campaign. The Age of Jackson had ended. ✓

Check Your Progress

1. What did supporters and opponents of the second Bank believe?

____

____

____

2. What caused the nullification crisis?

____

____

____

Vocabulary Builder

To *nullify* means "to make of no value." To nullify a law means to take away its power. How was nullification supposed to protect states' rights?

____

____

____

✓ Checkpoint

Name the act of Congress that South Carolina was trying to nullify.

____

____

✓ Checkpoint

Name the crisis that ruined Van Buren's presidency.

____

____

Section 5 Notetaking Study Guide

Question to Think About As you read Section 5 in your textbook and take notes, keep this section focus question in mind: **How did old issues take a new shape in the conflict over a national bank and tariffs?**

► Use these charts to record key information from the section.

Economic Challenges
The second Bank of the United States held the ____________ government's money and lent money to ____________ banks. It also issued paper money, which helped create a ____________ currency.
Many people blamed the Bank for the ____________.
In 1832, Jackson ____________ the bill to renew the Bank's charter. He won the 1832 election while ____________ the Bank, which closed when its charter ran out in ____________.

States' Rights and the Nullification Crisis
Americans had always debated about the balance between the powers of the ____________ and ____________ governments. The Constitution gave the federal government ____________. The Tenth Amendment ____________ federal power by stating that ____________.
Congress passed a law in 1828 raising tariffs. It helped northern manufacturers, but ____________ felt the law was unfair.
____________ argued that states had the right of nullification, which means they could ____________. This theory was based on the idea that Union was formed from a voluntary agreement between ____________.
The clearest argument against nullification came from ____________. He argued that the Union was formed by ____________, not the states.
After Congress passed another tariff in 1832, ____________ voted to nullify the tariffs. It threatened to ____________ if the federal government interfered. Federal threats to ____________ as well as a lowering of the ____________ led ____________ to vote to ____________.

The End of the Jackson Era
Jackson's choice to succeed him was ____________, who won the presidential election of 1836. However, soon afterward, an economic collapse, called the ____________, occurred. As a result of the hard times that followed, Van Buren did not ____________.

Refer to this page to answer the Chapter 6 Focus Question on page 108.

Chapter 6 Assessment

Directions: Circle the letter of the correct answer.

1. Which of the following cases established the principle that a state cannot pass a law that breaks a federal law?

- **A** *Marbury* v. *Madison*
- **B** *McCulloch* v. *Maryland*
- **C** *Gibbons* v. *Ogden*
- **D** *Dartmouth College* v. *Woodward*

2. What did the Monroe Doctrine declare?

- **A** The United States would consider any European interference in Latin America to be a threat to American peace and security.
- **B** The United States and Spain would protect new Latin American nations.
- **C** The United States would support European nations that wanted to regain their colonies in Latin America.
- **D** The United States would not get involved in Latin American affairs.

3. What is the name given to the journey to Indian Territory made by the Cherokees in the winter of 1838–39?

- **A** The Great Migration
- **B** The Long Walk
- **C** The Trail of Tears
- **D** The Overland Trail

Directions: Follow the steps to answer this question:

What was the basis of the disagreement over nullification?

Step 1: Recall information: Briefly describe what those who supported nullification believed. Then briefly describe what those who opposed it believed.

Beliefs of Supporters of Nullification	Beliefs of Opponents of Nullification

Step 2: Compare information: What justification did each side give for its position?

Arguments For Nullification	Arguments Against Nullification

Step 3: Draw conclusions: Complete the topic sentence that follows. Then write two or three more sentences that support your topic sentence.

Supporters and opponents of nullification disagreed about ____________________

____

____

____

____

Chapter 6 Notetaking Study Guide

Now you are ready to answer the Chapter 6 Focus Question: **How did the nation reflect a growing sense of national pride and identity?**

► Fill in the following chart to help you answer this question. Use the notes that you took for each section.

Building a National Identity

U.S.–Foreign Relations

- The Monroe Doctrine stated that ______________________________ ______________________________.
- How relations with Canada changed after the War of 1812: ______________________

Federal Government Versus States' Rights

Key Supreme Court cases that strengthened the power of the federal government:

1. ______________________________
2. ______________________________
3. ______________________________

- South Carolina said that states had the right to ______________________.

Indian Removal

- Why there was a conflict over land between white settlers and Native Americans: ______________________________ ______________________________
- Native Americans were forced ______________________________.
- The Cherokees called their journey ______________________________.

Democratic Reforms in the Age of Jackson

- States dropped property requirements for voting.
- Presidential electors were chosen by __________, not by __________.
- Candidates for office were chosen by ______________ instead of caucuses.

A National Economy

- The second Bank of the United States
  - made loans to businesses.
  - was a safe place for the ______________________ to keep its money.
  - issued ______________ that formed a stable ______________.
- However, many Americans opposed the bank because ______________________ ______________________________.

Refer to this page to answer the Unit 3 Focus Question on page 109.

Unit 3 Pulling It Together Activity

What You Have Learned

Chapter 4 As the nation's first President, George Washington established the U.S. government's authority in domestic as well as foreign affairs. Political divisions and strife with France rocked John Adams's presidency.

Chapter 5 The Louisiana Purchase of 1803 doubled the size of the United States. At the same time, the United States struggled to remain neutral in its foreign policy. British support of Native Americans led to the War of 1812.

Chapter 6 During the early 1800s, the federal government increased its authority. At the same time, the Monroe Doctrine expanded U.S. influence in Latin America.

Think Like a Historian

Read the Unit 3 Focus Question: **What problems might a new nation face?**

► Use the organizers on this page and the next to collect information to answer this question.

What types of national problems did the new nation face? Some of them are listed in this organizer. Review your section and chapter notes. Then complete the organizer.

National Issues Facing the New Nation

Powers of National Government

- Whiskey Rebellion
-

Political Divisions

-

States' Rights

-
-

Relations With Native Americans

- Indian Removal Act
-

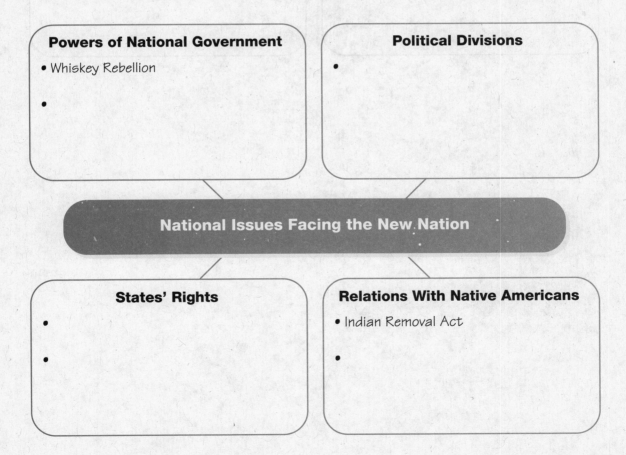

What types of international problems did the new nation face? The organizer below gives you a part of the answer. Review your section and chapter notes. Then fill in the rest of the organizer.

International Issues Facing the New Nation

Trade

-

War of 1812

- impressment of sailors
-

National Borders

- Adams-Onís Treaty
-
-

Western Hemisphere

-

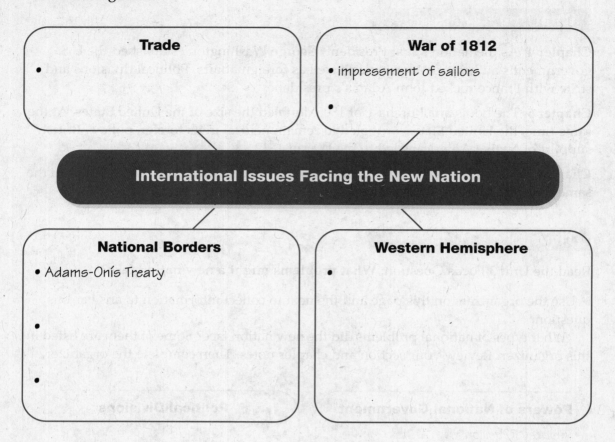

Unit 4

The Nation Expands and Changes

What You Will Learn

Chapter 7 The North industrialized and urbanized rapidly in the early to mid-1800s. The South became highly dependent on cotton and the slave labor needed to cultivate it. Tensions between North and South spread to the western territories.

Chapter 8 By the mid-1800s, Americans were seeking reform in education and abolition. Some sought equality for women. Artists and writers also began to develop a distinct style.

Chapter 9 In the mid-1800s, many Americans wanted the nation to expand westward to the Pacific Ocean. American settlers overcame hardships in making this happen.

Focus Your Learning As you study this unit and take notes, you will find the information to answer the questions below. Answering the Chapter Focus Questions will help build your answer to the Unit Focus Question.

Chapter 7 Focus Question
Why did Americans take different paths in the early 1800s?
(page 112)

Unit 4 Focus Question
What forces unite and divide a nation?
(page 154)

Chapter 8 Focus Question
How did reformers and writers inspire change and spark controversy?
(page 126)

Chapter 9 Focus Question
How did westward expansion change the geography of the nation and demonstrate the determination of its people?
(page 140)

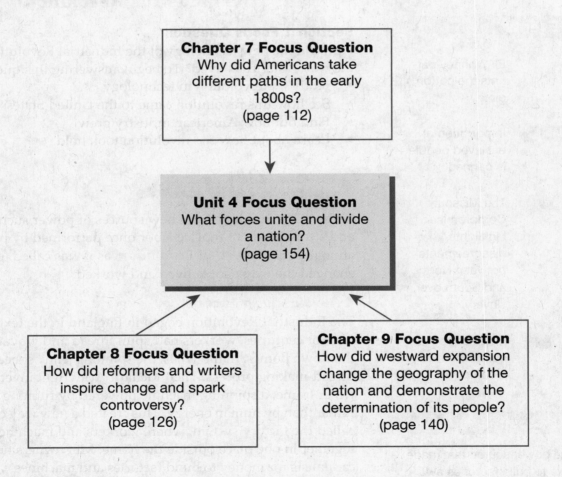

Chapter Standards

History-Social Science 8.6.1, 8.6.2, 8.6.3, 8.6.4, 8.7.1, 8.7.2, 8.7.3, 8.7.4, 8.9.5

Chapter 7

North and South Take Different Paths

(1800–1845)

What You Will Learn

The North industrialized and urbanized rapidly in the early to mid-1800s. The South became highly dependent on cotton and the slave labor needed to cultivate it. Tensions between North and South spread to the western territories.

Chapter 7 Focus Question

As you read through the sections in this chapter, keep this question in mind: **Why did Americans take different paths in the early 1800s?**

Section 1

The Industrial Revolution

Section 1 Focus Question

How did the new technology of the Industrial Revolution change the way Americans lived? To begin answering this question,

- Study the revolution in technology.
- See how this revolution came to the United States.
- Find out how American industry grew.
- Learn about how the revolution took hold.

Section 1 Summary

In the 1700s, machines and new sources of power such as water and steam began to replace labor once performed by people and animals. This **Industrial Revolution,** as it was called, greatly changed the way people lived and worked.

A Revolution in Technology

The Industrial Revolution began in England in the textile industry. For centuries, workers had spun thread and woven cloth in their own homes. In the 1760s, the spinning jenny speeded up the thread-making process. Then Richard Arkwright invented the water frame, a spinning machine powered by running water rather than by human energy. This created a new way of working called the **factory system,** where workers and machines come together in one place outside the home. Mill owners turned to capitalists for money to build factories and machines. **Capitalists** invest capital, or money, in a business to earn a profit. The use of steam power in the 1790s allowed factories to be built away from rivers. ✓

Key Events

1794	Eli Whitney patents the cotton gin.
1808	Importation of enslaved people is banned.
1820	The Missouri Compromise highlights disagreements between North and South over slavery.
1830	Peter Cooper builds the steam locomotive.

✓ Checkpoint

Name the power source that made it possible to build factories away from running water.

____

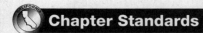

The American Industrial Revolution

Britain tried to guard its secrets of industrial success. Skilled workers were forbidden to leave the country. In 1789, a young apprentice in one of Arkwright's factories named Samuel Slater immigrated to America. Working from his memory of Arkwright's factories, Slater built new spinning machines for American merchant Moses Brown. Slater's mill became a great success. ✓

American Industry Grows

The success of Slater's mill marked the beginning of American industrialization. Industrialization began in the Northeast. U.S. industry did not grow significantly until the War of 1812. Without British imports, Americans had to depend on their own industries. **Francis Cabot Lowell** built a mill that combined spinning and weaving in a single factory. This idea led to the growth of a mill town called Lowell. The workforce was made up of young women known as "Lowell girls," who lived in boarding houses. ✓

The Revolution Takes Hold

Another key innovation in American industry was the invention of **interchangeable parts**—identical pieces that could be quickly put together by unskilled workers. Traditional craftsmen had built machines by hand. No two parts were the same, making machinery slow to build and hard to repair. Eli Whitney came up with the idea for interchangeable parts in the 1790s. The idea led to **mass production**—the rapid manufacture of large numbers of identical objects. As a result, many goods became cheaper and American industry continued to grow.

Many factories, mines, and mills employed children as young as 7 or 8. These children had little chance for an education and worked in difficult conditions. Working conditions for adults were no better. Many spent the 12- or 14-hour workday in poorly lit factories with little fresh air. The machines were often dangerous and injuries were common. There were no payments for disabled workers. By 1844, workers were demanding shorter days. Conditions gradually improved, but the eight-hour workday was far in the future. ✓

Check Your Progress

1. How did the Industrial Revolution change working life?

____

____

____

2. How do interchangeable parts make mass production possible?

____

____

____

✓ Checkpoint

Name the person who brought new spinning technologies from England to the United States.

____

✓ Checkpoint

What were workers in the Lowell mills called?

____

Vocabulary Builder

How would replacing the word *exactly* with the word *mostly* change the meaning of the following sentence? "Interchangeable parts were exactly alike." Would this make interchangeable parts more or less useful?

____

✓ Checkpoint

Name a reason that factory work was unhealthy and dangerous.

____

____

Section 1 Notetaking Study Guide

Question to Think About As you read Section 1 in your textbook and take notes, keep this section focus question in mind: **How did the new technology of the Industrial Revolution change the way Americans lived?**

► Use these charts to record key information from the section. Some information has been filled in to get you started.

The Industrial Revolution
In the Industrial Revolution, <u>machines</u> took the place of many hand tools. Much of the power once provided by ______ and ______ began to be replaced, first by ______ and then by ______.
For centuries, workers had ______ in their ______ on spinning wheels. In the 1760s, the ______ speeded up the thread-making process.
This system of working was replaced by the ______, which brought workers and ______ together in one place.
In 1764, ______ invented the ______, a spinning machine powered by ______ rather than human energy. Textile mills began to be built on ______.
In 1790, ______ built the first steam-powered ______. Factories no longer had to be built on ______.
______ built the first water-frame-style spinning machine in the United States.
In the 1790s, inventor ______ devised a system of ______, identical pieces that could be assembled quickly by ______.
During the <u>War of 1812</u>, the British navy blockaded U.S. ports. This caused ______ to grow significantly.
Francis Cabot Lowell and his partners built a mill that was organized a new way. It combined ______ and ______ in one building. Later, the town of Lowell, Massachusetts, was built. Factories there employed ______ from nearby farms.

Typical Factory Working Conditions
Length of workday: <u>12–14 hours</u> Factory conditions: ______ Safety conditions: ______ Treatment of disabled workers: ______

Refer to this page to answer the Chapter 7 Focus Question on page 125.

Section 2

The North Transformed

Section 2 Focus Question

How did urbanization, technology, and social change affect the North? To begin answering this question,

- Learn about northern cities.
- Explore the growth of northern industry.
- Find out about the transportation revolution.
- Learn about a new wave of immigrants.
- Examine the lives of African Americans in the North.

Section 2 Summary

New inventions and breakthroughs in transportation helped industry expand in the United States. Much of this industry was located in the North, where it encouraged the growth of cities.

Northern Cities

In the 1800s, the Industrial Revolution led to **urbanization,** or the growth of cities due to movement of people from rural areas to cities. As capitalists built more factories, agricultural workers were attracted to the new types of work available in the cities. As cities in the East became crowded, newly arrived immigrants headed westward. Growing cities faced many problems. Poor sewers, a lack of clean drinking water, and filthy city streets encouraged the spread of disease. Citywide fires were another major concern. Most city buildings were made of wood. Cities relied on volunteer firefighters who had little training or equipment. ✓

The Growth of Northern Industry

American inventors helped industry grow. In 1844, **Samuel F.B. Morse** tested the **telegraph,** an invention that used electrical signals to send messages very quickly over long distances. The telegraph revolutionized communication. In the Midwest, Cyrus McCormick built a mechanical reaper that cut wheat much faster than could be done by hand. Such machines allowed more wheat to be grown and harvested using fewer workers. This made it easier for farmers to settle the prairies of the Midwest. Other inventions revolutionized the way goods were made. The invention of the sewing machine made the production of clothing in quantity more efficient. Introduced in 1846 by Elias Howe and improved by Isaac Singer, sewing machines could make clothes faster and cheaper than ever before.

By 1860, New England and the Mid-Atlantic states were producing most of the nation's manufactured goods. Ninety percent of business investment was concentrated in the North. ✓

Key Events

1794 Eli Whitney patents the cotton gin.

1808 Importation of enslaved people is banned.

1820 The Missouri Compromise highlights disagreements between North and South over slavery.

1830 Peter Cooper builds the steam locomotive.

✓ Checkpoint

List three factors that led to the spread of disease in cities.

____

____

____

✓ Checkpoint

Name two key American inventors and their inventions.

Inventor: ______________________

Invention: ______________________

Inventor: ______________________

Invention: ______________________

A Transportation Revolution

Improvements in transportation also spurred the growth of industry. Better transport allowed factories to make use of raw materials from farther away, and manufactured goods could be delivered to distant markets. American Robert Fulton built the first practical steamboat, the *Clermont*, in 1807. But in 1850, a new type of American-built ship appeared, the clipper ship. Long and slender, with tall masts, clipper ships were the fastest vessels on the ocean. But the Yankee clippers, as they were called, were eventually replaced by faster oceangoing steamships.

Of all the forms of transportation, railroads did the most to tie together raw materials, manufacturers, and markets. In 1830, Peter Cooper built the first American-made steam locomotive. By 1840, there were 3,000 miles of railroad track in the United States. ✓

✓ Checkpoint

List three major breakthroughs in transportation.

___

___

___

A New Wave of Immigrants

In the 1840s, millions of immigrants came to the United States, mainly from western Europe. In 1845, disease wiped out the potato crop in Ireland. Because the potato was the staple food for most of the population, Ireland suffered from a **famine**, or widespread starvation. Huge numbers of Irish came to America, most of them former farm laborers. Many took jobs laying railroad track, or as household workers. Many Germans also came to the United States, fleeing failed revolutions in Germany. Unlike the Irish, German immigrants came from many levels of society. Most moved to the Midwest.

Some Americans worried about the growing foreign population. These were **nativists**, or people who wanted to preserve the country for white, American-born Protestants. ✓

✓ Checkpoint

Name the countries most immigrants to the United States in the 1840s came from.

___

___

African Americans in the North

African Americans in the North also faced **discrimination**, or the denial of equal rights or treatment based on race, religion, culture, or nationality. Though free, African Americans were often not allowed to vote or work in factories and skilled trades. Public schools and churches were often segregated. So African Americans formed their own churches. They also started their own newspapers and magazines. ✓

✓ Checkpoint

Define discrimination.

___

___

Check Your Progress

1. Name the invention that revolutionized communication.

___

2. How did better transportation help industry?

___

___

___

Section 2 Notetaking Study Guide

Question to Think About As you read Section 2 in your textbook and take notes, keep this section focus question in mind: **How did urbanization, technology, and social change affect the North?**

► Use these charts to record key information from the section. Some information has been filled in to get you started.

Key Inventions

Invention	Inventor(s)	When	What It Did
Sewing machine	Elias Howe and Isaac Singer	1846	Made sewing clothes faster and cheaper
			Harvested more wheat with fewer workers
			Made river travel faster and cheaper
	Peter Cooper		
		1844	
Clipper ship	No single inventor		

Changes in Population

	What Happened?	Why Did It Happen?	Results
Cities	Cities began growing rapidly, especially in the northeast.	Factories moved to cities, followed by people moving from rural areas for factory jobs.	Cities faced the spread of disease and the threat of fire.
Immigration	Millions of immigrants from ____________, particularly Ireland and Germany, came to the U.S. in the 1840s.	The Irish came to escape ____________.	Nativists: ____________ ____________
		The Germans came to escape ____________.	Know-Nothings: ____________ ____________
African Americans in the North	African Americans formed their own schools, churches, and publications.	____________ ____________ ____________ ____________ ____________	African Americans continued to face ____________. They were often denied the right to ____________. They were not allowed to work in factories or in ____________.

Refer to this page to answer the Chapter 7 Focus Question on page 125.

Section 3

The Plantation South

Key Events

- **1794** Eli Whitney patents the cotton gin.
- **1808** Importation of enslaved people is banned.
- **1820** The Missouri Compromise highlights disagreements between North and South over slavery.
- **1830** Peter Cooper builds the steam locomotive.

Section 3 Focus Question

How did cotton affect the social and economic life of the South? To begin answering this question,

- Find out about the "Cotton Kingdom."
- Examine the life of African Americans in the South.

Section 3 Summary

Cotton production expanded in the South to supply the textile industry. Whether free or enslaved, African Americans in the South faced many hardships.

The Cotton Kingdom

As the textile industry in the North grew, the demand for cotton rose. Eli Whitney's invention of the **cotton gin** allowed the South to meet this demand. The cotton gin used a spiked wooden cylinder to remove seeds from cotton fibers.

Boom in textiles creates demand for cotton.

→ Eli Whitney's cotton gin removes seeds from cotton fibers 50 times faster than by hand.

→ Enslaved African Americans grow much of the South's cotton on plantations. As cotton becomes more important, so does slavery. By 1860 there are nearly 4 million enslaved African Americans in the South.

→ There is a boom in cotton production, especially in states like Alabama, Louisiana, Mississippi, and Tennessee.

Vocabulary Builder

Gin is early English slang for "engine" or machine. What do you think the term *cotton gin* refers to?

____

Cotton became the greatest source of wealth for the United States. The southern "Cotton Kingdom" society was dominated by slaveholding owners of large plantations. Most southern whites accepted the system of slavery. Supporters of slavery said that the system was more humane than the free labor system of the North. But critics pointed out that factory workers could quit a job if conditions became too harsh. Also, critics said, people held in slavery often suffered physical or other abuse from white owners. By the 1830s, some northerners were urging that slavery be banned. ✓

✓ Checkpoint

Why did the invention of the cotton gin lead to a boom in cotton production?

____

____

____

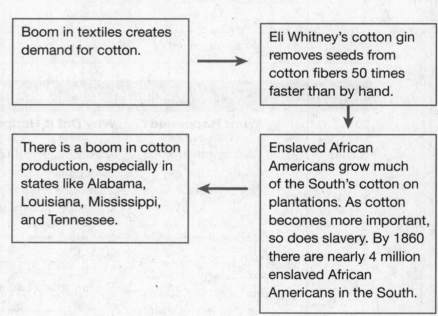

African Americans in the South

About six percent of African Americans in the South were free. Many had purchased their freedom. But laws denied them even basic rights. By law they were excluded from most jobs. They could not vote, serve on juries, testify against whites in court, or attend public schools. Free African Americans were even discouraged from traveling. They also risked being kidnapped and sold into slavery. Many free African Americans still made valuable contributions to southern life.

However, enslaved African Americans faced greater trials. They had no rights at all. Laws called **slave codes** controlled every aspect of their lives. A Kentucky court ruled in 1828 that "...a slave by our code is not treated as a person but as a ...thing..." Most enslaved African Americans did heavy farm labor, but many became skilled workers. Some worked in households. Wherever they worked, they faced the possibility of violent punishment for many offenses. Enslaved African Americans had only one protection against mistreatment: Owners looked on them as valuable property that they needed to keep healthy and productive.

Families of enslaved African Americans were often broken apart when slave owners sold one or more of their family members. And, after 1808, it was illegal to import enslaved Africans to the United States. Yet African Americans kept many African customs alive, including styles of music and dance. Many looked to the Bible for hope. African Americans composed **spirituals**—religious folk songs that blended Biblical themes with the realities of slavery.

African Americans found ways to resist slavery. Some worked slowly, broke equipment, and even fled to seek freedom in the North. Some led rebellions. **Nat Turner** led the most famous slave uprising in 1831. He and his companions killed some 60 whites. In reprisal, many innocent African Americans were executed. ✓

Check Your Progress

1. How were cotton and slavery connected?

___

___

___

2. In what ways did free African Americans in the South have their rights taken away?

___

___

___

✓ Checkpoint

List three ways African Americans resisted slavery.

___

___

___

Section 3 Notetaking Study Guide

Question to Think About As you read Section 3 in your textbook and take notes, keep this section focus question in mind: **How did cotton affect the social and economic life of the South?**

► Use these charts to record key information from the section. Some information has been filled in to get you started.

The Southern Economy	
Cotton gin	**What it was:** a machine invented by ________ that speeded the processing of cotton **Impact on Economy:** • made cotton growing more ________ • increased the use and value of ________ • led to huge growth in ________ • made cotton the greatest ________ in the United States
Slave labor	**Argument for slave labor:**
	Arguments against slave labor: • •

African American Life in the South	
What	**Effect on African American Life**
Restrictions placed on free African Americans' rights	Could hold only ________. They were not allowed to: ________, ________, ________, ________. They were discouraged from ________.
Hardships faced on plantations	Enslaved African Americans • received ________ • had to perform ________ • families were often ________
Types of work enslaved African Americans performed	• • •
African American culture	Preserved African ________, ________, and ________. Composed ________.
Ways of resisting slavery	• • • •

Refer to this page to answer the Chapter 7 Focus Question on page 125.

Section 4

Americans Move Westward

Section 4 Focus Question

How did Americans move west and how did this intensify the debate over slavery? To begin answering this question,

- Follow along as Americans move west.
- Learn about roads and turnpikes.
- Find out about canals.
- Examine the extension of slavery.

Section 4 Summary

As the U.S. population grew, more people moved west to find new land. A transportation system of new roads and canals kept the country connected. Increasing differences between North and South became apparent when Missouri asked to join the Union as a slave state.

Moving West

By the 1750s, the Scotch-Irish and Germans of Pennsylvania began settling the backcountry between the Atlantic Coast and the Appalachian Mountains. In 1775, pioneer **Daniel Boone** helped create the Wilderness Road, a new route to the West. By the early 1800s, the flow of immigrants to the West had become a flood. As western populations grew, many areas applied to become states. Between 1792 and 1819, eight states joined the Union: Kentucky (1792), Tennessee (1796), Ohio (1803), Louisiana (1812), Indiana (1816), Mississippi (1817), Illinois (1818), and Alabama (1819). ✓

Roads and Turnpikes

Traveling west was not easy. Roads were unpaved, rough, and easily washed out by rain. The nation needed better roads. Farmers and merchants had to have a way to move their goods to market quickly and cheaply. Private companies began building **turnpikes,** or toll roads. One example was the Lancaster Turnpike in Pennsylvania, the nation's first long-distance stone road. In marshy areas, builders constructed **corduroy roads** out of sawed-off logs laid side by side. These roads were bumpy and dangerous to horses. The first road built with federal money was the National Road. Begun in 1811 in Cumberland, Maryland, the road eventually stretched hundreds of miles, reaching Vandalia, Illinois, by 1850. ✓

Canals

Roads were still a slow and costly way to ship goods between East and West. The fastest, cheapest way to ship goods was by water. The solution was to build **canals**—channels that are dug across

Key Events

1794	Eli Whitney patents the cotton gin.
1808	Importation of enslaved people is banned.
1820	The Missouri Compromise highlights disagreements between North and South over slavery.
1830	Peter Cooper builds the steam locomotive.

✓ Checkpoint

Name two states admitted to the Union in the 1790s.

____

____

✓ Checkpoint

Name the first road built with federal money.

____

land and filled with water. Canals allow boats to reach more places. In 1808, Governor DeWitt Clinton of New York suggested that a canal be built to connect the Hudson River and Lake Erie. Building the canal was challenging for engineers and workers. Locks had to be built to raise or lower boats in the canal. Within two years of its opening in 1825, the canal had paid for itself. Produce from the Midwest came across Lake Erie, passed through the Erie Canal, and was carried down the Hudson River to New York City. New York City soon became the richest city in the nation. The success of the Erie Canal sparked a surge of canal building. ✓

✓ Checkpoint

Name the two places connected by the Erie Canal.

____

The Extension of Slavery

In 1819, the nation consisted of 11 "slave states" and 11 "free states." Since 1817, Missouri had been seeking admission as a slave state. Adding another slave state would upset the balance in the Senate, where each state had two votes. Adding two more senators from a slave state would make the South more powerful than the North. Representative James Tallmadge of New York proposed that Missouri be admitted as a slave state. Once admitted, however, no more slaves could be brought into the state. The bill failed in the Senate. Then Maine applied to join the Union as a free state. The admission of both a free state and a slave state would maintain the balance in the Senate. In 1820, Senator **Henry Clay** persuaded Congress to adopt the Missouri Compromise. This permitted Maine to be admitted to the Union as a free state and Missouri to be admitted as a slave state. In addition, the Compromise provided that the Louisiana Territory north of the southern border of Missouri would be free of slavery. It also gave southern slave owners a clear right to pursue escaped fugitives into "free" regions and return them to slavery.

The Missouri Compromise revealed how much sectional rivalries divided the states of the Union. The Compromise seemed to balance the interests of the North and the South. However, the South was not happy that Congress was becoming involved in the issue of slavery. The North was not happy that Congress had admitted another slave state into the Union. The bitterness of feelings about slavery posed a serious threat to national unity. ✓

✓ Checkpoint

Name the two states admitted to the Union under the Missouri Compromise.

____

____

Check Your Progress

1. Why were canals and better roads needed?

____

____

2. What was the Missouri Compromise?

____

____

____

____

Section 4 Notetaking Study Guide

Question to Think About As you read Section 4 in your textbook and take notes, keep this section focus question in mind: **How did Americans move west and how did this intensify the debate over slavery?**

► Use these organizers to record key information from the section. Some information has been filled in to get you started.

Roads and Canals		
Term	**What it was**	**Why it was important**
turnpike	A type of privately built toll road	Provided a much-needed way to move people and goods over land
	A road made of sawed-off logs	
		Allowed boats to reach more places
Project	**What it was and when it started**	**Why it was important**
	Road running from Cumberland, Maryland, to Vandalia, Illinois; 1811	
Erie Canal		• started a canal building boom • allowed goods to be shipped more ______ and cheaply between ______ and Midwest • helped make ______ the richest city in the nation

The Missouri Compromise

In 1820, Senator Henry Clay ______ persuaded Congress to approve the Missouri Compromise. Its provisions:

1. ______ was admitted as a free state.
2. ______ was admitted as a slave state.
3. ______ north of Missouri's southern border was free of slavery.
4. Southern slave owners gained the right to pursue ______ into free regions.

Refer to this page to answer the Chapter 7 Focus Question on page 125.

Chapter 7 Assessment

Directions: Circle the letter of the correct answer.

1. The rapid manufacture of large numbers of identical objects is called
- **A** the Industrial Revolution.
- **B** mass production.
- **C** the factory system.
- **D** the Lowell system.

2. Which of the following inventors made a major contribution to the Transportation Revolution?
- **A** Richard Arkwright
- **B** Francis Cabot Lowell
- **C** Cyrus McCormick
- **D** Robert Fulton

3. Which of the following inventions transformed the southern economy?
- **A** the cotton gin
- **B** the telegraph
- **C** the clipper ship
- **D** the mechanical reaper

4. The Missouri Compromise involved a debate over what issue?
- **A** the right of way for western railroads
- **B** the borders of the new Indian Territory
- **C** the westward expansion of slavery
- **D** the admission of California into the Union

Directions: Follow the steps to complete this task: **Compare the economy of the North with the economy of the South.**

Step 1: Recall information: List one characteristic of the northern economy and one characteristic of the southern economy.

Section	Economy
North	
South	

Step 2: Compare and contrast: Record how the characteristics of the economies are alike and how they are different.

	How They Are Alike	How They Are Different
Economies		

Step 3: Complete the topic sentence that follows. Then write two or three more sentences that support your topic sentence.

The economies of the North and South ______________________________

____

____

____

____

Chapter 7 Notetaking Study Guide

Now you are ready to answer the Chapter 7 Focus Question: **Why did Americans take different paths in the early 1800s?**

► Fill in the following charts to help you answer this question. Use the notes that you took for each section. .

The North and South Take Different Paths

The North	The South
Economy • Depended on industry • Some important inventions of Industrial Revolution: 1. spinning jenny 2. 3. • The factory system is the ______________ ______________. • Labor conditions were poor. • ____________ labor was often used.	**Economy** • Depended on slavery • Eli Whitney's invention of the ______________ increased the South's dependency on slavery. • Cotton plantations were important because cotton became America's greatest ______________.
Society • Urbanization: the growth of cities due to movement from rural to urban areas. • Urban problems included __________ and poor ______________. • New advances in transportation included ______________, ______________, and ____________. These allowed goods to be shipped to distant markets. • Immigration provided ____________ for industry and caused a rapid growth in ______________.	**Society** • Society was dominated by ______________. • Slave codes gave slaves no __________ and allowed every aspect of their lives to be ____________. • Free African Americans were not allowed to ____________ in elections or serve on ____________. Their children could not attend ______________, and they were discouraged from ______________.

Growing Sectional Differences

In 1820, Senator Henry Clay proposed the Missouri Compromise.

- What this proposal involved: ______________________________
- How this revealed sectional tensions:
  1. Southerners were not happy because ______________________________.
  2. Northerners were not happy because ______________________________.

Refer to this page to answer the Unit 4 Focus Question on page 154.

Chapter Standards

History-Social Science 8.4.4, 8.6.5, 8.6.6, 8.6.7, 8.9.1, 8.9.2, 8.9.3

Chapter 8

An Age of Reform (1820–1860)

What You Will Learn

By the mid-1800s, Americans were seeking reform in education and slavery. Some sought equality for women. Artists and writers also began to develop a distinct style.

Chapter 8 Focus Question

As you read through the sections in this chapter, keep this question in mind: **How did reformers and writers inspire change and spark controversy?**

Key Events

1831 William Lloyd Garrison founds antislavery newspaper.

1848 Women's rights convention is held in Seneca Falls, New York.

1850s American writers publish *The Scarlet Letter, Moby-Dick, Walden,* and *Leaves of Grass*.

Section 1

Improving Society

Section 1 Focus Question

How did key people bring about reform in education and society? To begin answering this question,

- Learn about the roots of the reforming spirit.
- Find out about temperance and prison reform.
- Explore education reform.

Section 1 Summary

The expansion of democracy during the presidency of Andrew Jackson and the Second Great Awakening led many to organize efforts to reform American society.

The Reforming Spirit

In the 1830s, many Americans became interested in **social reform**, or organized attempts to improve conditions of life. Social reform had its roots in both politics and religion. The expansion of democracy during the Age of Jackson helped encourage reform. As the political system became more fair, more people began to support causes such as rights for women and the end of slavery.

Religious ideas were another factor encouraging reform. In the early 1800s, some ministers began questioning traditional views, a movement known as the Second Great Awakening. Leaders of the movement questioned **predestination**, the idea that God decided the fate of a person's soul even before birth. They argued that people's own actions determined their salvation, an idea called the "doctrine of free will." In 1826, the minister **Charles Finney** held the first of many **revivals**, or huge outdoor religious meetings, to convert sinners and urge people to reform.

The Second Great Awakening promoted improvement of self and society.

The idea of creating a more perfect society led some to experiment with building utopian, or ideal, communities. In 1825, Robert Owen founded a utopian community called New Harmony in Indiana. Residents were supposed to produce enough food and other goods to make the community self-sufficient. However, like most utopian communities, New Harmony did not last very long. ☑

Social Reformers at Work

While utopian reformers attempted to create perfect communities apart from the larger community, others tried to change the existing society. The **temperance movement** was an organized effort to end alcohol abuse and the problems created by it. This would be difficult since alcohol was widely used in the United States. Many women were drawn to this movement. Most citizens favored temperance, or moderation in drinking. But other people supported **prohibition,** or a total ban on the sale and consumption of alcohol. Those who supported prohibition were able to get nine states to pass laws banning the sale of alcohol.

Some reformers sought to improve the prison system. **Dorothea Dix,** a schoolteacher, took up this cause. She supported the building of new, more sanitary, and more humane prisons. She also urged the government to create separate institutions, called asylums, for people with mental illnesses. ☑

Education Reform

Education was another area reformers hoped to change. The Puritans of Massachusetts established the first **public schools,** or free schools supported by taxes, in 1642. Many reformers believed public schools created better-informed voters, and could help immigrants assimilate, or become part of, American culture.

The leader of education reform was **Horace Mann.** With his encouragement, colleges were created to train teachers, the salaries of teachers were raised, and the school year was lengthened. These improvements did little for African Americans. However, in 1855, Massachusetts became the first state to admit African Americans to public schools. ☑

Check Your Progress

1. What religious movement contributed to reform?

____

2. What is the difference between temperance and prohibition?

____

____

✓ Checkpoint

Name the person who held the first revival meetings.

____

✓ Checkpoint

Name the schoolteacher who took up the cause of prison reform.

____

✓ Checkpoint

Name the main leader of the movement for education reform.

____

Section 1 Notetaking Study Guide

Question to Think About As you read Section 1 in your textbook and take notes, keep this section focus question in mind: **How did key people bring about reform in education and society?**

► Complete this chart to record key information from the section.

Improving Society
The Reforming Spirit of Jacksonian Democracy
Some people worked to make the political system fairer. They supported causes such as legal rights for ______________ and the end of ______________.
How the Second Great Awakening encouraged reform: • Doctrine of free will: ______________ • Charles Finney: ______________ • If people had the power to improve themselves, they could ______________.
Utopian Communities • Definition: <u>communities that tried to create perfect societies</u> • Robert Owen: ______________ • Results: ______________
Social Reformers at Work
Temperance Movement • Definition: an organized effort to ______________ • Many women supported this movement because ______________. • Some reformers supported prohibition, which is ______________.
Movement to Reform Prisons • Dorothea Dix worked to support the building of ______________. • Dix urged the government to create <u>asylums</u> for ______________.
Education Reform • Public schools were supported as a way to create more informed ______________ and help new ______________ • Horace Mann: reformer from Massachusetts who ______________ • Reformers of African American education ______________. • First state to admit African Americans to public schools: ______________ • Ashmun Institute: ______________

Refer to this page to answer the Chapter 8 focus question on page 139.

Section 2
The Fight Against Slavery

Section 2 Focus Question

How did abolitionists try to end slavery? To begin answering this question,

- Learn about the roots of the antislavery movement.
- Discover why there was growing opposition to slavery.
- Find out about the Underground Railroad.
- Explore why some opposed the abolition of slavery.

Section 2 Summary

The reform movement of the 1800s led to growing calls to end slavery. However, other Americans continued to defend slavery.

Roots of the Antislavery Movement

Many leaders of the early republic, such as Alexander Hamilton and Benjamin Franklin, opposed slavery. They believed that slavery violated the principle that "all men are created equal." In 1780, Pennsylvania became the first state to pass a law gradually ending slavery. By 1804, every northern state had either ended or pledged to end slavery.

In 1817, the American Colonization Society began an effort to gradually free and then send slaves back to Liberia, a colony in Africa. The colonization movement was unsuccessful. The majority of enslaved people had been born in America and did not want to return to Africa. By 1830, only about 1,400 African Americans had migrated to Liberia. ✓

Growing Opposition to Slavery

Antislavery opinion increased during the Second Great Awakening when preachers like Charles Finney began to condemn slavery. By the mid-1800s, more Americans had become **abolitionists**, reformers who wanted to abolish slavery. Instead of gradual emancipation, they supported a complete and immediate end to slavery. **William Lloyd Garrison** was an important abolitionist leader who founded an abolitionist newspaper, the *Liberator*, in 1831. He supported giving all African Americans full political rights. Garrison also cofounded the New England Anti-Slavery Society.

African Americans in the North also joined the abolitionist movement. In 1829, David Walker wrote his *Appeal: to the Coloured Citizens of the World*, which called on slaves to rebel to gain their freedom. Perhaps the most powerful speaker for abolitionism was **Frederick Douglass.** He was a former slave who had escaped to freedom. Douglass often spoke to large crowds and published an antislavery newspaper, the *North Star*.

Key Events

1831	William Lloyd Garrison founds antislavery newspaper.
1848	Women's rights convention is held in Seneca Falls, New York.
1850s	American writers publish *The Scarlet Letter*, *Moby-Dick*, *Walden*, and *Leaves of Grass*.

✓ Checkpoint

Name the first state to pass a law gradually ending slavery.

____

Vocabulary Builder

What word in the underlined sentence could be replaced by the word *oppose*?

____

Abolitionists won the support of a few powerful people. Former president John Quincy Adams, now a member of Congress, supported abolition. He read antislavery petitions in the House of Representatives and introduced a constitutional amendment to ban slavery in new states.

Later, Adams spoke to the Supreme Court for nine hours to help captive Africans aboard the slave ship *Amistad* regain their freedom. ✓

✓ Checkpoint

Name the organization William Lloyd Garrison cofounded.

____

The Underground Railroad

Some abolitionists helped people escape from slavery using a system known as the Underground Railroad. In spite of its name, the system was neither underground nor a railroad. It was a network of people—both black and white and both northerners and southerners—who secretly helped slaves reach freedom. Known as "conductors," these people helped runaway slaves move between "stations," which were usually abolitionists' homes. They could also be churches or caves.

One Quaker, Levi Coffin, helped 3,000 slaves escape. Escaped slave **Harriet Tubman** escorted over 300 slaves to freedom. Each year, hundreds of slaves moved along the Underground Railroad to freedom in the North or in Canada. In total, perhaps as many as 50,000 may have gained their freedom in this way. ✓

✓ Checkpoint

Name the escaped slave who led over 300 slaves to freedom on the Underground Railroad.

____

Opposing Abolition

Abolitionists faced obstacles in the North and the South. Northern textile mill owners and merchants relied on cotton produced by slave labor. Northern workers feared that freed slaves might take their jobs. Some northerners reacted violently towards abolitionists. In 1835, a mob dragged William Lloyd Garrison through the streets of Boston with a rope around his neck.

Southerners had long defended slavery as a positive force. As support for abolition grew, they went on the offensive. Southerners won passage of a "gag rule" in Congress that blocked discussion of antislavery petitions. ✓

✓ Checkpoint

Why did some northern factory owners oppose abolitionism?

____

____

Check Your Progress

1. Describe Frederick Douglass' roles in abolitionism.

____

____

2. What was the Underground Railroad?

____

____

Section 2 Notetaking Study Guide

Question to Think About As you read Section 2 in your textbook and take notes, keep this section focus question in mind: **How did abolitionists try to end slavery?**

► Complete this chart to record key information from the section.

The Fight Against Slavery

Roots of the Antislavery Movement

- 1780: Pennsylvania became the first state to pass a law gradually ending slavery.
- Ohio was the first state to ____________________.
- By 1804, ____________________ had ended or pledged to end slavery.
- The American Colonization Society ____________________, but it was ____________________.

Growing Opposition to Slavery

Abolitionists
- definition: ____________________

William Lloyd Garrison
- important abolitionist leader who founded the newspaper ____________ in 1831
- supported giving all African Americans ____________________
- cofounded the ____________________

David Walker
- wrote ____________________ in 1829, a pamphlet that called on enslaved people to ____________________

Frederick Douglass
- an escaped ____________ and powerful ____________
- published the *North Star*, an ____________________

John Quincy Adams
- As a member of Congress, he read ____________________.
- spoke to the Supreme Court for ____________________

The Underground Railroad

- definition: ____________________
- "conductors": people who helped runaway slaves move between "stations"
- "stations": usually ____________________
- Harriet Tubman: nicknamed ____________, escorted ____________________

Opposition to Abolition

In the North:
- Northern textile mill owners and merchants relied on cotton produced by ____________________.
- Northern workers feared that ____________________.

In the South:
- defended slavery as a ____________________
- Southerners in Congress won passage of a "gag rule," which blocked discussion of ____________________.

Refer to this page to answer the Chapter 8 focus question on page 139.

Section 3

A Call for Women's Rights

Key Events

1831 William Lloyd Garrison founds antislavery newspaper.

1848 Women's rights convention is held in Seneca Falls, New York.

1850s American writers publish *The Scarlet Letter*, *Moby-Dick*, *Walden*, and *Leaves of Grass*.

Section 3 Focus Question

How did the women's suffrage movement begin? To begin answering this question,

- Learn about the beginnings of the women's rights movement.
- Read about the Seneca Falls Convention.
- Find out about new opportunities for women.

Section 3 Summary

Women reformers organized the women's rights movement, which led to new civil and legal rights and new educational and career opportunities for women.

The Struggle Begins

In 1820, women had limited civil and legal rights. They could not vote or serve on juries, attend college, or enter professions like medicine or law. They also had limited educational opportunities. Married women could not even own property or keep their own wages. Women were expected to remain in the private world of the home.

Women who were active in abolition and other reform movements began to demand rights as equal citizens. Among these women was Sojourner Truth. **Sojourner Truth** was an illiterate former slave who spoke on behalf of both African Americans and women. **Lucretia Mott**, a Quaker, was also an abolitionist. Mott had organization skills and public speaking experience that most women of her day did not. ✓

✓ Checkpoint

List three things women could not do in 1820.

____

____

____

Seneca Falls Convention

In 1840, Mott traveled to London to attend an antislavery convention. There, she met another abolitionist, **Elizabeth Cady Stanton.** They were infuriated to learn that women were excluded from taking an active role in the proceedings. They organized a convention for women's rights held in Seneca Falls, New York in 1848. Over 300 men and women attended, among them, Frederick Douglass.

Stanton wrote a Declaration of Sentiments based on the Declaration of Independence. It declared that all men and women are created equal and listed injustices against women. The declaration demanded full equality for women in all areas of life. Stanton's argument was the beginning of the battle for **women's suffrage,** or the right of women to vote. Other delegates, including Lucretia Mott, feared that demanding suffrage might harm other causes because it was so controversial. Still, the convention narrowly voted to support the demand for women's suffrage. ✓

Vocabulary Builder

Exclude in the underlined sentence means to "keep out" or "reject." What would be an antonym of *exclude*?

____

✓ Checkpoint

Name the document that demanded full equality for women in all areas of life.

____

New Opportunities for Women

The Seneca Falls Convention was the birthplace of the women's rights movement. The **women's rights movement** was the organized effort to improve the political, legal, and economic status of women in American society. Stanton and **Susan B. Anthony** worked closely together. As an unmarried woman, Anthony, a former schoolteacher, abolitionist, and temperance supporter, was able to travel to promote their cause. Stanton, who was raising a family, often wrote speeches from home. Together, Stanton and Anthony founded the National Women's Suffrage Association in 1869. They also convinced New York to pass a law protecting women's property rights. Many other states followed, some even revising their laws to allow married women to keep their wages.

Even before Seneca Falls, reformers worked to provide educational opportunities for girls. American schools emphasized education for boys. Girls seldom studied advanced subjects like math and science. The women's rights movement focused much attention on education. In 1821, Emma Willard founded the Troy Female Seminary in New York, which served as a model for girls' schools everywhere. Other women also started schools. In 1837, Mary Lyon founded the first college for women, Mount Holyoke Female Seminary.

American society came to accept that girls could be educated, and women could be teachers. More and more schools began hiring women who had been trained at one of the new academies or colleges for women. Some women tried to enter other professions as well. Margaret Fuller, a journalist, scholar, and literary critic, wrote about the need for women's rights in the book *Women in the Nineteenth Century*. Other women entered scientific fields. Elizabeth Blackwell was the first woman to graduate from a medical school. Astronomer Maria Mitchell was the first professor hired at Vassar College and the first woman elected to the American Academy of Arts and Sciences. ✓

✓ Checkpoint

Name the first college for women in the United States.

____

Check Your Progress

1. Why did many reformers, including Lucretia Mott, oppose the demand for women's suffrage?

____

____

2. What movement were both Sojourner Truth and Lucretia Mott involved in before they began to demand rights for women?

____

Section 3 Notetaking Study Guide

Question to Think About As you read Section 3 in your textbook and take notes, keep this section focus question in mind: **How did the women's suffrage movement begin?**

► Complete this chart to record key information from the section.

Women's Rights Movement
Roots of the Movement
Important leaders • Sojourner Truth: former slave who spoke on behalf of African Americans and women • Lucretia Mott: ____________ • Elizabeth Cady Stanton: ____________
Seneca Falls Convention
How it came about: Lucretia Mott and Elizabeth Cady Stanton were not allowed to take an active role in an ____________ convention. In response, they organized a ____________ in Seneca Falls, New York, in 1848.
Declaration of Sentiments • the beginning of the battle for ____________ • It demanded ____________.
Suffrage • definition: ____________
New Opportunities for Women
The Seneca Falls Convention launched the women's rights movement. • Stanton and Susan B. Anthony founded ____________ in 1869. • In 1860, Stanton and Anthony convinced New York to pass a law ____________.
Education • Emma Willard: founded ____________, which served as ____________ • Mary Lyon: founded ____________, the first ____________
Careers • Margaret Fuller: wrote ____________, which was about the need for women's rights • Elizabeth Blackwell: the first ____________ • Maria Mitchell: the first ____________ and the first ____________

Refer to this page to answer the Chapter 8 focus question on page 139.

Section 4

American Literature and Arts

Section 4 Focus Question

How did American literature and arts have an impact on American life? To begin answering this question,

- Discover how a distinctly American culture developed.
- Find out about the flowering of American literature.
- Learn about new American styles of art and music.

Section 4 Summary

In the 1800s, America developed its own unique culture. This included new ideas and changes in literature, art, and music.

An American Culture Develops

Before 1800, American writers and artists modeled their work on European styles. Most American artists trained in Europe. By the mid-1800s, Americans had begun to develop their own styles that reflected the optimism of the reform era.

Writer Washington Irving based many of his stories, such as "The Legend of Sleepy Hollow" and "Rip Van Winkle," on the Dutch history of early New York. James Fenimore Cooper wrote about a character named Natty Bumppo, a frontiersman who kept moving westward.

By the early 1800s, a new artistic movement called Romanticism took shape in Europe. It was a style of writing and painting that placed value on nature, the emotions, or strong feelings, and the imagination. Americans developed their own form of Romanticism, called **transcendentalism.** Its goal was to explore the relationship between man and nature through emotions rather than through reason.

Transcendentalists tried to live simply, and sought an understanding of beauty, goodness, and truth. The writings and lectures of **Ralph Waldo Emerson** reflected transcendentalism. Emerson stressed **individualism,** or the unique importance of the individual. He influenced **Henry David Thoreau,** another important writer and thinker. In his 1854 book, *Walden,* Thoreau urged people to live simply. He also encouraged **civil disobedience,** the idea that people should disobey unjust laws if their consciences demand it. ✓

Flowering of American Literature

Herman Melville and **Nathaniel Hawthorne** changed the optimistic tone of American literature by introducing psychological themes and extreme emotions. Melville's novel, *Moby-Dick* (1851), was the story of an obsessed ship captain who destroyed himself, his ship, and his crew in pursuit of a whale. Hawthorne's stories

Key Events

1831	William Lloyd Garrison founds antislavery newspaper.
1848	Women's rights convention is held in Seneca Falls, New York.
1850s	American writers publish *The Scarlet Letter, Moby-Dick, Walden,* and *Leaves of Grass.*

Vocabulary Builder

If the word *optimum* means "best" and the suffix *-ism* means "belief," what do you think *optimism* in the underlined sentence means?

____

____

✓ Checkpoint

List two important United States transcendentalists.

____

____

used historical themes to explore the dark side of the mind. **Louisa May Alcott** was the first to write about a heroine as a believable, imperfect person, rather than as a shining ideal.

Poets helped create a new national voice. Henry Wadsworth Longfellow based poems on American history. He wrote "Paul Revere's Ride." His long poem, *The Song of Hiawatha*, was one of the first works to honor Native Americans.

Walt Whitman published *Leaves of Grass* in 1855. Whitman wrote about familiar subjects but his book of poems shocked many readers because he did not follow the accepted set of rules. Most important, Whitman is seen as the poet who best expresses the democratic American spirit. His poetry celebrated the common man. In his poem, "Song of Myself," Whitman reaches out to all people.

✓ Checkpoint

Name the first writer to create realistic heroines.

____

Other poets used their poetry for social protest and social reform. John Greenleaf Whittier was a Quaker from Massachusetts. Frances Watkins Harper was an African American woman from Maryland. Both Whittier and Harper wrote poems that described and condemned the evils of slavery. ✓

Art and Music

After 1820, artists also began to create a unique American style. They focused on the landscapes around them or the daily lives of Americans. Painter Thomas Cole was part of the Hudson River school, which was inspired by Romanticism. Artists in this school sought to stir emotion by reproducing the beauty and power of nature. Other painters, such as George Caleb Bingham, painted scenes of everyday life. George Catlin captured the ways and dignity of Native Americans.

✓ Checkpoint

Name the school of painting inspired by Romanticism.

____

American music also began to develop its own identity. A wide variety of new songs emerged, such as "Yankee Doodle." Other popular songs were work songs sung by men who worked on ships or the railroad. The era's most popular songwriter was Stephen Foster. Many of his tunes, such as "Camptown Races," are still familiar today. ✓

Check Your Progress

1. What aspect of the reform era was reflected in American literature and art?

____

2. How did Herman Melville and Nathaniel Hawthorne change the tone of American literature?

____

____

Section 4 Notetaking Study Guide

Question to Think About As you read Section 4 in your textbook and take notes, keep this section focus question in mind: **How did American literature and arts have an impact on American life?**

▶ Complete this chart to record key information from the section.

American Literature and Arts

Development of an American Culture

- Before 1800, American writers and artists modeled their work on ________.
- By the mid-1800s, American __writers__ and ________ developed styles that reflected American __optimism__ and ________.

Early Writers

- Washington Irving based many of his stories on the ________ ________; he wrote "The Legend of Sleepy Hollow" and "Rip Van Winkle."
- James Fenimore Cooper wrote about ________.

- Romanticism: a European ________ that placed value on ________
- Transcendentalism: goal was to explore ________ ________
  - Ralph Waldo Emerson stressed ________.
  - Henry David Thoreau urged people to ________ and encouraged civil disobedience.

Flowering of American Literature

Herman Melville and Nathaniel Hawthorne changed the tone of American literature by ________.

Louisa May Alcott: first to write about a heroine as a ________

Poetry

- Henry Wadsworth Longfellow based his poems on ________.
- Walt Whitman rejected ________ and expressed the ________.
- John Greenleaf Whittier and Frances Watkins Harper wrote poems that described and condemned ________.

Art

Hudson River school: The school's artists sought to reproduce ________. George Caleb Bingham's paintings showed ________. George Catlin's paintings showed ________.

Music

A new American style of song emerged, including ________ chanted by sailors and laborers, and ________ developed among African Americans.

Refer to this page to answer the Chapter 8 focus question on page 139.

Chapter 8 Assessment

Directions: Circle the letter of the correct answer.

1. Who was an important leader of education reform?
A Lucretia Mott
B Harriet Tubman
C William Lloyd Garrison
D Horace Mann

2. What document declared that all men and women are created equal and listed injustices against women?
A the U.S. Constitution
B the Declaration of Sentiments
C the Declaration of Independence
D *Moby-Dick*

3. Whose writings changed the tone of American literature by introducing psychological themes and extreme emotions?
A Charles Finney
B Henry David Thoreau
C Herman Melville
D Louisa May Alcott

Directions: Follow the steps to answer this question:

How did religious ideas encourage an era of social reform?

Step 1: Recall information: Define *social reform* and identify its roots.

Social Reform		
Concept	**Definition**	**Rooted In**
Social Reform		

Step 2: Explain the new religious movement and how it was spread.

Second Great Awakening	How It Was Spread

Step 3: Complete the topic sentence that follows. Then write two or three more sentences that support your topic sentence.

Religious ideas helped spark an era of social reform by ______________________

____

____

____

____

Chapter 8 Notetaking Study Guide

Now you are ready to answer the Chapter 8 Focus Question: **How did reformers and writers inspire change and spark controversy?**

► Complete the following chart to help you answer this question.

American Reforms and Ideas

Society and Education

Social reform: organized attempts to improve conditions of life.

- Two factors encouraging reform:
  1. ____________________
  2. ____________________
- The temperance movement was ____________________ ____________________.

Prison reform

- Dorothea Dix convinced states to build ____________ prisons and ____________ for the mentally ill.

Education reform

- ____________ called for colleges to train teachers and higher teacher salaries.
- ____________________ was the first state to admit African Americans to public schools.

Slavery

Abolitionists: reformers who wanted to abolish slavery.

- William Lloyd Garrison cofounded the *Liberator*, an ____________________ ____________________.
- Frederick Douglass: an escaped slave and powerful speaker

The Underground Railroad

- "Conductors" helped slaves move between "stations."
- ____________________, an escaped slave, escorted over 300 slaves to freedom.

Opposing Abolition

- Northerners relied on cotton produced by slaves.
- The "gag rule" blocked ____________ ____________________.

Women's Rights

Women's rights movement

- Women began to demand equal rights as citizens.
- Elizabeth Cady Stanton wrote ____________________.

The Seneca Falls Convention

- birthplace of ____________
- 1869: Stanton and Susan B. Anthony founded the ____________.

New Opportunities

- Women started schools for girls and women.
- career "firsts" in medicine, ____________, ____________

Culture

Ideas

- Transcendentalism was a form of ____________________, a European artistic movement.
- The writings of ____________ and ____________ reflected transcendentalism.
- Louisa May Alcott was the first to depict a woman as ____________ ____________________ ____________________.
- American artists began to focus on landscapes around them or ____________________ ____________________.

Refer to this page to answer the Unit 4 Focus Question on page 154.

Chapter Standards

History-Social Science 8.8.2, 8.8.3, 8.8.4, 8.8.5, 8.8.6

Chapter 9

Westward Expansion (1820–1860)

What You Will Learn

In the mid-1800s, many Americans wanted the nation to expand westward to the Pacific Ocean. American settlers overcame hardships in making this happen.

Chapter 9 Focus Question

As you read this chapter, keep this question in mind: **How did westward expansion change the geography of the nation and demonstrate the determination of its people?**

Key Events

1821	William Becknell opens the Santa Fe Trail.
1836	Texas declares independence from Mexico.
1849	California gold rush begins.

Section 1

The West

Section 1 Focus Question

What cultures and ideas influenced the development of the West? To begin answering this question,

- Explore what "the West" was.
- Learn about the Mexican settlements.
- Understand the concept of Manifest Destiny.

Section 1 Summary

The lands that made up the West were constantly shifting. They included lands under Mexican control. Americans believed they were destined to take possession of the West.

What Was "The West"?

As the nation grew, the lands that made up "the West" changed. When the United States first became a nation, the West meant the land between the Appalachian Mountains and the Mississippi River. By the 1820s, this land was almost completely settled. The West moved again, to the lands beyond the Mississippi.

The vast Great Plains lay between the Mississippi and the Rocky Mountains. But this land was overlooked by settlers, who believed it could never be farmed because it would be too hard to clear the thickly rooted grasses that covered it. Settlers looked past the Great Plains to the Northwest and Southwest.

The Northwest had fertile lands stretching from the Rocky Mountains to the Pacific Ocean. This region was claimed by the United States, Great Britain, Russia, and Spain.

The Southwest included present-day California, Utah, Nevada, Arizona, New Mexico, Texas, and half of Colorado.

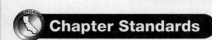

Ruled first by Spain, then by Mexico, this vast area was home to a culture that was very different from the one that existed in the United States. ☑

Mexican Settlements

Like England and France, Spain followed a policy of mercantilism in its colonies. It was illegal for settlers in New Spain to trade with other countries.

Over time, many Spanish settlers had children. These children were called creoles. In addition, Spanish settlers, Native Americans, and Africans would sometimes intermarry, and the children of these couples were called mestizos. By the 1800s, the combination of these ethnic groups had produced a Southwestern culture that was very different from the cultures that had previously existed in this part of the world.

Spanish missionaries tried to convert the local Native Americans to Catholicism. Many Native Americans were forced to live and work at missions. In the end, thousands of Native Americans died from overwork or disease.

Over the years, Spanish settlers mixed with Native Americans to create a blended culture. The region followed Spanish law and religion and used the Spanish language. Its foods and building materials were Native American.

In 1821, Mexico won its independence from Spain. The Mexican government opened up the region to trade with foreign countries, including the United States. It also removed the missions from church control and gave their lands in large **land grants,** or government gifts of land, to Mexican settlers. Many of these grants were made to **rancheros,** or owners of ranches. Much of this land belonged to Native Americans, who responded by raiding ranches. However, they were soon crushed, and their population in the Southwest was drastically reduced. ☑

Manifest Destiny

Many Americans were interested in westward **expansion**, or extending the nation beyond its existing borders. Under Jefferson, the Louisiana Purchase had doubled the size of the nation. But just forty years later, Americans were looking even farther west. A newspaper editor coined the phrase "manifest destiny" in 1845. The phrase described the belief that the United States was destined, or meant, to stretch from coast to coast. ☑

Check Your Progress

1. Why weren't the Great Plains settled quickly?

____

____

2. What phrase described American feelings about westward expansion?

____

✓ Checkpoint

List three areas that made up the West after the 1820s.

____

____

____

Vocabulary Builder

Reread the bracketed paragraph. Based on context clues in the paragraph, what do you think the word *missions* means?

____

____

____

✓ Checkpoint

Name two changes that Mexico made when it took control of the Southwest.

____

____

____

✓ Checkpoint

Name the term that described the idea that the United States should stretch from coast to coast.

____

Section 1 Notetaking Study Guide

Question to Think About As you read Section 1 in your textbook and take notes, keep this section focus question in mind: **What cultures and ideas influenced the development of the West?**

▶ Use this chart to record key information from the section. Some information has been filled in to get you started.

Westward Expansion

The Great Plains

Where: between the Mississippi River and the Rocky Mountains

Problem with land: ______

For many settlers, the Great Plains was: ______

The Northwest

Where: ______

Included present-day states of ______

Claimed by: ______

Settlers attracted to ______

Manifest Destiny

From the beginning, Americans were interested in westward expansion. The Louisiana Purchase, which doubled the territory of the nation, helped with this goal. Forty years later, the idea of Manifest Destiny became popular. It meant ______.

Mexican Settlement

The Southwest included the present-day states of: ______

Spanish Missions

- Purpose: ______
- Effect of missions on Indians: ______

Blended culture

- Spanish influence: ______
- Native American influence: ______
- Creoles were ______.
- Mestizos were ______.

Trade under Spanish rule: ______

Trade under Mexican rule: ______

Under Spanish rule, land grants were given mostly to ______.
Under Mexican rule, missions were removed from ______ control. Their lands were given as land grants to ______.
Much of this land belonged to ______, who responded by ______.
But soon ______ and their population ______.

Refer to this page to answer the Chapter 9 Focus Question on page 153.

Section 2

Trails to the West

Section 2 Focus Question

Why did people go west, and what challenges did they face? To begin answering this question,

- Learn how traders led the way into the West.
- Explore the Oregon Trail.
- Learn about life in the West.

Section 2 Summary

People went west for different reasons. Whether to find gold, become a trader, work as a missionary, or farm, people who went west suffered many hardships.

Traders Lead the Way

Trade drove the first western crossings. Traders were looking for new markets in which to sell their goods. In the process, they blazed important trails for those who followed.

After Mexico won independence, it allowed trade with the United States. In 1821, Captain **William Becknell** led a wagon train filled with merchandise from Independence, Missouri, to Santa Fe, New Mexico. It was a difficult journey, but Becknell's group reached Santa Fe. The Santa Fe Trail soon became a busy international trade route.

John Jacob Astor, a German fur merchant, sent the first American fur-trading expedition to Oregon. In 1808, he established the American Fur Company at Fort Astor, now Astoria, Oregon. Astor's expedition consisted of two groups. One group sailed around South America and up the Pacific coast, and the other group traveled across the continent. On the way, the second group found the South Pass through the Rocky Mountains, which became an important trade route that helped open up the Northwest for the missionaries and settlers who followed.

The fur trade made Astor the richest man in the country. **Mountain men**, or fur trappers of the Northwest, supplied him with furs. For most of the year, they lived <u>isolated</u> lives, but once a year they gathered for a **rendezvous** (RAHN day voo), or a meeting where they would trade furs for supplies.

Beaver fur was in great demand in the East. However, by the 1830s, the supply of beavers was nearly exhausted, so most of the trappers moved back east to become farmers, merchants, or even bankers. Others stayed as guides for the wagon trains that brought thousands of settlers west in the 1840s. ✓

The Oregon Trail

The first white easterners to build permanent homes in Oregon were missionaries, who began to travel west in the 1830s to bring

Key Events

1821	William Becknell opens the Santa Fe Trail.
1836	Texas declares independence from Mexico.
1849	California gold rush begins.

Vocabulary Builder

The word *isolated* comes from the Latin word *insula*, which means "island." Think about the position of an island relative to the mainland. What do you think the word *isolated* means as it is used in the text?

____

____

✓ Checkpoint

List three people or groups who developed trade in the West.

____

____

____

their religion to the Indians. The missionaries' glowing reports of Oregon led more easterners to make the journey west. Farmers sought the free and fertile land, the mild climate, and the plentiful rainfall in river valleys. Settlers from all over the country began to come down with "Oregon Fever."

Most settlers followed the Oregon Trail, a route that stretched over 2,000 miles from Missouri to Oregon. Travelers left in the spring and had five months to make their journey. If they were caught in the Rocky Mountains during the winter, their chances of survival were slim.

Pioneers on the Oregon Trail banded together in wagon trains for mutual protection. During the day, teams of horses or oxen would pull the long trains of covered wagons, which were filled with the settlers' food and possessions. Meanwhile, the pioneers would walk, often for 15 hours a day. At night, the wagons were drawn up in a circle to keep the cattle from wandering off. The trip was a great hardship and dangerous. As mile followed mile, people would begin to discard personal items to lighten their wagons. In addition, disease and accident killed one out of every ten travelers, and clean, safe water was hard to find. Still, over 50,000 people reached Oregon between 1840 and 1860. ✓

✓ Checkpoint

List two groups of people who went to Oregon.

____

____

Life in the West

Settlers in the West had few possessions and little money. They worked hard to clear land, plant crops, and build shelters. Disease, accidents, and such natural disasters as storms and floods were a constant threat.

Women in the West worked just as hard as men did. Because their labor was so necessary for a family's survival, women had a higher status in the West. In 1869, Wyoming Territory became the first area of the United States to grant women the vote.

Native Americans in Oregon lived in an uneasy peace with the white settlers. While Native Americans in southern Oregon usually got along with whites, in the north, Native Americans were angered by the presence of strangers on their land. When gold was discovered in northern Oregon in the 1850s, a large number of white and Chinese miners arrived in the area. In 1855, war broke out briefly between the Native Americans and miners. After the U.S. government intervened, the tribes were forced to accept peace treaties. ✓

✓ Checkpoint

List three dangers that settlers in Oregon faced.

____

____

____

Check Your Progress

1. What first drove people to find safe trails to the West?

____

____

2. Why did western women have a higher status?

____

____

Section 2 Notetaking Study Guide

Question to Think About As you read Section 2 in your textbook, keep this section focus question in mind: **Why did people go west, and what challenges did they face?**

► Use these charts to record key information from the section.

Traders Lead the Way

The Santa Fe Trail

- In 1821, ______________________ led a wagon train from ______________ to ______________________.
- Hardships experienced along the way: ______________________
- Importance: established a route for ____________ trade with ___________ that stretched about _____ miles

The Oregon Fur Trade

- John Jacob Astor sent the first American fur-trading expedition to Oregon and established the __________ Fur Company in 1808.
- Trappers who supplied furs were called ______________________.
- What happened to the fur trade in the 1830s: ______________________

____

The Oregon Trail

Missionaries Travel West to Oregon in the 1830s

- Purpose of missionaries: ______________________
- Famous missionary couple: ______________________
- How missionaries spurred settlement of the West: ______________________

____

On the Trail

- Trail stretched more than ______ miles from __________ to __________
- Travelers left in ___________ and had to reach Oregon in 5 months. If they did not make it in time, they risked ______________________.
- Between 1840 and 1860, more than _________ people reached Oregon.

Life in the West

Pioneer Life

- Settlers had only ______________ to clear the land, ______________, and build shelters.

Threats included ______________, ______________, and ______________.

Women in the West

- Reason women's status was raised in the West: ______________________

____

- In 1869, ______________ was the first area to grant women the right to ___________.

Native Americans and Settlers

- Relationship between the two groups: ______________________
- In the 1850s, ______________ brought large numbers of ______________ to ______________ Oregon. In 1855, ___________ broke out there briefly.

Refer to this page to answer the Chapter 9 Focus Question on page 153.

Section 3

Conflict With Mexico

Key Events

1821	William Becknell opens the Santa Fe Trail.
1836	Texas declares independence from Mexico.
1849	California gold rush begins.

Section 3 Focus Question

What were the causes and effects of the Texas War for Independence and the Mexican-American War? To begin answering this question,

- Find out how Texas won independence.
- Learn how Texas and Oregon were annexed by the United States.
- Discover the causes of the Mexican-American War.
- Explore how the United States achieved Manifest Destiny.

Section 3 Summary

In negotiations with Britain, the United States acquired Oregon, but U.S. expansion in the Southwest came at the cost of war with Mexico.

Texas Wins Independence

In 1820, the Spanish gave Moses Austin a land grant to establish a small colony in Texas. After Moses Austin died, his son, **Stephen Austin**, led a group of some 300 settlers there. After Mexico won its independence from Spain and took possession of Texas, Texans came into conflict with the Mexican government. Mexico had outlawed slavery, but settlers brought slaves in. Texans wanted a democratic government.

In 1833, General Antonio López de Santa Anna became president of Mexico. He overturned Mexico's democratic constitution and started a **dictatorship**, or one-person rule, that clamped down on Texas. Stephen Austin convinced Texans to declare independence from Mexico. The Republic of Texas was created in 1836.

When **Sam Houston**, commander of Texan forces, finally defeated Santa Anna, he became president of the Republic of Texas. Texans hoped the United States would **annex**, or add on, their republic to the Union. ✓

✓ Checkpoint

Name the three men who played major roles in the war over Texas.

____

____

____

Annexing Texas and Oregon

Annexation became a major political issue because Texas would come in as a slave state. How could the balance of slave and free states be maintained? President **James K. Polk** solved this problem by negotiating a treaty to acquire Oregon from Britain. In 1845, Texas was admitted as a slave state. Oregon was annexed as a free territory.

But trouble was looming. Mexico had never recognized Texas independence. Now Mexico claimed that the southern border of Texas was the Nueces River, not the Rio Grande. Polk pressured Mexico to accept the Rio Grande border.

Timeline of U.S. Southwestern Expansion

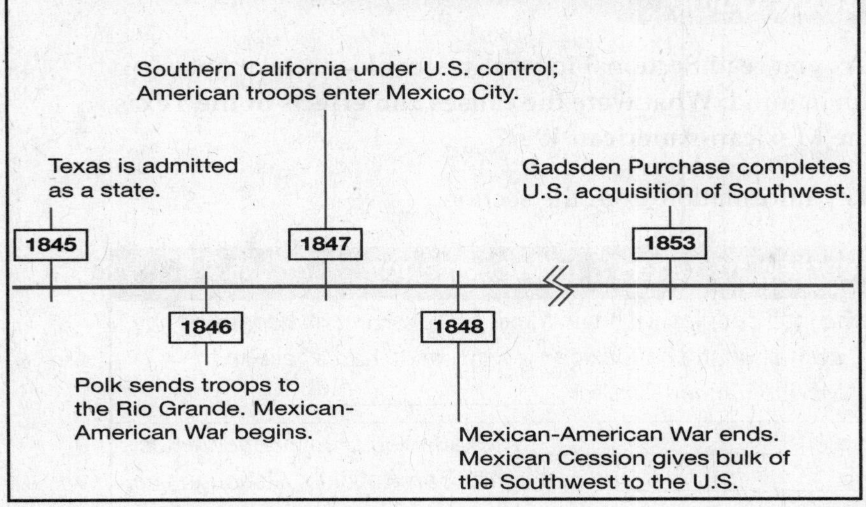

1845
Texas is admitted as a state.
1846
Polk sends troops to the Rio Grande. Mexican-American War begins.
1847
Southern California under U.S. control; American troops enter Mexico City.
1848
Mexican-American War ends. Mexican Cession gives bulk of the Southwest to the U.S.
1853
Gadsden Purchase completes U.S. acquisition of Southwest.

✓

✓ Checkpoint

List the two rivers that were claimed as Texas's southern border.

The Mexican-American War

Mexico would not accept the Rio Grande border. It also refused to **cede**, or give up, California and New Mexico to the United States when President Polk offered to purchase them. So Polk sent General Zachary Taylor to the Rio Grande border. The Mexican government saw this as an act of war and attacked. Polk then urged Congress to declare war. He sent Stephen Kearny to capture Santa Fe. **John C. Frémont**, an explorer, led a rebellion against Mexican rule in California. By early 1847, all of southern California was under U.S. control.

General Taylor invaded Mexico and defeated Santa Anna at the Battle of Buena Vista. General Winfield Scott marched to Mexico City. Santa Anna fled the city, and Mexico was under U.S. occupation. ✓

✓ Checkpoint

Name four Americans who led the United States in the Mexican-American War.

Achieving Manifest Destiny

The United States and Mexico signed the Treaty of Guadalupe-Hidalgo in 1848. Mexico recognized Texas as a U.S. state. Then in the Mexican Cession, it gave present-day California, Nevada, Utah, as well as parts of Wyoming, Colorado, Arizona, and New Mexico to the United States for $18 million.

In the Gadsden Purchase of 1853, the United States paid Mexico $10 million for a narrow strip of present-day Arizona and New Mexico. The United States had fulfilled what it saw as its destiny to occupy the West. ✓

✓ Checkpoint

List the two things that gave the United States the entire Southwest.

Check Your Progress

1. What did Texans want from the Mexican government?

2. What action started the Mexican-American War?

Section 3 Notetaking Study Guide

Question to Think About As you read Section 3 in your textbook and take notes, keep this section focus question in mind: **What were the causes and effects of the Texas War for Independence and the Mexican-American War?**

► Use these charts to record key information from the section.

Events Leading to Texas's Independence
American settlers in Texas came into conflict with the Mexican government because they were ___slaveholders___, even though the Mexican government had abolished ________. In 1830, Mexico banned further ________.
After Santa Anna established a(n) ________, Texans declared independence. Mexican troops laid siege to ________, a mission in San Antonio. Although the Texans were defeated, this event inspired ________. Later, the Texans defeated Santa Anna's army at ________.
________ became president of the new Republic of Texas. He hoped that the United States would ________ Texas. However, public opinion in the United States was divided because ________.

Annexing Texas and Oregon
James K. Polk negotiated a treaty with ___Britain___ to divide Oregon, which became the states of ________, ________, and ________.
Tensions with Mexico increased because Mexico had never ________. Also, the United States claimed that the southern Texas border was the ________, while Mexico claimed it was the ________.

The Mexican-American War
When war broke out between Mexico and the United States, it was most popular among ________ and ________, who wanted ________. Many ________, however, opposed the war because they thought it was an attempt to ________.
Stephen Kearny led troops that captured ________ and later ________.
________ won a victory at the Battle of Buena Vista. An American army under ________ captured Veracruz and then marched on to ________.
The Treaty of ________ formally ended the war. Under the treaty, Mexico recognized ________ and ceded a vast territory known as ________ to the United States. This territory included present-day ________.
In the ________ of 1853, the United States paid Mexico $10 million for a narrow strip of present-day ________.

Refer to this page to answer the Chapter 9 Focus Question on page 153.

Section 4
A Rush to the West

Section 4 Focus Question

How did Mormon settlement and the gold rush lead to changes in the West? To begin answering this question,

- Learn about Mormon settlement in Utah.
- Find out about the California gold rush.
- Explore California's changing population.

Section 4 Summary

While Mormons migrated to Utah in search of religious freedom, fortune seekers flocked to California in search of gold.

Mormons Settle Utah

In 1830, **Joseph Smith**, a New York farmer, founded the Church of Jesus Christ of Latter-day Saints. His followers were called the Mormons. The church grew quickly, but its teachings placed its followers in conflict with their neighbors. For example, Smith favored **polygamy**, or the practice of having more than one wife at a time.

Hostile communities forced the Mormons to move from New York to Ohio to Missouri to Illinois, where Joseph Smith was murdered. In 1847, **Brigham Young**, the new Mormon leader, led the group to the valley of the Great Salt Lake in Utah. Over the next few years, some 15,000 Mormons made the trek to Utah.

As a result of the Mexican Cession, Utah became part of the United States in 1848, and the U.S. government created the Utah Territory. The Mormons immediately came into conflict with the federal government over three issues. The first issue was the election process, which was controlled by the Mormon Church. As a result, non-Mormons had no say in the government. Another was the fact that the church supported Mormon-owned businesses, so non-Mormons had difficulty doing business in the territory. Third, polygamy was illegal in the rest of the country. In time, Congress passed a law that took control of elections away from the Mormon Church, and church leaders agreed to ban polygamy and to stop favoring Mormon-owned businesses. ✓

The California Gold Rush

After the Mexican Cession, easterners began migrating to California. At the time, there were about 10,000 Californios, or Mexican Californians, living in the territory.

California history changed forever when gold was discovered in 1848 at Sutter's Mill near Sacramento. News of the discovery spread quickly, and the prospect of finding gold drew about 80,000 fortune seekers. These people who came to California in search of gold were known as the **"forty-niners."** In just two

Key Events

1821	William Becknell opens the Santa Fe Trail.
1836	Texas declares independence from Mexico.
1849	California gold rush begins.

✓ Checkpoint

List three issues that were a source of conflict between the Mormons and the U.S. government.

____

____

____

Vocabulary Builder

Reread the underlined sentence. Which of the following words could replace *prospect*, as it is used in the sentence?

a. hope
b. guarantee
c. agreement

years, California's population zoomed from 14,000 to 100,000. Prospectors, or gold seekers, searched throughout the Sacramento Valley for gold.

Since much of California was desert, disputes over water rights were common. **Water rights** are the legal rights to use the water in a river, stream, or other body. Often, such disputes erupted in violence.

Mining towns sprang up overnight and emptied just as quickly when news spread of a gold strike somewhere else. These towns attracted miners and people hoping to make money from miners. Since California was not yet a state, federal law did not apply within mining towns. Often **vigilantes**, or self-appointed law enforcers, punished people for crimes, although such vigilantes had no legal right to do so.

Other migrations in U.S. history included men and women, young and old. The forty-niners, however, were mainly young men. Still, some women did come to California, which offered women profitable work.

Few forty-niners struck it rich, and after the gold rush ended, many people continued to search for gold throughout the West. Others settled in the West for good. ✓

✓ Checkpoint

Name one way the gold rush was different from other migrations in U.S. history.

____

____

____

California's Changing Population

The gold rush brought enormous ethnic diversity to California. People came from Europe, Asia, Australia, and South America. After news of the gold rush reached China, about 45,000 Chinese men went to California. They faced prejudice and were generally hired only for menial labor.

Although some southerners brought slaves with them during the gold rush, slavery did not take root in California. Other miners objected to anyone profiting from mining who did not participate in the hard labor of finding gold.

The gold rush brought tragedy for Native Americans in California. Miners swarmed onto Indian lands, and vigilante gangs killed many Indians. About 100,000 Indians, nearly two thirds of the Native American population, died during the gold rush period.

By 1850, only 15 percent of Californians were Mexican. Laws were passed that discriminated against Californios, and many lost their land as a result. ✓

✓ Checkpoint

Describe one reason why slavery did not take root in California.

____

____

____

Check Your Progress

1. Why did the Mormons migrate to Utah?

____

____

2. How did California's population change after gold was discovered in the state?

____

____

Section 4 Notetaking Study Guide

Question to Think About As you read Section 4 in your textbook, keep this question in mind: **How did Mormon settlement and the gold rush lead to changes in the West?**

► Use these charts to record key information from the section.

Mormons Move West
Seeking Refuge The Mormon Church was founded by Joseph Smith in 1830. Hostility forced the Mormons to move from ____________ to ____________, and then to ____________. After ________ was murdered, ______________ led the Mormons to the valley of Utah's ____________.
Conflict With the Government Utah became part of the United States in ______. The Mormons almost immediately came into conflict with the U.S. government over three issues: 1. *Problem*: ______________________________ *Solution*: 1. Congress took away control of elections from the Mormon Church. 2. *Problem*: ______________________________ *Solution*: ______________________________. 3. *Problem*: Polygamy, which is ______________________________, was illegal in the United States. *Solution*: ______________________________ Finally, in ________, Utah became a state.

The California Gold Rush
Gold Is Discovered In January ______, gold was discovered at Sutter's Mill near ____________. Fortune seekers, called ______________, came to California in search of gold. In just two years, the population of settlers in California zoomed from __________ to __________.
Miners and Mining Towns Mining towns supplied miners with __________, ____________, and ______________. Since California was not yet a state, federal law did not apply within mining towns, so ______________, or ____________________, punished people for crimes.
California's Changing Population During the gold rush, people from __________, __________, __________, and ______________ came to California. Chinese workers faced ____________ and were usually hired only for ______________. Some southerners brought their slaves to California, but slavery did not take root because ______________________________ ______________________________. California's Native American population declined by about ________ thirds during the gold rush. They were killed by __________ gangs who wanted their land. By 1850, only ______ percent of Californians were ______________________________.

Refer to this page to answer the Chapter 9 Focus Question on page 153.

Chapter 9 Assessment

Directions: Circle the letter of the correct answer.

1. The largest region of the West was
- **A** the Southwest.
- **B** the Northwest.
- **C** the Great Plains.
- **D** the Pacific Coast.

2. Most early travelers to the West were
- **A** missionaries.
- **B** farmers.
- **C** traders.
- **D** merchants.

3. Which of the following was a result of the Mexican-American War?
- **A** the Mexican Cession
- **B** the annexation of Texas
- **C** the annexation of Florida
- **D** the Gadsden Purchase

4. Which of the following was a result of the gold rush in California?
- **A** Many people became rich from mining.
- **B** Slavery became widespread in the territory.
- **C** California's population became more diverse.
- **D** Native Americans were forced to move to Indian Territory.

Directions: Follow the steps to answer this question:

How did the Mexican-American War help achieve Manifest Destiny?

Step 1: Define Manifest Destiny.

____

____

____

Step 2: Recall information: Describe the results of the Mexican-American War.

Results of the Mexican-American War
•
•

Step 3: Complete the topic sentence that follows. Then write two or three more sentences that support your topic sentence.

The effect of the Mexican-American War helped achieve Manifest Destiny by ______

____

____

____

____

____

Chapter 9 Notetaking Study Guide

Now you are ready to answer the Chapter 9 Focus Question: **How did westward expansion change the geography of the nation and demonstrate the determination of its people?**

► Complete the following chart to help you answer this question. Use the notes that you took for each section.

Westward Expansion Changes the Nation's Geography
The West

• **What was the West?** By the 1820s, lands west of the Mississippi
  • **Northwest:** Land that stretched from ___the Rockies___ to the ____________; in the early 1800s was claimed by ____________
  • **Southwest:** Lands in the southwest that included present-day California, Utah, Nevada, Arizona, New Mexico, Texas, and half of Colorado; ruled first by Spain, then by Mexico
• **What was Manifest Destiny?** ____________

Trails to the West

• **The Santa Fe Trail:** overland trade route that carried merchandise from Independence, Missouri, to Santa Fe, New Mexico
• **The Oregon Trail:** ____________
• **Life in the West**
  • **For women:** ____________
  • **For Native Americans and settlers:** ____________

Texas and the Mexican-American War
• **Texans rebel against Mexico because** of religious differences, conflicts over slavery, and a lack of democracy . • **Annexation of Texas was controversial in the United States because** ____________ • **The solution that led to the annexation of Texas was that** ____________ • **Causes of the Mexican War:** ____________ • **Results of the Mexican War:** The nation's geography greatly changed after the United States acquired a vast territory under the Mexican Cession.
A Rush to the West
• **Who were the Mormons?** a religious group founded by Joseph Smith in 1830 • **Why did they migrate to Utah?** to escape conflict with ____________ • **Discovery in 1848 that changed California's history:** ____________

Refer to this page to answer the Unit 4 Focus Question on page 154.

Unit 4 Pulling It Together Activity

What You Have Learned

Chapter 7 The North industrialized and urbanized rapidly in the early to mid-1800s. The South became highly dependent on cotton and the slave labor needed to cultivate it. Tensions between North and South spread to the western territories.

Chapter 8 By the mid-1800s, Americans were seeking reform in education and abolition. Some sought equality for women. Artists and writers also began to develop a distinct style.

Chapter 9 In the mid-1800s, many Americans wanted the nation to expand westward to the Pacific Ocean. American settlers overcame hardships in making this happen.

Think Like a Historian

Read the Unit 4 Focus Question: **What forces unite and divide a nation?**

► Use the organizers on this page and the next to collect information to answer this question.

What forces united the nation? Some of them are listed in this chart. Review your section and chapter notes. Then complete the chart.

Factors That United the North and the South, 1800–1860	
Area	**Uniting Factors**
Economy	• transformed by the Industrial Revolution
Technology	• new methods of transportation: steamboat, railroad • •
Labor	•
Arts	•
Issues	• •

Look at the second part of the Unit Focus Question. It asks about the forces that divide a nation. The chart below gives you a part of the answer. Review your section and chapter notes. Then fill in the rest of the chart.

Factors That Divided the North and the South, 1800–1860		
Area	**In North**	**In South**
Economy	• industrial • based on manufacturing and trade	• agricultural • dependent on cotton
Key technology	• •	•
Where people lived and worked	• •	•
Source of labor	•	•
Reform movements	• •	•
Slavery	• •	• •

Unit 5

Civil War and Reunion

What You Will Learn

Chapter 10 With the addition of new western lands, tension over the slavery issue erupted into violence. The election of Abraham Lincoln led to seven states leaving the Union and marked the coming of the Civil War.

Chapter 11 People in the North and the South hoped for an early victory, but the Civil War went on for years. Hundreds of thousands of Americans were killed before the war ended.

Chapter 12 At the end of the Civil War, Americans faced the problem of how to reunite the nation. Disagreements over Reconstruction led to conflicts in government and in the South. With the end of Reconstruction, African Americans in the South lost many of the rights they had gained.

Focus Your Learning As you study this unit and take notes, you will find the information to answer the questions below. Answering the Chapter Focus Questions will help build your answer to the Unit Focus Question.

Chapter 10 Focus Question
How did the nation try but fail to deal with growing sectional differences?
(page 157)

Unit 5 Focus Question
How was the Civil War a political, economic, and social turning point?
(page 199)

Chapter 11 Focus Question
How did people, places, and things affect the outcome of the Civil War?
(page 171)

Chapter 12 Focus Question
What were the short-term and long-term effects of the Civil War? (page 188)

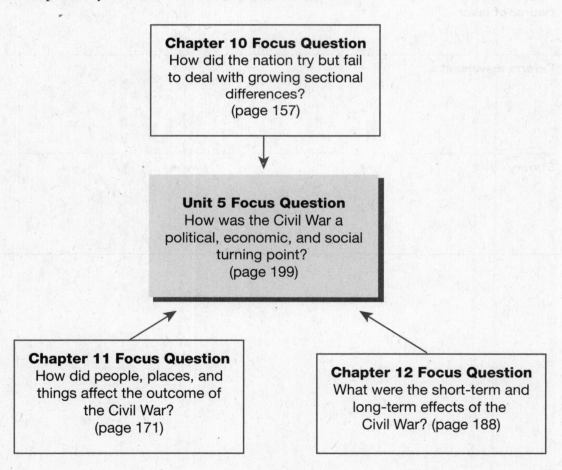

Chapter 10

The Nation Divided (1846–1861)

What You Will Learn

With the addition of new western lands, tension over the slavery issue erupted into violence. The election of Abraham Lincoln led to seven states leaving the Union and marked the coming of the Civil War.

Chapter 10 Focus Question

As you read through this chapter, keep this question in mind: **How did the nation try but fail to deal with growing sectional differences?**

Section 1

Growing Tensions Over Slavery

Section 1 Focus Question

How did the question of admission of new states to the Union fuel the debate over slavery and states' rights? To begin answering this question,

- Learn about slavery and the Mexican-American War.
- Explore the bitter debate over slavery in the United States.

Section 1 Summary

The vast new lands the United States won in the Mexican-American War recharged the national debate on slavery.

Slavery and the Mexican-American War

Between 1820 and 1848, the balance between free and slave states was maintained. However, the Missouri Compromise did not apply to the huge territory gained from Mexico in 1848. Would this territory be organized as states that allowed slavery?

The issue was important to northerners who wanted to stop slavery from spreading. Fearing that the South would gain too much power, Representative David Wilmot of Pennsylvania proposed in 1846 that Congress ban slavery in all southwestern lands that might become states. This was called the Wilmot Proviso. The proviso passed in the House, but not the Senate. Slaveholding states saw it as a northern attack on slavery.

Neither the Democrats nor the Whigs wanted to take a strong stand on slavery. Each party needed support in both the North and the South to win the presidential election of 1848.

The Democratic presidential candidate in 1848 was Senator Lewis Cass of Michigan. He came up with a slavery plan he

Chapter Standards

History-Social Science 8.9.1, 8.9.4, 8.9.5, 8.10.1, 8.10.3, 8.10.4

Key Events

1852 Harriet Beecher Stowe publishes *Uncle Tom's Cabin*.

1857 Supreme Court ruling in Dred Scott case declares Missouri Compromise unconstitutional.

1861 The Civil War begins with Confederate bombardment of Fort Sumter.

Vocabulary Builder

Sovereign comes from a Latin word meaning "above." If the states were sovereign, and made their own laws, what law would they be above?

____

✓ Checkpoint

List the three parties and their candidates in the 1848 election.

____

____

____

✓ Checkpoint

List two issues that caused debate in the Congress.

____

____

____

____

thought would work in both the North and South. His idea was to let people in each new territory that applied for statehood decide for themselves whether to allow slavery. This **popular sovereignty** meant that people in each territory would vote directly on the issue, rather than having their elected representatives decide for them.

Many antislavery Whigs and Democrats wanted to take a stronger stand. They created their own party, called the Free-Soil Party. They wanted to ban slavery in all territory gained in the Mexican-American War—to make it "free soil." The party chose former Democratic President Martin Van Buren as its candidate. Although Van Buren did poorly in the election, he took enough votes from Cass to keep him from winning. General Zachary Taylor of the Whig Party became President. ✓

A Bitter Debate

Both sides realized that California's entrance into the Union would upset the balance of free and slave states. Southerners feared that if free states gained the majority in the Senate, the South could no longer block antislavery proposals. Southern leaders threatened to **secede,** or withdraw, from the Union if California were admitted as a free state.

There were other bitter divisions between North and South. Northerners wanted the slave trade abolished in Washington, D.C. Southerners wanted laws forcing northerners to return **fugitive,** or runaway, enslaved people.

For a time, it seemed that a satisfactory conclusion was not possible. Then in January 1850, Senator **Henry Clay** of Kentucky made a series of proposals to save the Union, which led to a great Senate debate. South Carolina Senator **John C. Calhoun** was against Clay's compromises. He wrote that if California joined the Union as a free state, only a constitutional amendment protecting states' rights or secession could save the South's way of life.

Arguing the other side, Senator **Daniel Webster** of Massachusetts stated that Clay's compromises were necessary to preserve the Union. Both sides seemed deadlocked. ✓

Check Your Progress

1. What was the Wilmot Proviso?

____

____

____

2. Why did southerners fear California entering the Union as a free state?

____

____

____

Section 1 Notetaking Study Guide

Question to Think About As you read Section 1 in your textbook and take notes, keep this question in mind: **How did the question of admission of new states to the Union fuel the debate over slavery and states' rights?**

► Use this chart to record key information from the section. Some information has been filled in to get you started.

The Debate Over Slavery and States' Rights		
If	**Then**	**Who Benefits?**
The Wilmot Proviso passes,	1. slavery will be banned in all territory from the Mexican-American War that becomes part of the United States; slave states will be outnumbered and weakened.	North
Lewis Cass (Democrat) becomes President,	2. ______	
Martin Van Buren (Free-Soil) becomes President,	3. ______	
Zachary Taylor (Whig) becomes President,	4. ______	
California enters the Union as a free state,	5. ______	
Fugitive slave laws are enforced,	6. slavery is enforced in the North and the South.	South
Henry Clay's proposals are accepted,	7. according to Calhoun, the South ______	
Slavery remains an unresolved issue,	8. ______	

Refer to this page to answer the Chapter 10 Focus Question on page 170.

Section 2
Compromises Fail

Key Events

1852	Harriet Beecher Stowe publishes *Uncle Tom's Cabin*.
1857	Supreme Court ruling in Dred Scott case declares Missouri Compromise unconstitutional.
1861	The Civil War begins with Confederate bombardment of Fort Sumter.

Section 2 Focus Question

What was the Compromise of 1850, and why did it fail? To begin answering this question,

- Learn about the Compromise of 1850.
- Find out about the impact of *Uncle Tom's Cabin*.
- Learn about the Kansas-Nebraska Act.
- Read about the violence in Bleeding Kansas.

Section 2 Summary

Efforts to calm the slavery debate, such as the Compromise of 1850, ultimately failed, and the debate only grew fiercer.

The Compromise of 1850

In 1850, Congress passed and President Millard Fillmore signed a series of five bills known as the Compromise of 1850 that were based on Henry Clay's proposals. To please the North, California was admitted as a free state, and the slave trade was banned in the nation's capital. To please the South, popular sovereignty would be used to decide the slavery issue in the rest of the Mexican Cession. Southerners also got a tough fugitive slave law.

The Fugitive Slave Act of 1850 allowed government officials to arrest any person accused of being a runaway slave. Suspects had no right to prove they had been falsely accused in a trial. All that was needed to deprive someone of his or her freedom was the word of one white person. In addition, northerners were required to help capture runaway slaves if authorities requested assistance.

The Fugitive Slave Act became the most controversial part of the Compromise of 1850. Northerners hated the new law. Many swore they would resist it. They were outraged to see African Americans suddenly arrested and shipped South. Thousands of northern African Americans fled to Canada for safety, including many who had never been enslaved. ✓

✓ Checkpoint

Name two parts of the Fugitive Slave Act.

____

____

____

____

Uncle Tom's Cabin

Harriet Beecher Stowe was a northerner committed to fighting slavery. In 1852, she published *Uncle Tom's Cabin*, about a kind slave who is abused by a cruel master. Many white southerners attacked the book as **propaganda**, false or misleading information that is spread to further a cause. The book was a bestseller in the North. It shocked thousands of people who were previously unconcerned about slavery. Stowe's book showed that slavery was not just a political conflict, but a real human problem. ✓

✓ Checkpoint

What was the reaction of many northerners to *Uncle Tom's Cabin*?

____

____

The Kansas-Nebraska Act

In 1853, Illinois Senator **Stephen A. Douglas** suggested forming two new territories—the Kansas Territory and the Nebraska Territory. Southerners objected because both territories lay in an area closed to slavery by the Missouri Compromise. This meant that the states created from these territories would enter the Union as free states.

To win southern support, Douglas proposed that slavery in the new territories be decided by popular sovereignty. In effect, this undid the Missouri Compromise. Northerners were angered that the slavery issue was to be reopened in the territories. Southerners, however, supported Douglas's proposal, which enabled the Kansas-Nebraska Act to pass in both houses of Congress. ✓

Bleeding Kansas

Both proslavery and antislavery settlers flooded into Kansas within weeks after Douglas's bill became law. Each side was determined to hold the majority in the territory when it came time to vote.

In March 1855, Kansas held a vote on whether to enter the Union as a free or slave state. Thousands of proslavery people from Missouri voted illegally. Kansas had only 3,000 voters, but 8,000 votes were cast. A proslavery government was elected. Antislavery Kansans refused to accept these results and put a second government in place.

Violence soon broke out. Pro- and antislavery groups terrorized the countryside, attacking and killing settlers. It was so bad that the territory earned the name Bleeding Kansas.

Violence even spilled onto the floor of the U.S. Senate. After Massachusetts Senator Charles Sumner attacked a South Carolina senator in a fiery speech, the senator's nephew attacked Sumner in the Senate chamber. Many southerners felt that Sumner got what he deserved. To northerners, however, it was further evidence that slavery was brutal and inhumane. ✓

Check Your Progress

1. What did each side get in the Compromise of 1850?

____

____

____

2. What was the effect of the Kansas-Nebraska Act?

____

____

____

Vocabulary Builder

Circle the definition of *propose* that most closely matches the meaning used in the underlined sentence.

A. to put forward for consideration
B. to nominate for an office
C. to make an offer of marriage

✓ Checkpoint

Name the method used to determine the status of slavery in the Kansas and Nebraska territories.

____

✓ Checkpoint

Kansas election of 1855:

Number of voters:

____

Number of votes cast:

____

Section 2 Notetaking Study Guide

Question to Think About As you read Section 2 in your textbook and take notes, keep this section focus question in mind: **What was the Compromise of 1850, and why did it fail?**

► Use this chart to record key information from the section. Some information has been filled in to get you started.

Compromises Fail		
Compromise of 1850 Proposed by ____________	**Terms:** • California admitted as a __________ • Slave trade banned in ____________ • ____________ would decide slavery in the rest of the Mexican Cession. • Southerners got a tough new ____________________	**Goal of Compromise:** To end slavery crisis by giving supporters and opponents of slavery some of what they wanted.
Fugitive Slave Act of 1850	**Terms:** • Government officials may arrest any person accused of being a __________ __________ by any white person. • Suspects had no right to a __________. • ____________ were required to help authorities capture accused runaway slaves if asked.	**Results:** • Most __________ part of the Compromise of 1850 • Thousands of northern African Americans fled to __________.
Kansas-Nebraska Act of 1854 Proposed by ____________	**Terms:** • Slavery in the new Kansas and Nebraska territories was to be decided by ____________________.	**Results:** • Undid the __________ __________ • Reopened the issue of __________ in territories • __________ outraged
Kansas Election of 1855	**Events:** • Both proslavery and antislavery settlers flooded Kansas and wanted to hold the ____________ in the territory. • Thousands of Missourians entered Kansas illegally to select a ____________________. • Anti-slavery settlers held a second ____________.	**Results:** • Kansas now had two __________. • Violence broke out and earned Kansas the name __________ __________.

Refer to this page to answer the Chapter 10 Focus Question on page 170.

Section 3

The Crisis Deepens

Section 3 Focus Question

Why did the Lincoln-Douglas debates and John Brown's raid increase tensions between the North and South? To begin answering this question,

- Learn how a new antislavery party came to be.
- Explore the impact of the Dred Scott decision.
- Find out about the Lincoln-Douglas debates.
- Learn about John Brown's raid.

Section 3 Summary

The Lincoln-Douglas debates and John Brown's raid caused more controversy and anger over slavery.

A New Antislavery Party

The Whig Party split apart in 1854 when Whigs who were willing to take a strong antislavery stand joined the new Republican Party. Its main platform was to keep slavery from spreading to the western territories.

Joined by northern Democrats and by Free-Soilers, the Republican Party quickly became powerful. It won 105 of 245 seats in the House in the election of 1854. In 1856, John C. Frémont was the first Republican candidate for President. Although Frémont won 11 of the 16 free states, the Democrat candidate, James Buchanan, was elected President. ✓

The Dred Scott Decision

In 1857, the Supreme Court delivered a blow to antislavery forces. It decided the case of *Dred Scott* v. *Sandford*. **Dred Scott** was an enslaved person who sued for his freedom because he had lived with his master in states where slavery was illegal.

Supreme Court Chief Justice **Roger B. Taney** ruled that Scott had no right to sue in federal court because African Americans were not citizens. Taney also declared that living in a free state did not make enslaved people free. They were property, and the property rights of their owners were protected in all states.

This meant that Congress did not have the power to prohibit slavery in any territory, and that the Missouri Compromise was unconstitutional. Slavery was legal again in all territories. Supporters of slavery rejoiced at this ruling. Northerners, however, were stunned. ✓

The Lincoln-Douglas Debates

Abraham Lincoln, an Illinois attorney, was elected to the House as a Whig, where he voted for the Wilmot Proviso. After one term, he returned to his Springfield law practice.

Key Events

1852 Harriet Beecher Stowe publishes *Uncle Tom's Cabin*.

1857 Supreme Court ruling in Dred Scott case declares Missouri Compromise unconstitutional.

1861 The Civil War begins with Confederate bombardment of Fort Sumter.

✓ Checkpoint

List three groups that joined the Republican Party.

____

____

____

✓ Checkpoint

Name the kind of right that protected slavery in all states, according to the Dred Scott decision.

____

Vocabulary Builder

Entitle, in the underlined sentence, means "to give a right to something." What does this tell you about the way Lincoln felt about the rights of African Americans?

____

____

✓ Checkpoint

List two points Lincoln made in the debates about slavery and African Americans.

____

____

____

____

✓ Checkpoint

Name the part of the country in which John Brown was considered a hero.

____

Lincoln's opposition to the Kansas-Nebraska Act brought him back into politics. In 1858, Lincoln ran for the Illinois Senate seat against Stephen Douglas, the author of the Kansas-Nebraska Act. When Lincoln accepted the Republican nomination, he made a stirring speech in favor of the Union. He said the country could not survive "half slave and half free."

Many southerners believed that Lincoln was an abolitionist. Lincoln then challenged Douglas to a series of public debates, and thousands gathered to hear them speak.

Douglas strongly defended popular sovereignty. He said people in each state could decide the slavery issue for themselves and shouldn't worry about what other states did. He also painted Lincoln as a dangerous abolitionist who wanted equality for African Americans.

Lincoln declared, "If slavery is not wrong, nothing is wrong." He predicted that slavery would die on its own. In the meantime, slavery had to be kept out of the West. While Lincoln did not promote equal rights for African Americans, he stated that they should be "entitled to all the rights" in the Declaration of Independence.

Douglas won the Senate election, but the debates made Lincoln nationally known. Two years later, the men would be rivals again for the presidency. ✓

John Brown's Raid

John Brown was an abolitionist who had been driven out of Kansas after the Pottawatomie Massacre. He returned to New England and hatched a plot to raise an army to free people in the South who were enslaved. In 1859, Brown and a small band of supporters attacked Harpers Ferry, Virginia. His goal was to seize guns the U.S. Army stored there. He would give the arms to enslaved African Americans and lead them in a revolt.

Brown and his men were captured. Brown was executed, but his cause was celebrated in the North, where many considered him to be a hero. More than ever, southerners were convinced that the North was out to destroy their way of life. ✓

Check Your Progress

1. What was the Republican Party's main platform?

____

____

____

2. Why did John Brown attack Harpers Ferry?

____

____

____

Section 3 Notetaking Study Guide

Question to Think About As you read Section 3 in your textbook and take notes, keep this section focus question in mind: **Why did the Lincoln-Douglas debates and John Brown's raid increase tensions between the North and South?**

► Use these charts to record key information from the section. Some information has been filled in to get you started.

The Dred Scott Decision

- Dred Scott was an enslaved person who sued for his freedom.
- Supreme Court Chief Justice ______________ ruled that Scott had no right to sue in federal court because African Americans were not ______________.
  - Slaves were property, and the ______________ of their owners were protected in all states.
- This meant Congress did not have the power to prohibit slavery in any territory, and the ______________ was unconstitutional.
- Supporters of slavery ______________ at this ruling but northerners were ______________.

Abraham Lincoln-Stephen Douglas Debates

- Occurred during Illinois Senate race in the year ________.
- Lincoln's opposition to the ______________ led him to run as a Republican against Senator Stephen Douglas, the author of the ______________.
- The goal of the new Republican party was to ______________ ______________.

Douglas's stand on popular sovereignty:	Lincoln's stand on African Americans:	Lincoln's stand on slavery:	Lincoln's position on the Union:
______________	a. ______________ b. ______________	a. ______________ b. ______________ c. ______________	______________

John Brown's Raid

Who was John Brown?	His plan in 1859:	Southerners were worried because:
______________	______________	______________

Refer to this page to answer the Chapter 10 Focus Question on page 170.

Section 4

The Coming of the Civil War

Key Events

1852 Harriet Beecher Stowe publishes *Uncle Tom's Cabin*.

1857 Supreme Court ruling in Dred Scott case declares Missouri Compromise unconstitutional.

1861 The Civil War begins with Confederate bombardment of Fort Sumter.

Section 4 Focus Question

Why did the election of Abraham Lincoln spark the secession of southern states? To begin answering this question,

- Learn how the nation divided.
- Find out how the Civil War began.

Section 4 Summary

By the time Lincoln became President, the division over slavery was too deep to heal. The Civil War began.

The Nation Divides

As the election of 1860 drew near, Americans everywhere felt a sense of crisis. The long and bitter debate over slavery had left the nation seriously divided. Southern Democrats wanted the party to support slavery in the territories. But northerners refused to do so, and the party split in two.

Northern Democrats nominated Stephen Douglas. But southern Democrats picked Vice President John Breckinridge from Kentucky. Some southerners still hoped to heal the split between North and South. They formed the Constitutional Union Party and nominated John Bell of Tennessee, who promised to protect slavery *and* keep the nation together. The Republicans chose Abraham Lincoln as their candidate. His criticisms of slavery during his debates with Stephen Douglas made him popular in the North.

The election showed just how fragmented the nation had become. Lincoln won every free state. Breckinridge won every slaveholding state except four. Bell won Kentucky, Tennessee, and Virginia. Douglas won only Missouri. Although he carried only 40 percent of the popular vote, Lincoln received enough electoral votes to win the presidency.

To many southerners, Lincoln's election meant that the South no longer had a voice in the national government. They believed that the President and Congress were set against their interests. South Carolina was the first southern state to secede from the Union. Six more states followed.

Not all southerners favored secession. But they were overwhelmed by those who did. By February 1861, leaders from the seven seceding states had met in Montgomery, Alabama, and formed a new nation they called the Confederate States of America. By the time Lincoln took office in March, the Confederate leaders had written a constitution and named former Mississippi Senator Jefferson Davis as their president. ✓

Vocabulary Builder

Confederate comes from a Latin word meaning "to unite." The Confederate States of America, then, means what?

____

____

✓ Checkpoint

List the four presidential candidates in 1860.

____

____

____

____

The Civil War Begins

In Lincoln's inaugural address, he assured the seceding states that he meant them no harm. He stated that he had no plan to abolish slavery where it already existed. Lincoln's assurance of friendship was rejected. The seceding states took over post offices, forts, and other federal property within their borders.

One of those forts was Fort Sumter, on an island in the harbor of Charleston, South Carolina. The fort's commander would not surrender. South Carolina authorities decided to starve the fort's troops into surrender. They had been cut off from supplies since late December and could not hold out much longer.

Lincoln did not want to give up the fort, but he feared that sending troops might cause other states to secede. He decided to send food to the fort, but on supply ships carrying no troops or guns. Confederate leaders decided to capture the fort while it was still cut off from supplies. On April 12, they opened fire. After 34 hours, with the fort on fire, the troops inside finally surrendered.

This attack marked the beginning of the American Civil War. A **civil war** is a war between opposing groups of citizens of the same country.

The Civil War probably attracts more public interest today than any other event in American history. Americans continue to debate whether it could have been avoided.

In 1850, southerners might have been satisfied if they had been left alone. But by 1861, the North and South were so bitterly opposed that most Americans saw war as inevitable. At stake was the nation's future. ✓

✓ Checkpoint

Name the event that marked the beginning of the American Civil War.

____

Check Your Progress

1. How did Lincoln win the presidential election without receiving a majority of the popular vote?

____

____

____

2. What is a civil war?

____

____

____

Section 4 Notetaking Study Guide

Question to Think About As you read Section 4 in your textbook and take notes, keep this question in mind: **Why did the election of Abraham Lincoln spark the secession of southern states?**

► Use this chart to record key information from the section. Some information has been filled in to get you started.

Chain of Events Leading to Civil War	

The Election of 1860	• There were four candidates in the election because ______
	  • Northern Democratic candidate: ______
	  • Southern Democratic candidate: ______
	  • Constitutional Union candidate: ______
	  • Republican candidate: ______
	• Although he did not receive a majority of the popular vote, Lincoln received enough ______ to win the election.
	• The election showed how ______ the nation was.

Secession	• After South Carolina learned that Lincoln had won the election, it responded by ______ • Southern leaders who opposed secession: 1. ______ 2. ______ • First state to secede from the Union: ______ • Name of the new southern nation: ______ • President of the southern nation: ______ • Lincoln's message to seceding states: ______ • Response of seceding states to Lincoln's message: 1. ______ 2. ______
Fort Sumter	• Lincoln's plan to deal with the siege of Fort Sumter: ______ • South Carolina's response to Lincoln's plan: ______

Refer to this page to answer the Chapter 10 Focus Question on page 170.

Chapter 10 Assessment

Directions: Circle the letter of the correct answer.

1. The main question raised by the Southwest territory was
   - A should slavery be abolished?
   - B should the Missouri Compromise be used?
   - C would slavery be allowed in the west?
   - D should California come in as a free state?

2. What was an effect of the Kansas-Nebraska Act?
   - A *Uncle Tom's Cabin* gained popularity.
   - B It undid the Missouri Compromise.
   - C The Free-Soil Party was formed.
   - D Abraham Lincoln became President.

3. The Republicans' first presidential candidate was
   - A Abraham Lincoln.
   - B Stephen Douglas.
   - C Martin Van Buren.
   - D John C. Frémont.

4. Most southerners believed Lincoln
   - A would abolish slavery.
   - B would defend Fort Sumter.
   - C would accept secession.
   - D would not become President.

Directions: Follow the steps to answer this question:

How did the issue of slavery bitterly divide the nation?

Step 1: Recall information: Describe each of the following pieces of legislation.

Legislation	What It Said
Wilmot Proviso	
Fugitive Slave Act of 1850	

Step 2: How did these acts affect the nation?

____

____

____

Step 3: Complete the topic sentence that follows. Then write two or three more sentences that support your topic sentence.

Legislation like the Wilmot Proviso and the Fugitive Slave Act of 1850 ______________

____

____

____

____

Chapter 10 Notetaking Study Guide

Now you are ready to answer the Chapter 10 Focus Question: **How did the nation try but fail to deal with growing sectional differences?**

► Complete the following chart to help you answer this question. Use the notes that you took for each section.

The Nation Divided

Growing Tensions Over Slavery

The Wilmot Proviso	**California**
• *Description:* _______________ _______________ *Its fate:* Blocked in __________, slaveholding states saw it as an __________ on slavery.	• Both sides realized its admission to the Union would upset the balance of free and slave states. • *The South threatens:* __________

Compromises Fail

To please the North, the Compromise of 1850	*To please the South, the Compromise of 1850*
• admitted California as a free state. •	• •

The Kansas-Nebraska Act essentially undid _______________.

Harriet Beecher Stowe published _______________ in 1852. A bestseller in the North, it was written off as _______________ in the South.

The Crisis Deepens

In the *Dred Scott* case, the Supreme Court declared _______________ unconstitutional and opened all territories _______________.

- Abraham Lincoln ran against _______________ for the Illinois Senate in 1858.
- In their debates, Lincoln took a stand against slavery saying African Americans should be entitled to the rights stated in _______________.
- After he was executed for raiding Harpers Ferry and trying to lead a slave revolt, _______________ was considered a hero by many northerners.

The Coming of the Civil War

To many southerners, the election of Lincoln meant that the South no longer had a voice in _______________.	Lincoln's assurance of friendship in his inaugural address was _______________ by the seceding states.

The Confederate attack on _______________ marked the beginning of the Civil War.

Refer to this page to answer the Unit 5 Focus Question on page 199.

Chapter 11

The Civil War (1861–1865)

What You Will Learn

People in the North and the South hoped for an early victory, but the Civil War went on for years. Hundreds of thousands of Americans were killed before the war ended.

Chapter 11 Focus Question

As you read this chapter, keep this question in mind: **How did people, places, and things affect the outcome of the Civil War?**

Section 1

The Call to Arms

Section 1 Focus Question

Why did each side in the Civil War think the war would be won easily? To begin answering this question,

- Discover how sides were taken in the war.
- Explore the strengths of the North and the South.
- Learn the two sides' strategies.
- Find out about the First Battle of Bull Run.
- Explore the details of a soldier's life.

Section 1 Summary

As the Civil War began, North and South prepared for a short war. They soon realized they were in for a long struggle.

Taking Sides in the War

After Fort Sumter was captured, President Lincoln declared that a rebellion existed in the South. He requested troops to subdue the Confederacy. Some states supplied more than enough volunteers, some refused to comply, and some did not respond. More southern states seceded.

There were four **border states**—slave states that did not secede. These were Delaware, Kentucky, Missouri, and Maryland. Delaware supported the Union. Kentucky started out **neutral**, not favoring either side, but it supported the Union after it was invaded by southern forces in September 1861.

Most people in Maryland and Missouri favored the South. Lincoln sent troops to occupy Missouri. If Maryland seceded, the U.S. capital would be in Confederate territory, so eastern Maryland was put under **martial law**. This is a type of rule in which the military is in charge and citizens' rights are suspended. ✓

Chapter Standards

History-Social Science 8.10.2, 8.10.3, 8.10.4, 8.10.5, 8.10.6, 8.10.7

Key Events

1861 Eleven states secede from the Union, creating the Confederacy.

1863 Lincoln delivers the Emancipation Proclamation.

1864 Grant invades South and lays siege to Petersburg.

1865 Lee's surrender at Appomattox brings Union victory.

✓ Checkpoint

List the four border states.

____

____

____

____

North Against South

When the war began, people on both sides were confident of victory. To win the war, the North had to invade the South. Southerners would be fighting on their own territory, and they would be led by some of the nation's best officers. The North also had some advantages. It had a larger population, more farmland, and more factories.

✓ Checkpoint

List three advantages the North had in the war.

____

____

____

Two thirds of northern men aged 18 to 45 served in the military. In the South, three fourths of free men the same age served. But the North had 3.5 million men in this age group, whereas the South had only 1 million. The North thus had a much larger army than the South. ✓

The Two Sides Plan Strategy

To isolate the South, the North set up a naval **blockade,** a military action to prevent traffic to and from an area. If the South could not sell cotton to Britain, it would run out of money to fight. The North planned to control the Mississippi River and seize Richmond, Virginia, the Confederate capital.

✓ Checkpoint

Name the main goal of the Union blockade.

____

____

Southerners had a simple strategy: defend their land until northerners gave up. They would finance the war with continued trade with Britain. They also hoped Britain would support the South. ✓

First Battle of Bull Run

Northerners wanted to end the war quickly with a decisive battle. Popular demand led Union General Irvin McDowell to march into Virginia before his troops were fully trained. The First Battle of Bull Run was fought along Bull Run, a river near Manassas, Virginia, on July 21, 1861. The South held firm, and the poorly trained Union troops panicked and retreated. ✓

✓ Checkpoint

Name the Union army's goal in marching into Virginia.

____

A Soldier's Life

✓ Checkpoint

List two dangers faced by soldiers in prison camps.

____

____

Soldiers spent most of their time in camp, not fighting. They spent much of the time training. Camp conditions were often miserable, especially in wet weather. Soldiers often did not have clean water, which led to outbreaks of disease.

Conditions in prison camps were even worse. In overcrowded camps, prisoners died each day from starvation and exposure. ✓

Check Your Progress

1. What were the Union and Confederate war strategies?

____

____

____

2. What was the result of the First Battle of Bull Run?

____

____

Section 1 Notetaking Study Guide

Question to Think About As you read Section 1 in your textbook and take notes, keep this section focus question in mind: **Why did each side in the Civil War think the war would be won easily?**

► Use this chart to record key information from the section. Some information has been filled in to get you started.

The Call to Arms

The North

1. How did two border states bolster northern confidence? Kentucky and Delaware supported the Union.
2. What Virginia event helped the North? ________
3. What four things did the North have much more of than the South had? ________
4. What were three parts of the Northern strategy? ________
5. Who was the Union general in the First Battle of Bull Run? ________

The South

1. How did two border states bolster southern confidence? Maryland and Missouri supported the South, and northern troops had to be used to subdue them.
2. Which generals left the U.S. Army to join the Confederate Army? ________
3. What were two advantages the South had? ________
4. What was the South's strategy? ________
5. Why was the South hopeful that Britain would support it? because Britain was a major trading partner that needed southern cotton

Hardships of Both Sides

1. What effect did the war have on American families? ________
2. What were the camp conditions for soldiers? often miserable and diseased, lack of clean water
3. What were the conditions for prisoners of war in the North and the South? ________

Refer to this page to answer the Chapter 11 Focus Question on page 187.

Key Events

1861 Eleven states secede from the Union, creating the Confederacy.

1863 Lincoln delivers the Emancipation Proclamation.

1864 Grant invades South and lays siege to Petersburg.

1865 Lee's surrender at Appomattox brings Union victory.

✓ Checkpoint

List three ways rifles were better than older guns.

____

____

____

Vocabulary Builder

Fill in the first blank below with a synonym for *reinforce.* Fill in the second blank with an antonym for *reinforce.*

Union delays allowed Confederates to ____________ their army near Richmond. McClellan thought that not having enough troops would ______________ his army.

Section 2

Early Years of the War

Section 2 Focus Question

How did each side in the war try to gain an advantage over the other? To begin answering this question,

- Learn about new technology of the war.
- Read about the war in the East.
- Find out about the war in the West.

Section 2 Summary

Unable to win a quick victory, Union forces met Confederate troops in a series of battles made more bloody by new technology.

New Technology in the War

New weapons made the Civil War more deadly than any previous war. Traditionally, generals had relied on an all-out charge of troops to overwhelm the enemy. But new rifles and cannons were far more accurate and had a greater range than the old muskets and artillery. They could also be loaded much faster. As a result, the attacking army could be bombarded long before it arrived at the defenders' position.

Unfortunately, Civil War generals were slow to recognize the problem and change tactics. Thus, thousands of soldiers died charging across open fields during the Civil War.

Ironclads, or warships covered with protective iron plates, were another new invention. Cannonfire bounced harmlessly off these ships. The Confederacy used ironclads against the Union's naval blockade, and the Union used them in their efforts to control the Mississippi River. ✓

The War in the East

After its demoralizing defeat at Bull Run, the Union army got a new commander, General **George McClellan.** He was an excellent organizer, but he was also a very cautious leader. He spent seven months training his army instead of attacking the Confederate enemy. In March 1862, he finally moved 100,000 soldiers by boat to a point southeast of Richmond. He knew that his troops could easily have defeated the 15,000 Confederate soldiers facing them, but the cautious McClellan stopped to ask Lincoln to send him more men. Almost a month passed before he resumed the march.

This delay gave the Confederates plenty of time to reinforce their small army. They stopped McClellan's advancing forces outside Richmond on May 31, 1862, then forced the Union army to retreat in late June.

General Lee decided to invade the North, reasoning that a victory on Union soil would win the Confederacy European support. He moved his army into western Maryland.

When McClellan learned that Lee had divided his army, he attacked the larger half at Antietam Creek near Sharpsburg, Maryland, on September 17, 1862. It was the bloodiest day of the Civil War. In attack after attack, McClellan's troops charged into the gunfire that came from the Confederate lines. The Union suffered 12,000 **casualties**, which is a military term for persons killed, wounded, or missing in action. The South lost nearly 14,000 soldiers, and Lee began a forced retreat back to Virginia. McClellan could have pursued Lee's battered army, but he did not. ✓

✓ Checkpoint

Name the error McClellan made before facing Lee's troops near Richmond.

___

___

The War in the West

In the West, Union generals were not so cautious. General **Ulysses S. Grant**, the most successful of these generals, was a man who took chances. In February 1862, Grant captured Fort Henry, just south of the Kentucky-Tennessee border. Then he took Fort Donelson. These victories opened the South up to invasion from two different water routes. Grant's forces continued south along the Tennessee River to Corinth, Mississippi, an important railroad center.

Before Grant could advance on Corinth, Confederate General Albert Sidney Johnston attacked. On April 6, 1862, he surprised Grant's forces at a church in the town of Shiloh. The Battle of Shiloh was costly for both sides. The South suffered nearly 11,000 casualties. The toll for the North was more than 13,000. However, the Union army was successful in forcing the Confederate army to withdraw from the railroad center, and in the process, it won control of Corinth. The Union now controlled western Tennessee and part of the Mississippi River.

Two weeks after the Battle of Shiloh, Union commander David Farragut entered the Mississippi River from the Gulf of Mexico and captured New Orleans. By the summer of 1862, the Union controlled almost all of the Mississippi River. ✓

✓ Checkpoint

List three key places Grant and his troops captured.

___

___

___

Check Your Progress

1. What effect did rifles have at the beginning of the Civil War?

___

___

___

___

2. What two events show the differences between Grant's and McClellan's approaches after victory?

___

___

___

___

Section 2 Notetaking Study Guide

Question to Think About As you read Section 2 in your textbook and take notes, keep this section focus question in mind: **How did each side in the war try to gain an advantage over the other?**

► Use this chart to record key information from the section. Some information has been filled in to get you started.

Early Years of the War		
New Technology		
New ______________ and ______________ were more accurate and had greater range than previous weapons. ______________ were a great improvement over older wooden warships.		
Event	**Military Leader**	**Outcome**
Forts Henry and Donelson, February 1862	Union: Grant	• The Union takes control of two water routes into the western Confederacy .
Use of ironclads		• ______________ • ______________
Battle of Shiloh, April 1862	Union: Grant Confederacy: A. S. Johnston	• ______________
New Orleans, April 1862	Union:	• The North controls almost all of the Mississippi River.
Outside Richmond, Virginia, May and June 1862	Union:	• ______________
Battle of Antietam, September 1862	Union: Confederacy:	• ______________

Refer to this page to answer the Chapter 11 Focus Question on page 187.

Section 3

The Emancipation Proclamation

Section 3 Focus Question

What were the causes and effects of the Emancipation Proclamation? To begin answering this question,

- Find out about emancipating the enslaved.
- Learn how African Americans helped the Union.

Section 3 Summary

After the Emancipation Proclamation was issued, the Civil War became a struggle to end slavery as well as a battle to save the Union.

Emancipating the Enslaved

Northern abolitionists assumed that Lincoln's main war goal was to end slavery because that was what they wanted most. But Lincoln's main goal was to preserve the Union. If that could be done without outlawing slavery, Lincoln would not outlaw slavery. He did not want to free the slaves at the outset of the war because it might provoke the border states into secession. Furthermore, he knew that most northerners did not care enough about slavery to fight a war to end it. Lincoln had no plan to **emancipate**, or free, enslaved people in 1861.

But by mid-1862, Lincoln realized that slavery was important to the southern war effort. Slaves kept farms and factories producing when their owners were away fighting the war. Lincoln decided slavery had to end.

On January 1, 1863, Lincoln issued the Emancipation Proclamation. He had been ready to do this in the summer of 1862, but nervous Cabinet members, fearing that the people would not like it, had urged him to wait until the Union army had more victories under its belt. Then northerners would still be willing to fight, even if they did not care about ending slavery.

The proclamation was not the sweeping rejection of slavery abolitionists wanted and expected. It freed slaves only in areas that were fighting the Union. Slaves in border states and the west were not affected, and southern states already under Union control were not affected. States that had seceded did not have to obey the law because they did not recognize the U.S. government. In short, very few slaves were actually freed in 1863.

Some abolitionists protested that the proclamation did not go far enough; others accepted it as a start. Northern African Americans rejoiced, while white southerners claimed Lincoln was trying to start a slave rebellion. For the most part, Union soldiers supported the law because they knew it dealt a blow to the South's ability to fight. Whether people embraced the proclamation or not,

Key Events

1861	Eleven states secede from the Union, creating the Confederacy.
1863	Lincoln delivers the Emancipation Proclamation.
1864	Grant invades South and lays siege to Petersburg.
1865	Lee's surrender at Appomattox brings Union victory.

Vocabulary Builder

Proclamation comes from a Latin word that means "to cry out." Use context clues from this section to write your own short definition of *proclamation*.

____

____

____

✓ Checkpoint

Name Lincoln's main goal in fighting the Civil War.

____

____

it changed the nature of the Civil War. It was no longer just a fight to save the nation. It was now also a war to end slavery.

Also, the proclamation ended all hope the South had of being supported by Britain. Britain would not support a government identified as fighting for slavery. ✓

African Americans Help the Union

African Americans in the North were not allowed to fight in the Union army at first. Even after Congress allowed it in 1862, few state governments mobilized African American volunteers. After the Emancipation Proclamation, it was easier for African Americans to enlist. By the end of the war, 189,000 had served in the army or navy. Over half of these soldiers were former slaves who had escaped or been freed by Union soldiers when they took over southern territory.

All African Americans fighting in the Civil War faced grave danger—slavery or death—if taken prisoner by southerners. They served in all-black regiments in the army and served alongside whites in the navy. They were paid less than white soldiers. Still, they fought bravely, often deep in southern territory. Free northern and emancipated southern African Americans also served in the Union army as cooks, wagon drivers, and hospital aides.

✓ Checkpoint

List four ways that African Americans served in the Union army and navy.

____

____

____

____

People enslaved in the South during the war did what they could to hurt the Confederate war effort. Some provided information to the Union army. Enslaved people had always quietly resisted slavery by deliberately working slowly or damaging equipment. But with many slaveholders off fighting the war, large numbers of slaves refused to work. ✓

Check Your Progress

1. How did the Emancipation Proclamation change the Civil War?

____

____

2. What were some of the extra risks African Americans took by serving in the Union army?

____

____

Section 3 Notetaking Study Guide

Question to Think About As you read Section 3 in your textbook and take notes, keep this section focus question in mind: **What were the causes and effects of the Emancipation Proclamation?**

► Use this chart to record key information from the section. Some information has been filled in to get you started.

The Emancipation Proclamation
Emancipating the Enslaved
Lincoln's main war goal was to ______________________. He did not free slaves at the beginning of the war in order to avoid ______________________ ______________________.
Lincoln issued the ______________________ on January 1, 1863. However, it only freed slaves in ______________________, so very few enslaved people were immediately freed. Most Union soldiers supported the proclamation because it ______________________.
The Emancipation Proclamation caused the Civil War to become a ______________________. It also kept Britain from ______________________.
African Americans Help the Union
More than half of African American volunteers serving in the Union army were ______________________.
Confederates did not treat captured African American soldiers as ______________; they faced ______________________.
Noncombat positions held by free African Americans in the Union army: • • wagon drivers •
Ways enslaved African Americans hurt the Confederate war effort: • •

Refer to this page to answer the Chapter 11 Focus Question on page 187.

Section 4

The Civil War and American Life

Key Events

1861 Eleven states secede from the Union, creating the Confederacy.

1863 Lincoln delivers the Emancipation Proclamation.

1864 Grant invades South and lays siege to Petersburg.

1865 Lee's surrender at Appomattox brings Union victory.

Vocabulary Builder

The term *habeas corpus* comes from a Latin phrase meaning "to have the body." Why would the term *habeas corpus* be used to describe imprisonment?

____

____

____

✓ Checkpoint

Name three ways people disrupted the war effort.

____

____

____

Section 4 Focus Question

How did the war affect people and politics in the North and the South? To begin answering this question,

- Explore divisions over the war.
- Find out about the draft laws.
- Learn about the economic strains caused by the war.
- Explore the role of women in the Civil War.

Section 4 Summary

Neither the North nor the South presented a united front in the war. Divisions existed between states and social classes.

Divisions Over the War

The North may have faced the South in the war, but each side experienced divisions over the war and slavery. Not all northerners supported a war to end slavery. Many opposed the Emancipation Proclamation. Nor did all northerners support restoring the Union. Some felt the South should be allowed to secede. Some northerners blamed Lincoln and the Republicans for forcing the South into a war. Northern Democrats who opposed the war were called Copperheads, after the poisonous snake. Copperheads criticized the war and called for peace with the Confederacy.

Not all southerners supported slavery or secession. Poor backcountry regions with few enslaved people were less supportive of the war than regions with large slaveholding populations. Strong support for states' rights created other divisions. For example, the governors of Georgia and North Carolina did not want the Confederate government to force men from their states to do military service.

People on both sides tried to disrupt the war effort by helping prisoners of war escape, encouraging soldiers to desert, and holding peace protests. Both Abraham Lincoln and Jefferson Davis tried to keep order by suspending the right of **habeas corpus,** the constitutional protection against unlawful imprisonment, during the war. ✓

The Draft Laws

Desertion was a problem for both sides. Between 300,000 and 550,000 Union and Confederate soldiers left their units and went home. Some returned after their crops were planted or harvested. To meet the need for troops, both North and South established a **draft,** a system of required military service. The southern draft began in 1862, and the northern draft began in 1863; all eligible men were required to enlist in the army or navy.

But there were ways around the draft. The wealthy could hire substitutes to serve for them. In the South, a man who held at least 20 enslaved people did not have to serve. In the North, anyone who paid $300 to the government was allowed to stay home. Only the well-off could afford this amount.

People on both sides objected that poor people were fighting the war. Draft riots broke out in many northern cities in 1863 as poor people who could not pay their way out of the draft destroyed draft offices and other property. ✓

The War and Economic Strains

While northern industries thrived on war production, the amount of money coming in to the government did not cover the costs of the war, so Congress introduced the first **income tax** in August 1861. This is a tax on the money people receive. Congress also printed $400 million in paper money. This was the first federal paper money, and it led to **inflation,** or a general rise in prices. In the North, prices went up 80 percent on average.

The Union blockade prevented the South from raising money by selling cotton overseas. Shortages of goods became severe as income from cotton dropped ever lower. On top of this, food production fell as Union armies invaded farmland. Food shortages led to riots in southern cities. ✓

Women in the Civil War

Women in the North and South contributed to the war effort in many ways. Some disguised themselves as men and enlisted in the army, and some were spies. But most women took up the roles their male family members had played in society. Women ran businesses and farms, worked in factories, taught school, and served on the battlefield, in army camps, and in hospitals. Elizabeth Blackwell, the first American woman to earn a medical degree, trained nurses for the Union army. Clara Barton cared for Union soldiers on the battlefield and later founded the American Red Cross. ✓

Check Your Progress

1. Why would suspending habeas corpus help keep the peace?

____

____

2. How did most women support the war effort?

____

____

✓ Checkpoint

List three ways someone could avoid the draft.

____

____

____

✓ Checkpoint

Name the effect the printing of paper money had in the North.

____

✓ Checkpoint

Name two women who helped heal soldiers during the war.

____

____

Section 4 Notetaking Study Guide

Question to Think About As you read Section 4 in your textbook, keep this section focus question in mind: **How did the war affect people and politics in the North and the South?**

► Use this chart to record key information from the section.

The Civil War's Effect on American Life

Divisions

In the North, some people:	Areas of South less supportive of war:
• • believed the South had the right to secede • Northern Democrats opposed to the war were called ________.	• Opposition to the war was strongest in ________ and ________. Divisions were also created by strong support for ________.

Disruptions

Ways people disrupted the war effort:

- encouraged soldiers to desert
-
-
-

Both sides dealt with disruptions in some areas by ________.

Draft Laws

- ________ was a problem for both sides. Many soldiers left their units to ________.
- Each side established a ________, a system of required ________. Anger at exceptions to this requirement caused ________ in many places.

Economic Strains

Congress levied the first __income tax__ to pay for the war.
The Union printed large amounts of ________, causing the cost of goods to ________.
Union blockades of the South caused ________ that made goods ________.

Women in the Civil War

Women's contributions to the war effort on both sides:

- disguised themselves as men to join the army
-
-
-

Barriers for women fell, especially in the field of ________.

Refer to this page to answer the Chapter 11 Focus Question on page 187.

Section 5
Decisive Battles

Section 5 Focus Question

How did Lincoln and his generals turn the tide of the war? To begin answering this question,

- Learn how the tide of war turned.
- Find out how the Union closed in on the Confederacy.
- Discover how peace came at last.

Section 5 Summary

Under Grant's leadership, the Union finally defeated the Confederacy. Both sides suffered terrible losses in the final two years of the war.

The Tide Turns

The Union army had a new commander in 1862, General Ambrose Burnside, who was determined to act more boldly than General McClellan had. Burnside marched toward Richmond in December 1862 to attack Confederate General Lee's army. Burnside ordered traditional charges, sending thousands of men running into Confederate gunfire. The Union lost 13,000 men in the Battle of Fredericksburg. The South lost 5,000.

Burnside was replaced by General Joseph Hooker, who also marched toward Richmond. In May 1863, his army was defeated at the Battle of Chancellorsville by a southern force half its size. The South, however, lost General Stonewall Jackson in the battle.

After these victories, Lee determined once more to launch an attack in the North. His forces were outside the town of Gettysburg, Pennsylvania, on July 1, 1863, when they encountered Union troops, now led by General George Meade. Fighting broke out that lasted for three days. When the Battle of Gettysburg was over, the Union had won. The South had lost 28,000 men, and the North had lost 23,000.

The day after the Battle of Gettysburg ended, the city of Vicksburg, Mississippi—one of the last cities on the river still in southern hands—fell to Union General Grant. Grant had laid **siege** to the city for two months. A siege is an attempt to capture a place by surrounding it with troops and cutting it off until its people surrender. Grant's victory at Vicksburg and Lee's defeat at Gettysburg were the turning points of the war, giving the Union the advantage. ✓

Closing in on the Confederacy

President Lincoln decided to put General Grant in charge of the Union army. Grant marched toward Richmond, fighting a series of battles in Virginia in the spring of 1864 in which he lost about 55,000 men. The Confederacy lost 35,000. Grant knew his men

Key Events

1861	Eleven states secede from the Union, creating the Confederacy.
1863	Lincoln delivers the Emancipation Proclamation.
1864	Grant invades South and lays siege to Petersburg.
1865	Lee's surrender at Appomattox brings Union victory.

✓ Checkpoint

Name three Union commanders.

____

____

____

could be replaced, but he also knew that the South was running out of soldiers and supplies. He settled into a siege at Petersburg, south of Richmond, to wait the Confederates out.

During this siege, another Union general, **William Tecumseh Sherman,** was driving his army across the South. In his march, he practiced **total war**, or all-out attacks aimed at destroying not only an enemy's army, but also its resources and its people's will to fight. His troops set fire to buildings, seized crops and livestock, and pulled up railroad tracks. Sherman captured Atlanta on September 2, 1864. He then marched east toward the Atlantic Ocean. Sherman's "March to the Sea" brought devastation to an area 60 miles wide.

Steps to a Union Victory

1. Meade defeats Lee at Gettysburg.
2. Vicksburg falls to Grant.
3. Grant is made commander of the Union army.
4. Grant fights a series of battles that cost Lee soldiers who cannot be replaced.
5. Sherman's "March to the Sea" devastates land, resources, and people.
6. Grant reinforces his army and captures Richmond.

✓

✓ Checkpoint

Name the general who practiced total war and led the Union "March to the Sea."

____

Peace at Last

By March 1865, Grant had extended his armies, encircling Lee. Lee knew that the war was lost. Lincoln knew it too and asked the American people to welcome the South back to the Union. He said, "with malice toward none, [and] charity for all; . . . let us strive together . . . to bind up the nation's wounds."

Vocabulary Builder

Using everyday language, write your own version of Lincoln's statement "with malice toward none, and charity for all; ... let us strive together ... to bind up the nation's wounds."

____

____

____

On April 2, Grant broke the Confederate line and captured Richmond. After briefly retreating west, Lee offered to surrender. On April 9, Grant and Lee met in a home in the town of Appomattox Court House, Virginia, to sign the surrender agreement. The Union generously allowed the Confederates to return home without punishment.

The war was over, but its effects lasted long afterward. Around 260,000 southerners had died, along with over 360,000 northerners, including 37,000 African Americans. ✓

✓ Checkpoint

How many soldiers died in the Civil War?

Northerners: ___________________

Southerners: ___________________

Check Your Progress

1. Why did Burnside suffer such high casualties?

____

____

2. What happened to Confederate soldiers under the terms of the surrender agreement?

____

____

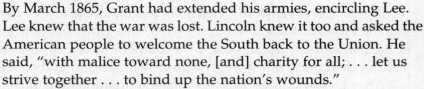

Section 5 Notetaking Study Guide

Question to Think About As you read Section 5 in your textbook and take notes, keep this section focus question in mind: **How did Lincoln and his generals turn the tide of the war?**

► Use these charts to record key information from the section.

Turning the Tide of War

General	Battle(s)	Result
1. Ambrose Burnside	______	______
2. Joseph Hooker	______	______
3. George Meade	Gettysburg	Union victory that forced Lee out of the North and cost Lee nearly a third of his soldiers, who could not be replaced.
4. Ulysses Grant	Vicksburg	______
5. Ulysses Grant	______	______
6. ______	Atlanta	______
7. William Sherman	"March to the Sea"	______
8. ______	Richmond	Confederate national capital is taken and Lee is forced to surrender his army.

The End of the War

Lincoln looked ahead to victory in a speech in 1863 called ______.
The capture of Atlanta gave Lincoln a ______.
Number of Union soldiers killed in the Civil War: ______
Number of Confederate soldiers killed in the Civil War: ______
Key results of the Civil War:

-
- It put an end to slavery.

Refer to this page to answer the Chapter 11 Focus Question on page 187.

Chapter 11 Assessment

Directions: Circle the letter of the correct answer.

1. Which does NOT describe public reaction to the start of the Civil War?
- **A** Most believed the war would be short.
- **B** The border states all sided with the Confederacy.
- **C** Not everyone supported the war.
- **D** Most people in Maryland and Missouri favored the South.

2. Where were slaves actually freed by the Emancipation Proclamation?
- **A** areas outside of Union control
- **B** parts of the South already under Union control
- **C** the border states
- **D** the western territories

3. In what year did the Union take the upper hand in the Civil War?
A 1862 **B** 1863 **C** 1864 **D** 1865

Directions: Follow the steps to answer this question:

How did the North finally gain the upper hand in the Civil War?

Step 1: Recall information: In the chart, fill in the result of each Union victory.

Event	Result
Gettysburg	1.
Vicksburg	2.
Battles in northern Virginia	3.
Sherman's "March to the Sea"	4.

Step 2: How did these events affect the North and the South?

Events' Effects on North and South	
North	
South	

Step 3: Complete the topic sentence that follows. Then write two or three more sentences that support your topic sentence.

By 1864, the tide had turned in the North's favor because ______________________

____

____

____

____

Chapter 11 Notetaking Study Guide

Now you are ready to answer the Chapter 11 Focus Question: **How did people, places, and things affect the outcome of the Civil War?**

► Complete the following chart to help you answer this question. Use the notes that you took for each section.

People, Places, and Things That Affected the Outcome of the Civil War

People	Places	Things
Lincoln: • His main goal was to restore the Union. • Effects of the Emancipation Proclamation: 1. 2.	Border states: The Union's control over these states helped the Union war effort.	Railroads: The North had many more miles of railroad tracks than the South.
	First Battle of Bull Run: ______	Manufacturing: ______
	Shiloh: ______	New rifles and cannons were deadlier than earlier weapons: • more accurate • had a longer range •
Ulysses S. Grant: • Attacks in the West led to Union control of the Mississippi. • He became the Union army's top commander.	Antietam: ______	Ironclads: • protected from cannon fire • used against Union naval blockade •
African Americans served in the army and navy as: • • • •	Gettysburg: important Union victory stopped the Confederate advance into northern territory	
	Vicksburg: led to ______	Economic challenges:
How women participated: • • • •	Battles in northern Virginia/ Petersburg: • •	In the North: • Congress levied the first income tax to pay war costs. • Increased currency supply led to inflation and higher prices. In the South: • •

Refer to this page to answer the Unit 5 Focus Question on page 199.

Chapter Standards

History-Social Science 8.10.7, 8.11.1, 8.11.2, 8.11.3, 8.11.4, 8.11.5

Key Events

1863	President Lincoln proposes a mild Reconstruction plan.
1867	Radical Reconstruction begins.
1870	The 15th Amendment is ratified by the states.
1896	Supreme Court upholds separate facilities for blacks and whites.

Vocabulary Builder

If *strict* is the opposite of *lenient*, what do you think *lenient* as used in the underlined sentence means?

____

____

____

Chapter 12

Reconstruction and the New South

(1863–1896)

What You Will Learn

At the end of the Civil War, Americans faced the problem of how to reunite the nation. Disagreements over Reconstruction led to conflicts in government and in the South. With the end of Reconstruction, African Americans in the South lost many of the rights they had gained.

Chapter 12 Focus Question

As you read through the sections in this chapter, keep this question in mind: **What were the short-term and long-term effects of the Civil War?**

Section 1

Rebuilding the Nation

Section 1 Focus Question

How did the government try to solve key problems facing the nation after the Civil War? To begin answering this question,

- Explore the challenges of preparing the nation for reunion.
- Learn about the services of the Freedmen's Bureau.
- Find out about Lincoln's assassination and its aftermath.

Summary

As the Civil War came to a close, the United States faced the enormous challenges of reuniting the nation. **Abraham Lincoln** and Congress were divided on how to restore the Union. With the assassination of President Lincoln in 1865, hopes of a lenient Reconstruction policy faded.

Preparing for Reunion

As the Civil War ended, enormous problems faced the nation. Much of the South lay in ruins, the homeless needed food and shelter, and many in the North and the South held hard feelings toward their former foes. The process of bringing the North and the South back together again, known as Reconstruction, would occupy the nation for years to come.

Lincoln and some fellow Republicans thought a lenient Reconstruction policy would strengthen the Republican Party in the South. The Radical Republicans disagreed and claimed only a "hard," or strict, Reconstruction policy would keep the South from rising again.

Reconstruction	
Lenient	**Strict**
Lincoln: Ten Percent Plan - loyalty oath from 10% of state's voters needed to create new state government - abolition of slavery by state government - former Confederates who swear loyalty pardoned	**Radical Republicans: Wade-Davis Bill** - loyalty oath from 50% of state's voters needed to reenter Union - abolition of slavery by state government - Confederate volunteers barred from voting and holding office

✓

The Freedmen's Bureau

It was urgent to deal with the needs of the **freedmen**, enslaved people who had been freed by war, as well as other war refugees. Congress created the Freedmen's Bureau in March of 1865. The bureau's first duty was to provide emergency relief to people displaced by war.

The Freedmen's Bureau set up schools to teach freedmen to read and write, and it helped to start schools at which African Americans could extend their education. The Freedmen's Bureau also helped freedmen find jobs and settled disputes between blacks and whites. ✓

Lincoln Is Murdered

As the war drew to a close, President Lincoln hoped for a peaceful Reconstruction. But Lincoln had no chance to put his plans into practice. He was shot on April 14, 1865, by **John Wilkes Booth**, a Confederate sympathizer. Lincoln died a few hours later.

News of Lincoln's death shocked the nation. His successor as President was Andrew Johnson from Tennessee. A southern Democrat who had remained loyal to the Union, Johnson had expressed bitterness toward the Confederates. Many expected him to take a hard line on Reconstruction. ✓

Check Your Progress

1. What were two major differences between the Ten Percent Plan and the Wade-Davis Bill?

____

____

2. How did the Freedmen's Bureau help former slaves?

____

____

✓ Checkpoint

List two key issues that faced the nation during Reconstruction.

____

____

✓ Checkpoint

What was the main purpose of the Freedmen's Bureau?

____

____

____

✓ Checkpoint

Name the person who succeeded Abraham Lincoln as President.

____

Section 1 Notetaking Study Guide

Question to Think About As you read Section 1 in your textbook and take notes, keep this section focus question in mind: **How did the government try to solve key problems facing the nation after the Civil War?**

▶ Use this chart to record key information from the section. Some of the information has been filled in to get you started.

Rebuilding a Nation

Challenges That the Nation Faced	Proposed Solutions
1. How would Confederate states and sympathizers be treated?	a. Lincoln's Ten Percent Plan • loyalty oath: 10% of each state's voters must take oath • slavery: each state's government must abolish slavery • former Confederates: pardoned if signed loyalty oath
	b. The Wade-Davis Bill • loyalty oath: __________ • former Confederates: __________
2. What provisions would be made for those freed from slavery?	The Freedmen's Bureau a. main purpose: __________ b. examples: • • •

Murder of Abraham Lincoln		Vice President Becomes President	
When	April 14, 1865	Who	Andrew Johnson
How		From where	
By whom		Political party	
National reaction		Expected impact on Reconstruction	

Refer to this page to answer the Chapter Focus Question on page 198.

Section 2

The Battle Over Reconstruction

Section 2 Focus Question

How did disagreements over Reconstruction lead to conflict in government and in the South? To begin to answer this question,

- Learn how conflict grew between the President and Congress during Reconstruction.
- Discover the significance of the Fourteenth Amendment.
- Understand the policies of Radical Reconstruction.

Summary

As the struggle for Reconstruction continued into the Johnson Administration, there were many clashes between Congress and the President. The Radical Republicans took hold of Congress, and African Americans made strides into politics for the first time.

A Growing Conflict

Like President Lincoln, **Andrew Johnson** wanted to restore the Union quickly and easily, so he proposed a lenient plan for Reconstruction. Johnson's plan required southern states to ratify the Thirteenth Amendment, which banned slavery and forced labor. His plan also offered amnesty to most Confederates and allowed southern states to form new governments and to elect representatives to Congress.

Congress rejected Johnson's plan and appointed a committee to form a new plan for the South. The committee learned that some southern states passed **black codes,** or laws to control African Americans. In response, Congress adopted a harder line against the South. The Radical Republicans took the hardest stance. They wanted to prevent former Confederates from regaining control of southern politics and to make sure that freedmen had the right to vote. ✓

The Fourteenth Amendment

The struggle for Reconstruction was focused on the President and Congress during 1866. Congress passed the Civil Rights Act of 1866, but President Johnson vetoed it and another bill extending the Freedmen's Bureau. Congress overrode both vetoes.

Congress also drew up the Fourteenth Amendment, which declared all people born or naturalized in the United States citizens. It barred the states from passing laws to take away a citizen's rights. Nor can a state take away a person's property or liberty "without due process of the law." In addition, any state that prevented its adult males from voting would have its representation in Congress reduced. Despite opposition from President Johnson, the amendment was ratified in 1868. ✓

Key Events

1863	President Lincoln proposes a mild Reconstruction plan.
1867	Radical Reconstruction begins.
1870	The 15th Amendment is ratified by the states.
1896	Supreme Court upholds separate facilities for blacks and whites.

✓ Checkpoint

List two goals of the Radical Republicans.

____

____

____

____

✓ Checkpoint

Name two elements of the Fourteenth Amendment.

____

____

____

____

Radical Reconstruction

As the elections of 1866 approached, violence directed at African Americans erupted in southern cities. Outrage at this violence led Congress to push a stricter form of Reconstruction, called Radical Reconstruction. The Reconstruction Act of 1867 threw out the governments of all states that refused to adopt the Fourteenth Amendment. It also imposed military rule on these states. By June of 1868, all of these states had ratified the Fourteenth Amendment and written new constitutions. They also allowed African Americans to vote.

For the first time, African Americans in the South played an important role in politics, serving as sheriffs, mayors, judges, and legislators. Sixteen African Americans served in the House of Representatives and two served in the Senate. Some other accomplishments of Radical Reconstruction include public schools opening in southern states, even taxation, and property rights to women. Bridges, roads, and buildings destroyed by the war were rebuilt.

Meanwhile, the Radical Republicans **impeached** and tried to convict President Johnson in order to remove him from office. To impeach means to bring formal charges against an elected official. Johnson barely escaped removal by one vote.

Ulysses S. Grant won the presidential election for the Republicans in 1868. With the South under military rule, some 500,000 African Americans voted. Grant was a war hero and a moderate with support from many northern business owners. Radicals then began to lose their grip on the Republican Party.

Despite Democratic opposition, Congress approved the Fifteenth Amendment in 1869. It barred all states from denying the right to vote "on account of race, color, or previous condition of servitude."

Angry at being shut out of power, some whites resorted to violence. They formed secret societies, such as the Ku Klux Klan, to terrorize African Americans and their white allies. Congress passed laws barring the use of force against voters, but the damage had been done. In the face of threats and violence from the Klan and other groups, voting by African Americans declined. The stage was set for the end of Reconstruction. ✓

Vocabulary Builder

Servitude comes from the Latin word *servus*, which means "slave." What do you think *servitude* means?

____

____

✓ Checkpoint

List two effects of the Reconstruction Act of 1867.

____

____

____

____

Check Your Progress

1. What were the main features of Andrew Johnson's plan for Reconstruction?

____

____

2. List three accomplishments of Reconstruction.

____

____

____

Section 2 Notetaking Study Guide

Question to Think About As you read Section 2 in your textbook and take notes, keep this section focus question in mind: **How did disagreements over Reconstruction lead to conflict in government and in the South?**

▶ Use these organizers to record key facts from the section. Some information has been filled in to get you started.

Reconstruction

Johnson's Plan
- issued broad amnesty to Confederates
- allowed southern states to organize new governments and ________

Congress
- refused to seat southern representatives
- appointed committee to ________
- passed ________ of 1866, which granted citizenship to African Americans and guaranteed their civil rights

Johnson
- ________ the Civil Rights Act of 1866
- vetoed a bill that extended the life of ________

Congress
- ________ Johnson's vetoes
- passed ________
  - All people born or naturalized in the United States are citizens.
  - All citizens are guaranteed rights.
  - Citizens are promised due process of law.
  - Black males have the right to vote.

Radical Reconstruction

Actions of the Radicals
- imposed military rule on states that rejected ________
- to join the Union, states had to:
  1. ________
  2. ________
- allowed ________ to register to vote
- opened ________ in the South
- built a strong following with three key groups:
  1. ________
  2. ________
  3. ________
- spread out ________ more evenly
- gave ________ to women
- impeached ________
- passed ________
  - states could not deny the right to vote based on ________, ________, or previous condition of servitude

Responses to Radicals

- General ________ elected President in 1868
- ________ terrorized African Americans and their white allies

Refer to this page to answer the Chapter Focus Question on page 198.

Section 3
The End of Reconstruction

Key Events

1863 President Lincoln proposes a mild Reconstruction plan.

1867 Radical Reconstruction begins.

1870 The 15th Amendment is ratified by the states.

1896 Supreme Court upholds separate facilities for blacks and whites.

Section 3 Focus Question

What were the effects of Reconstruction? To begin to answer this question,

- Understand how Reconstruction ended.
- Learn how African Americans lost many rights with the end of Reconstruction.
- Discover how many freedmen and whites became locked in a cycle of poverty.
- Find out how the end of Reconstruction marked a start of industrial growth in the South.

Summary

Support for Radical Republicans and their policies declined. Reconstruction came to a halt with the election of 1876. Southern African Americans gradually lost their rights and fell into a cycle of poverty. Meanwhile, the South's economy flourished.

Reconstruction's Conclusion

Support for Radical Republicans declined as Americans shifted focus from the Civil War to their own lives. Many northerners lost faith in the Republicans and their policies as the Grant presidency suffered from controversy and corruption. Meanwhile, many northerners and southerners alike were calling for the withdrawal of federal troops from the South and amnesty for former Confederates. Beginning in 1869, Democrats regained power in the South state by state. Slowly they chipped away at the rights of African Americans.

The end of Reconstruction was finalized with the election of Rutherford B. Hayes in 1876. Although he was a Republican, he vowed to end Reconstruction to avoid a challenge to his election by Democrats. Hayes removed all federal troops from the South. ✓

✓ Checkpoint

List two reasons that Reconstruction came to an end.

____

____

____

____

African Americans Lose Rights

With the end of Reconstruction, African Americans began losing their remaining political and civil rights in the South. Southern whites passed a number of laws to prevent blacks from voting. As these laws could apply to blacks and whites, they did not violate the Fifteenth Amendment. A **poll tax**, or a tax to be paid before voting, kept many blacks and poor whites from voting. Another law required voters to pass a **literacy test**, or a test to see if a person could read or write before voting. Most southern blacks had not been educated and could not pass the test. In addition, whites whose fathers or grandfathers could vote in the South on January 1, 1867, did not have to take the test.

Southern states created laws, known as "Jim Crow" laws, requiring **segregation**, or enforced separation of races. In *Plessy* v. *Ferguson*, the Supreme Court ruled that law could require "separate" facilities as long as they were "equal." The "separate but equal" rule was in effect until the 1950s, but the facilities for African Americans were rarely equal. ✓

A Cycle of Poverty

At emancipation, most freedmen were very poor. Most freedmen in rural areas became sharecroppers. A **sharecropper** is a farmer who rents land and pays a share of each year's crop as rent. Sharecroppers hoped to save money and eventually buy land of their own. But weather conditions and the ups and downs of crop prices often caused sharecroppers to lose money and become locked in a cycle of debt. They would then become poorer and poorer each year.

[Opportunities also dwindled for African Americans in southern cities and towns. African Americans skilled in crafts and trades found such jobs closed to them in the segregated South. Those who were educated could possibly become schoolteachers, lawyers, or preachers in the black community. However, most urban African Americans had to take whatever menial jobs they could find.] ✓

Industrial Growth

During Reconstruction, the South's economy slowly began to recover. By the 1880s, new industries appeared. Agriculture was the first industry to recover, with cotton production setting new records by 1875. Farmers also started to put more land into tobacco production, and output grew.

Industries that turn raw materials into finished products, such as the textile industry, came to play an important role in the South's economy. New mills and factories also grew to use the South's natural resources, such as iron, timber, and oil. By 1900, the South was no longer dependent on "King Cotton." A "New South" based on manufacturing was emerging. ✓

Check Your Progress

1. How did the rights of African Americans change after the end of Radical Reconstruction?

____

____

____

2. What led to southern industrial growth in the 1880s?

____

____

✓ Checkpoint

Name two ways that southern African Americans were prevented from voting.

____

____

Vocabulary Builder

Use the context clues in the paragraph in brackets to write a definition of the word *menial*.

____

____

✓ Checkpoint

List two reasons that sharecropping was not profitable.

____

____

✓ Checkpoint

Name three industries that contributed to the South's economic recovery.

____

____

____

Section 3 Notetaking Study Guide

Question to Think About As you read Section 3 in your textbook and take notes, keep this section focus question in mind: **What were the effects of Reconstruction?**

► Use this organizer to record key information from the section. Some information has been filled in to get you started.

The End of Reconstruction

African Americans' Rights

- Southern states passed laws to prevent African Americans from voting. These included
  - ______________________
  - ______________________
  - grandfather clauses
- Southern states passed __________ laws, which enforced __________.

Freedmen in Poverty

- Most rural freedmen became ______________________.
  - rented land and paid with ______________________
  - dependent on __________ and crop prices
- Opportunities declined for urban African Americans.
  - skilled labor jobs closed to African Americans

Reconstruction's Conclusion

- Support for Radical Republicans declined.
- Many people called for:
  - withdrawal of troops from the South
  - ______________________
- Disputed Election of 1876
  - ______________________ vowed to end Reconstruction
  - all troops removed

Industrial Growth in the South

- Investors started or expanded industries to turn __________ into __________.
- The __________ industry came to play an important role in the southern economy.
- New mills and factories grew up to use the South's __________, __________, and __________.

Refer to this page to answer the Chapter 12 Focus Question on page 198.

Chapter 12 Assessment

Directions: Circle the letter of the correct answer.

1. The case of *Plessy* v. *Ferguson* provided the legal basis for
   - **A** poll taxes.
   - **B** sharecropping.
   - **C** impeachment.
   - **D** segregation.

2. Which of the following was a result of the Ku Klux Klan's campaign of violence?
   - **A** Andrew Johnson was impeached.
   - **B** Rutherford B. Hayes was elected President.
   - **C** The South became more industrialized.
   - **D** Fewer African Americans voted.

3. Slavery and forced labor were banned by the
   - **A** Emancipation Proclamation.
   - **B** Freedmen's Bureau Bill.
   - **C** Thirteenth Amendment.
   - **D** Reconstruction Act of 1867.

4. The process of bringing the North and the South together after the Civil War became known as
   - **A** Reconstruction.
   - **B** Emancipation.
   - **C** Radicalization.
   - **D** Bureaucratization.

Directions: Follow the steps to answer this question:

What do the differences between Johnson's plan and Radical Reconstruction say about their supporters' attitudes about the South?

Step 1: Recall information: List two policies of Johnson's plan. Then list two policies of Radical Reconstruction.

Johnson's Plan	Radical Reconstruction
•	•
•	•

Step 2: Compare these policies in the chart.

How Plans Differ	What Differences Suggest

Step 3: Complete the topic sentence that follows. Then write two or three more sentences that support your topic sentence.

The details of Johnson's plan and Radical Reconstruction reveal that ______________________

____

____

____

Chapter 12 Notetaking Study Guide

Now you are ready to answer the Chapter 12 Focus Question: **What were the short-term and long-term effects of the Civil War?**

► Complete the following chart to help you answer this question. Use the notes that you took for each section.

Rebuilding a Nation

As the Civil War ended, the nation faced enormous challenges:

- much of the South lay in ruins
-
-

Lincoln's Plan	Radical Republican Plan
Ten Percent Plan • • • 10% state voter loyalty oath	Wade-Davis Bill • • •

The first duty of the Freedmen's Bureau was to ______________________________ ______________________________.

Battle Over Reconstruction

Johnson's Plan	Radical Republican Goals
• Southern states ratify Thirteenth Amendment • •	• •

Radical Reconstruction

- ______________________ imposed military rule on all southern governments that did not ratify the Fourteenth Amendment.
- During Radical Reconstruction, ______________________ played an important role in politics, and women were given ______________________.
- Southern states opened ______________________ for the first time.
- Legislators spread ______________ more evenly and made fairer ______________.

End of Reconstruction

As Radical Republican support died, many called for local self-government and ______________________________.

The end of Reconstruction was finalized with ______________________________.

Southern whites prevented African Americans from voting with techniques such as ______________ and ______________.	The South's economy began to ______________ due to industries based on ______________.

Refer to this page to answer the Unit 5 Focus Question on page 199.

Unit 5 Pulling It Together Activity

What You Have Learned

Chapter 10 With the addition of new western land, tension over the slavery issue erupted into violence. The election of Abraham Lincoln led to seven states leaving the Union and marked the coming of the Civil War.

Chapter 11 People in the North and the South hoped for an early victory, but the Civil War went on for years. Hundreds of thousands of Americans were killed before the war ended.

Chapter 12 At the end of the Civil War, Americans faced the problem of how to reunite the nation. Disagreements over Reconstruction led to conflicts in government and in the South. With the end of Reconstruction, African Americans in the South lost many of the rights they had gained.

Think Like a Historian

Read the Unit 5 Focus Question: **How was the Civil War a political, economic, and social turning point?**

► Use the organizers on this page and the next to collect information to answer this question.

What political, economic, and social factors existed before the Civil War? Some of them are listed in this organizer. Review your section and chapter notes. Then complete the organizer.

Political
- nation deeply divided over slavery
-

The United States Before the Civil War

Economic
- North:
- South:

Social

North and South deeply divided
- South:
- North:

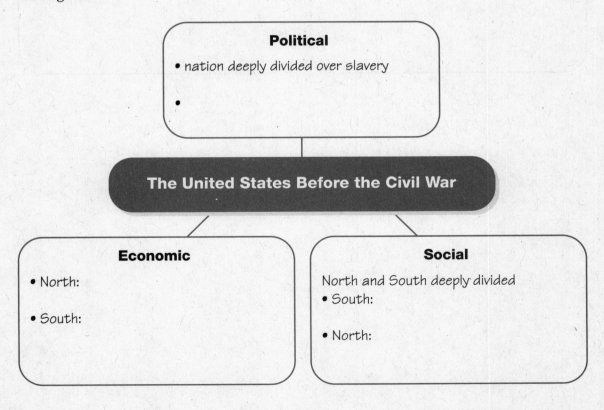

What political, economic, and social factors changed because of the Civil War? The organizer below gives you a part of the answer. Review your section and chapter notes. Then fill in the rest of the organizer.

The United States After the Civil War

Economic

- inflation
-
-
-

Political

- 13th Amendment abolished slavery
-
-
-
-

Social

- many people killed or injured
-
-
-
-

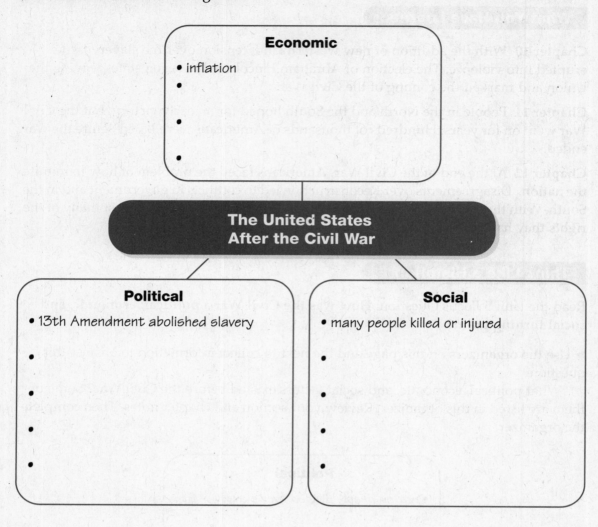

Unit 6

An Age of Industry

What You Will Learn

Chapter 13 Miners and railroad builders led to settlement of the West. Native Americans struggled to maintain their way of life. Western farmers faced many challenges.

Chapter 14 In the late 1800s, industrialization caused urban growth, altered the way business was run, and prompted reforms in education. A new wave of immigration to America occurred during this period.

Chapter 15 During the late 1800s and early 1900s, Americans organized to press for reforms in many areas of government and society.

Chapter 16 In the late 1800s, the United States began building an overseas empire and becoming more involved in foreign affairs.

Focus Your Learning As you study this unit and take notes, you will find the information to answer the questions below. Answering the Chapter Focus Questions will help build your answer to the Unit Focus Question.

Chapter 13 Focus Question
How did the growth of big business affect the development of the West?
(page 202)

Chapter 14 Focus Question
How did industrialization increase the speed of change?
(page 216)

Unit 6 Focus Question
How did the industrialization of the United States change the economy, society, and politics of the nation?
(page 261)

Chapter 15 Focus Question
How did society and politics change during the Progressive Era?
(page 233)

Chapter 16 Focus Question
How did a more powerful United States expand its role in the world?
(page 247)

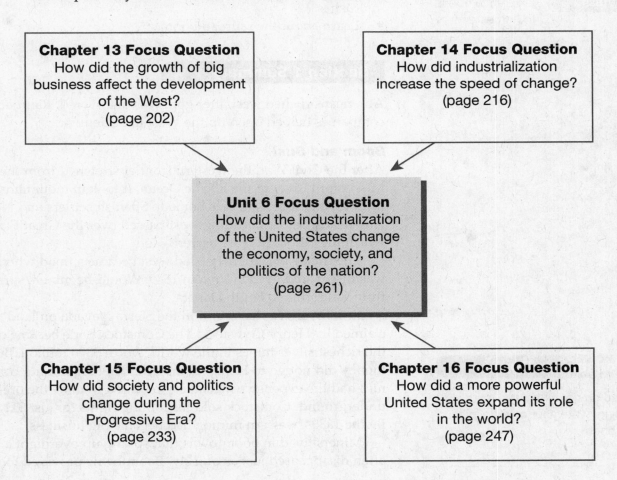

Chapter Standards

History-Social Science 8.12.1, 8.12.2, 8.12.3, 8.12.4, 8.12.8

Key Events

1867	First cattle drive on Chisholm Trail.
1887	Dawes Act breaks up Native American tribal lands.
1889	Oklahoma opens to homesteaders.

Chapter 13

The West Transformed (1860–1896)

What You Will Learn

Miners and railroad builders led to settlement of the West. Native Americans struggled to maintain their way of life. Western farmers faced many challenges.

Chapter 12 Focus Question

As you read this chapter, keep this question in mind: **How did the growth of big business affect the development of the West?**

Section 1

Mining and Railroads

Section 1 Focus Question

How did mining and railroads draw people to the West? To begin answering this question,

- Find out about the boom and bust of the gold and silver rushes.
- Learn about the railroad boom.

Section 1 Summary

Americans rushed west after gold was discovered. Railroad companies helped open up the West to settlement.

Boom and Bust

After the Civil War, the western frontier stretched from the Mississippi River to the Pacific Ocean. It took in mountains, prairies, and forests. It was home to Spanish settlers and Native Americans. Settlers heading west passed over the Great Plains, which they thought were barren.

The trickle of settlers headed west became a flood when gold was discovered in California in 1849. Would-be miners spread from California to South Dakota.

In 1859, silver was found in the Sierra Nevada on land claimed by Henry Comstock. The Comstock Lode became one of the richest silver mines in the world, worth $300 million. But the money did not go to Henry Comstock. Only big mining companies had the expensive machinery required to mine the ore deep underground. Comstock sold his mining rights for just $11,000. By the 1880s, western mining had become big business.

Miners lived in boomtowns that sprang up overnight and often disappeared just as quickly. Boomtowns provided food,

Vocabulary Builder

Based on context clues in your reading, write your own definition of a boom.

____

board, and equipment, all at greatly inflated prices. Women who joined the mining boom could make a good living running restaurants, laundries, and boarding houses.

Almost half of all miners were foreign-born. Foreign miners often faced hostility. For example, laws restricted Chinese miners to claims abandoned by others.

Mining towns sprouted so fast that law and order were hard to find. People formed groups of **vigilantes**, or self-appointed law keepers, to hunt down people they considered criminals and to punish people as they saw fit. Eventually, residents of western towns brought in judges and sheriffs as part of their push to become U.S. territories.

In some mining towns, all the ore was soon extracted. Mines shut down and miners moved away. Businesses failed and merchants left. Boomtowns became ghost towns. ✓

✓ Checkpoint

List three kinds of businesses women ran in boomtowns.

____

____

____

The Railroad Boom

Before 1860, the railroads stopped at the Mississippi River. The federal government offered the railroad companies **subsidies**, or grants of land and money, to extend their lines. For every mile of track they laid, railroads got ten square miles of land next to the track. Very quickly, the railroads owned over 180 million acres, an area the size of Texas. They also received federal loans.

In 1862, Leland Stanford and his partners won the right to build a railroad line eastward from California. Their company, called the Central Pacific Railroad, was to build the western portion of the **transcontinental railroad**, a railroad line that spanned the continent. At the same time, the Union Pacific Railroad was building west from Omaha. The two railroads hired thousands of workers, including native-born whites, Mexican Americans, African Americans, and immigrants from Mexico, Ireland, or China, to build each line. The work was hazardous, and the pay was low. Finally, on May 10, 1869, the lines met in Promontory, Utah.

With the transcontinental railroad in place, the West became a fixed part of the U.S. economy. Goods flowed between the East and the West, and railway stops turned into towns that grew rapidly. Eight western territories became states in the period from 1864 to 1890. ✓

✓ Checkpoint

Name the two companies that built the transcontinental railroad.

____

____

Check Your Progress

1. What was the Comstock Lode?

____

____

2. How did railroads come to own millions of acres of land?

____

____

Section 1 Notetaking Study Guide

Question to Think About As you read Section 1 in your textbook and take notes, keep this section focus question in mind: **How did mining and railroads draw people to the West?**

► Use these charts to record key information from the section. Some information has been filled in to get you started.

The Discovery of Gold and Silver in the West
The Comstock Lode • Discovered in Nevada in 1859 • Importance: one of the richest ____________ • Effect: made Nevada a center for ____________
The Boom Spreads • Few prospectors became rich because ____________ ____________. • By the 1880s, western mining had become ____________.
Life in Mining Towns • Tent cities arose around mining camps and quickly became boomtowns. • Nearly half of all miners were ____________. • Because mining towns grew so quickly, it was hard to find ________ and ________. So, miners formed groups of ____________, who ____________ and ____________. • As towns grew, local residents looked for more lasting forms of ____________. • In some towns, all the ore was soon extracted, and mines ____________, miners ____________, businesses ____________, and merchants ________.

The Railroad Boom
Aid to Railroads • To encourage the growth of railroads, the ____________ offered railroads ____________, which are ____________. • Railroads also received ____________.
The Transcontinental Railroad • A transcontinental railroad is a railroad line that ____________. • In 1862, the ____________ Railroad won the right to build a line eastward from ____________. The ____________ Railroad would build west from ____________. • The railroads hired thousands of workers, including 10,000 ____________. • On May 10, ______, the two lines met in ____________, ______.
Effects of the Railroads • On population: ____________ • Political changes: ____________ ____________

Refer to this page to answer the Chapter 13 Focus Question on page 215.

Section 2

Native Americans Struggle to Survive

Section 2 Focus Question

What were the consequences of the conflict between the Native Americans and white settlers? To begin answering this question,

- Discover who the people of the Plains were.
- Find out about broken treaties.
- Learn about the last stand for Custer and the Sioux.
- Read about Native American efforts at resistance.
- Understand the failure of reform.

Section 2 Summary

The gold rush and the railroads meant disaster for Native Americans of the West.

People of the Plains

People of the Plains lived by gathering wild foods, by hunting, and by fishing. Some raised crops. When Europeans arrived, they introduced horses and guns to Native Americans. This allowed Native Americans to kill more game, as well as travel faster and farther. Many Plains nations followed the buffalo herds. As a result, buffalo hunting played a key role in people's survival.

In many Plains nations, women managed village life. They cared for children, prepared food, carved tools, and made clothing and **tepees**. Tepees are cone-shaped tents made of buffalo skins. Men were hunters and warriors. Often, they also led religious life. ✓

Broken Treaties

U.S. treaties promised to safeguard Native American lands. As miners and settlers pushed west, they broke the treaties. In 1851, Plains nations signed the Fort Laramie Treaty. This treaty said their lands would be protected by the United States forever if they stopped following the buffalo. No sooner had Native Americans signed the treaty than settlers moved onto their land.

In the early 1860s, new treaties forced Native Americans to give up land around Pikes Peak. Native Americans protested by attacking supply trains and settlers' homes. In response, Colonel John Chivington and 700 militia volunteers attacked a band of Cheyenne under army protection at Sand Creek in eastern Colorado in 1864. The Cheyenne waved a white flag, but Chivington attacked anyway. The Sand Creek Massacre helped to ignite an era of war. ✓

Key Events

1867	First cattle drive on Chisholm Trail.
1887	Dawes Act breaks up Native American tribal lands.
1889	Oklahoma opens to homesteaders.

✓ Checkpoint

Describe the roles of women and men in the Plains nations.

Women: ______________________

____

Men: ______________________

____

✓ Checkpoint

Name the event that helped start an era of war.

____

Last Stand for Custer and the Sioux

Native Americans were moved to **reservations**, or land set aside for Native Americans to live on. But life on these reservations was a disaster. The poor soil of Oklahoma made farming extremely difficult. If gold was discovered on reservation land, a flood of miners would invade their land.

In June 1876, Colonel George Custer attacked a band of Sioux and Cheyenne in an attempt to force them onto a reservation. Chiefs **Sitting Bull** and Crazy Horse won this Battle of Little Bighorn, but the Sioux and Cheyennes were rounded up a winter or two later by a larger force. ✓

✓ Checkpoint

Name two Native American leaders who resisted the reservation system.

____

____

Other Efforts at Resistance

Under pressure, many Nez Percés agreed to go to a reservation. But Chief Joseph tried to flee to Canada rather than face this humiliation. He and his people were hunted down and finally caught near the Canadian border.

The Navajos of the Southwest resisted removal to reservations until 1864, when they were sent to the Pecos River in Arizona. The Apaches, led by Geronimo, fought until 1886, when they were sent to a reservation in Oklahoma.

In the 1880s, soldiers worried about the Ghost Dances, which Native Americans said gave them visions of returning to their old ways. In 1890, Sitting Bull was killed by Native American police sent to stop the dance. Then soldiers surrounded a group of Sioux fleeing to avoid more violence. While the Sioux were giving up their guns, a shot was fired. The army opened fire, killing nearly 200 Sioux men, women, and children. This Battle of Wounded Knee ended the Indian Wars. ✓

✓ Checkpoint

Name the event that marked the end of the Indian Wars.

____

The Failure of Reform

Reformers criticized the government for its harsh treatment of Native American nations. Susette La Flesche told of the destruction of native culture in lectures and articles. Alice Fletcher promoted Native American rights.

Hoping to improve Native American life, Congress passed the Dawes Act in 1887. It tried to end Native Americans' wandering and turn them into farmers. The act set up schools and gave Native American men 160 acres to farm. But few Native Americans took to farming, and with the buffalo hunt gone, they remained poor. Many grew dependent on the government for food and supplies. ✓

✓ Checkpoint

List two things the Dawes Act did.

____

____

Check Your Progress

1. What changed the western Native American way of life?

____

____

2. Why did the Dawes Act fail?

____

____

Section 2 Notetaking Study Guide

Question to Think About As you read Section 2 in your textbook and take notes, keep this section focus question in mind: **What were the consequences of the conflict between the Native Americans and white settlers?**

► Use this chart to record key information from the section. Some information has been filled in to get you started.

Native Americans in the West
People of the Plains • For centuries the Plains people lived by gathering wild foods, hunting, and fishing. • The Europeans introduced ____________ and ____________. • Many Plains nations began ______________________________.
Broken Treaties • As Americans moved west, U.S. officials tried to convince the Plains nations to stop ______________________ and <u>settle down permanently</u>. • In 1851, Native American leaders signed the ____________________ Treaty. The U.S. government promised to ________________________________. However, after the treaty was signed, ____. • In 1864, ______________________ attacked a band of ____________ at ______________. The ______________ helped ignite an era of war.
Native American Resistance • Southern Plains nations were moved to reservations in Oklahoma. Life there was a disaster because ____. • Many Sioux and Cheyennes gathered on land set aside for them in the ____________ of ______________. When a ______________ in 1874 brought ____________ to the area, ____________ and ______________ led attacks to keep whites out. • In 1876, ______________________ tried to force Native Americans onto a reservation. He and all his men died in the Battle of ______________. • Chief Joseph led the ______________ to ______________. The U.S. Army ________________________________, and Chief Joseph ______________. • After years of war, the ______________ were defeated in 1864 in Arizona, and they were forced to move to a spot near the ______________. • In the late 1880s, Native Americans began performing the ______________, which they believed would make their ______________ and the ____________ return and would cause ______________ to leave the Plains. Soldiers saw this as the beginning of an ______________. In a struggle, ______________ was killed. Later, troops killed nearly ______ Sioux men, women, and children at the Battle of ______________________.
Efforts at Reform • Congress passed the __________ Act in 1887, which gave Native American men ______________________ and set up ______________________________________. The measure failed because few Native Americans ____________________________.

Refer to this page to answer the Chapter 13 Focus Question on page 215.

Section 3

Cattle Kingdoms

Key Events

1867	First cattle drive on Chisholm Trail.
1887	Dawes Act breaks up Native American tribal lands.
1889	Oklahoma opens to homesteaders.

Section 3 Focus Question

What factors led to boom and bust in the cattle industry? To begin answering this question,

- Find out about the rise of the cattle industry.
- Explore life on the trail.
- Learn about the Wild West.
- Learn why the cattle boom went bust.

Section 3 Summary

Cattle towns and the life of the cowhand on the trail helped create the legend of the Wild West. But the boom was short-lived.

The Rise of the Cattle Industry

Wild longhorn cattle had roamed the **open range**, or unfenced land, of Texas for years. When the railroads crossed the Plains in the 1860s, Texas ranchers at last saw a way to get these cattle to market. They could drive the cattle to the railroad towns, where they would be shipped by rail to slaughterhouses and then sold in the East.

These **cattle drives** meant herding and moving cattle over very long distances. Texan cattle were driven as far as 1,000 miles to rail lines. ✓

✓ Checkpoint

Name the type of cattle that roamed the open range of Texas.

____

Life on the Trail

Cowhands who drove the cattle had to have nerves of steel. They had to control thousands of cows and keep the herds together through rivers, fires, and droughts. Cowhands earned less than a dollar a day.

The first cowhands were the Spanish and Mexican **vaqueros** (vah KAYR os). This Spanish word for cowhand or cowboy comes from *vaca*, the Spanish word for "cow." Americans learned how to ride, rope, and brand from vaqueros, and they adopted their spurs, chaps, and cowboy hats. About one third of all cowhands on the trails were Mexican, while many others were African American or white Civil War veterans. ✓

✓ Checkpoint

Name three types of clothes American cowhands borrowed from the vaqueros.

____

____

____

The Wild West

Railroad towns were the final destination of the cattle drives. Abilene, Kansas, was the first big **cow town**, or settlement at the end of a cattle trail. It was founded in 1867 by Joseph McCoy. He figured that after months on the trail, cowhands would spend their hard-earned money on a bath, a meal, a soft bed, and some fun. McCoy founded Abilene where the Chisholm Trail met the Kansas Pacific Railroad.

Cow towns were filled with unruly men. They were places of violence, adventure, and opportunity. There were saloons, dance halls, drinking, gambling, and gun fighting. These helped spread the myth of the Wild West.

William "Buffalo Bill" Cody did his best to promote the fantasy of the Wild West. He started his traveling Wild West show in 1883. It featured gun-slinging cowboys, Native Americans on horseback, and reenactments of battles from the Indian Wars. But even as Cody's show packed in eastern audiences, the West was being steadily transformed. It was changing into a place where Native Americans were forced onto reservations and big companies ran mining and ranching. Even cow towns were quieting down, a result of settlers and ministers who wanted peaceful communities. ✓

Boom and Bust in the Cattle Kingdom

The cattle boom lasted from the 1860s to the 1880s. At its height, ranchers could buy a calf for $5 and sell a grown steer for $60. Investors created huge cattle companies. One covered almost 800 square miles in three states. The ranching region, dominated by the cattle industry and its ranches, trails, and cow towns, became known as the **cattle kingdom**.

By the mid-1880s, more than 7 million cattle were on the open range. It was more than the land could support. Two years of hard weather in 1886 and 1887 killed millions of cattle. A depression in eastern cities lowered demand for beef, and farmers fenced in the open range. As railroads expanded and their lines moved closer to ranches, long cattle drives ended. All these factors led to the end of the cattle boom. ✓

Check Your Progress

1. Why did ranchers have to drive their cattle so far?

____

____

2. How was Buffalo Bill's Wild West show out of date?

____

____

____

____

Vocabulary Builder

Reread the bracketed paragraph. Based on context clues in the paragraph, write a definition of the word *transform*.

____

____

✓ Checkpoint

List three ways the West was changing in the 1880s.

____

____

____

____

____

____

✓ Checkpoint

List three factors that hurt the cattle industry.

____

____

____

Section 3 Notetaking Study Guide

Question to Think About As you read Section 3 in your textbook and take notes, keep this section focus question in mind: **What factors led to boom and bust in the cattle industry?**

► Use this chart to record key information from the section. Some information has been filled in to get you started.

Cattle Kingdoms: Causes and Effects	
Causes	**Effects**
1. Railroads swept across the Plains.	1. Texas ranchers began driving cattle to the rail lines to get cattle to distant __________. Cowhands followed trails such as the __________ Trail and the __________ Trail.
2. Cowhands who drove cattle needed to unwind at the end of the trail, where they faced dangers such as panicked animals, stampedes, fires, and thieves.	2. __________ sprang up along rail lines. Here, __________, __________, __________, and __________ served the cowhands.
3. Cowhands borrowed much from early __________ and __________ __________.	3. Cowhands learned how to ride, rope, and brand. They wore spurs and chaps and broad-brimmed hats.
4. __________ created a traveling __________ show.	4. The myth of the Wild West as a place of violence, adventure, and endless opportunity was spread.
5. Profits rose. New breeds of cattle had fewer __________ and more __________ than longhorns.	5. The cattle industry booms. Backers from the East and Europe invested __________ in __________.
6. In the 1880s, there was bad weather, economic depression, lower demand for beef, and competition with sheep. Farmers fenced in the open range.	6. The cattle industry __________.
7. Railroads expanded and their lines moved closer to the ranches.	7. Large roundups and long __________ vanished. The cattle boom __________.

Refer to this page to answer the Chapter 13 Focus Question on page 215.

Section 4
Farming in the West

Section 4 Focus Question

How did farmers on the Plains struggle to make a living? To begin answering this question,

- Find out about the impact of homesteading.
- Discover the hardships of life on the Plains.
- Learn about the last rush for land.
- Read about how farmers organized politically.

Section 4 Summary

Homesteading boomed in the West after the Civil War, but times were not easy for farmers.

Homesteading

During the Civil War, Congress passed the Homestead Act of 1862. It offered 160 acres on the Great Plains to those who agreed to live on the land and farm it for five years. This gave thousands of poor people the chance to be **homesteaders**, settlers who acquired free land offered by the government.

But only one third of homesteaders on the Great Plains lasted the required five years. On the dry Plains, 160 acres was not enough land to support a family.

The railroads also promoted farming on the Plains. The railroads owned millions of acres thanks to land grants. They recruited people to farm them because more farms meant more shipping for the railroads. ✓

A Hard Life on the Plains

Life on the Great Plains was not easy. Water was scarce, and crops were hard to grow. The soil of the Plains was fertile, but the tough **sod**, a thick layer of roots of grasses tangled with soil, had to be removed to expose clear soil for planting. Plains farmers were called **sodbusters** for this reason.

New farming methods helped Plains farmers. They used steel plows, which were stronger and lighter than other plows. New drills allowed them to bury seeds deep in the ground, where there was moisture. They used both windmills to pump water that lay hundreds of feet below ground and barbed wire to keep cattle from trampling their crops. Whole families, including young children, worked long days on the farm to keep it going.

Thousands of African Americans, many former slaves, also settled on the Plains. By the 1880s, 70,000 African Americans had settled in Kansas. They were known as Exodusters because they believed they were like the Jews who fled slavery in Egypt, a bible story told in the Book of Exodus.

Key Events

1867	First cattle drive on Chisholm Trail.
1887	Dawes Act breaks up Native American tribal lands.
1889	Oklahoma opens to homesteaders.

Vocabulary Builder

Based on context clues, define *homestead*.

____

____

✓ Checkpoint

Name two conditions that homesteaders had to live up to.

____

____

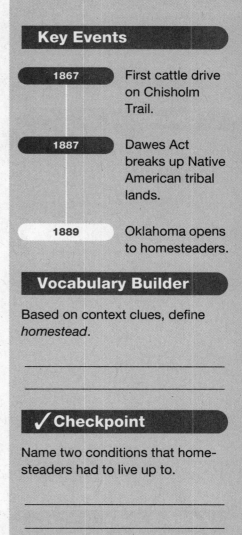

✓ Checkpoint

List two things that made farming the Plains so difficult.

____

____

✓ Checkpoint

How much land was up for grabs in the Oklahoma Land Rush?

____

✓ Checkpoint

Name two things that Populists wanted.

____

____

____

____

In the Spanish Southwest, the Spanish-speaking farmers and shepherds who had lived in the region for centuries were overrun by American settlers and immigrants from Mexico brought in to build railroad lines. ✓

A Last Rush for Land

By the late 1880s, free western land was finally running out. In 1889, nearly 100,000 people gathered at a line near present-day Oklahoma City to claim some of the two million acres of free land being offered in what was once Indian Territory. A few people, known as **sooners**, had already sneaked onto the land, and they came out of hiding to claim it. By 1890, the United States no longer had free land to give. ✓

Farmers Organize

As in mining and ranching, farming had a few big organizations that did well, while small farmers scraped by. Overproduction drove down prices. Small farmers borrowed money to expand or to buy new equipment. When prices for their crops fell, the farmers could not pay off the loans, and they lost their land.

Many farmers living in poverty and isolation formed **granges**, groups of farmers who met for lectures, sewing bees, and other events. In 1867, local granges joined to form the National Grange. In the 1870s and 1880s, National Grange members were demanding the same low rates from railroads and grain warehouses that big farmers received. They elected state officials who backed their views. The Farmers' Alliance was organized in the 1870s to set up **farm cooperatives**. These were groups of farmers who pooled their money to make large purchases of tools, seed, and other supplies at a discount.

In 1892, unhappy farmers joined labor unions to form the Populist Party. They pushed for social reforms like public ownership of railroads and warehouses to control rates, an income tax to replace property taxes, and an eight-hour workday. Populists also wanted the government to back the dollar with silver as well as gold. They hoped this would bring on **inflation**, or a general rise in prices, raising crop prices.

In the presidential election of 1896, Populists backed **William Jennings Bryan,** a Democrat who supported the silver plan. But Republican gold-alone backer William McKinley won, and Populism faded away. ✓

Check Your Progress

1. Why did railroads support farming on the Plains?

____

____

2. What did the National Grange demand?

____

____

Section 4 Notetaking Study Guide

Question to Think About As you read Section 4 in your textbook and take notes, keep this question in mind: **How did farmers on the Plains struggle to make a living?**

► Use this chart to record key information from the section.

Farming in the West	
Homestead Act of 1862	• Offered ___160___ acres to anyone who resided on the land for five years • Thousands became homesteaders, which were ________________ ________________.
Railroads	• To the railroads, more farms meant more ________. • So railroads gave away ________________ ________________.
New Farming Methods	• ___Steel plows___ that could break through sod • __________ to bury seed • __________ to harvest crops • __________ to beat off the hard coverings of grain
Farm Families	• Role of men: ________________ • Role of children: ________________ • Role of women: ________________
Exodusters	• Thousands of __________ came to the Plains. • They were known as Exodusters because ________________ ________________.
Spanish-speaking Farmers	• Many had been there since before ________________. • Mexican immigrants arrived with the coming of the ________. • Large landowners were known as ________.
Sooners	• The federal government opened up what was once ________ in ________________ to homesteaders in April 1889. • A few people known as sooners ________________.
Farmers Organize	• Granges were groups of farmers who met for lectures, sewing bees, and other events. In 1867, local granges ________________ ________________. • Grangers demanded ________________ ________________. • Farm cooperatives were groups of farmers who pooled their money to ________________. • ___Unhappy farmers___ joined with ________________ to form the Populist Party, which pushed for ________________.

Refer to this page to answer the Chapter 13 Focus Question on page 202.

Chapter 13 Assessment

Directions: Circle the letter of the correct answer.

1. Which of the following was true of miners in the late 1800s?
- **A** Most worked for big mining companies.
- **B** Most received government subsidies.
- **C** Almost half were foreign-born.
- **D** Almost half became wealthy.

2. What was the goal of the Dawes Act?
- **A** to protect Native Americans' way of life
- **B** to turn Native Americans into farmers
- **C** to prohibit settlers from trespassing on Native American lands
- **D** to offer employment opportunities to Native Americans

3. Which did NOT cause the end of the cattle kingdom?
- **A** two years of bad weather
- **B** extension of railroad lines into Texas
- **C** oversupply of cattle
- **D** an economic depression

4. Why did Populist farmers want inflation?
- **A** to increase demand for crops
- **B** to lower equipment prices
- **C** to hurt big farmers
- **D** to raise crop prices

Directions: Follow the steps to answer this question:

What was the main issue that led to the outbreak of the Indian Wars?

Step 1: Recall information: In the chart, recall the issues behind the events leading up to the Indian Wars.

Fort Laramie Treaty	Sand Creek Massacre
• Provision for Native Americans: ______ • In return, the U.S. wanted: ______ • What happened: ______	• Events leading up to massacre: ______ • What happened: ______ • Result: ______

Step 2: Decide: What was the basic conflict between the U.S. government and Native Americans? ______

Step 3: Complete the topic sentence that follows. Then write two or three more sentences that support your topic sentence.

The Indian Wars were caused by a conflict over ______

______

______

______

______

Chapter 13 Notetaking Study Guide

Now you are ready to answer the Chapter 13 Focus Question: **How did the growth of big business affect the development of the West?**

► Complete the following organizers to help you answer this question. Use the notes that you took for each section.

Mining and Railroads	Effects on Native Americans
Gold and silver rushes • People raced to the West to mine. • By the 1880s, big businesses had taken over mining.	**Gold discoveries** • Led miners onto traditional Native American lands • Conflict erupted
Railroads laid tracks to mines and boomtowns. Effects: • • Western population grew rapidly.	**Railroad expansion and the buffalo** Railroads had buffalo killed to • • Effect:
	Westward settlement • Native Americans were forced onto ____________, or areas set aside for them to live.

The Influence of Big Business on the West

Cattle Kingdoms	Farming in the West
Effect of railroads: •	**Railroads promoted farming by** •
Reasons the cattle industry boomed: • •	**Big farmers versus small farmers:** • Big farms tended to do well, while many small farms struggled.
Reasons the cattle boom ended: • • •	**Farm groups pushed for silver standard** • Why farmers wanted this: • Why banks and businesses opposed:
Reason cattle drives ended: •	• Result:

Refer to this page to answer the Unit 6 Focus Question on page 261.

Chapter Standards

History-Social Science 8.12.1, 8.12.3, 8.12.4, 8.12.5, 8.12.6, 8.12.7, 8.12.9

Chapter 14

Industry and Urban Growth (1865–1915)

What You Will Learn

In the late 1800s, industrialization caused urban growth, altered the way business was run, and prompted reforms in education. A new wave of immigration into America occurred during this period.

Chapter 14 Focus Question

As you read this chapter, keep this question in mind: **How did industrialization increase the speed of change?**

Key Events

1869	Knights of Labor, a major labor union, is formed.
1889	Jane Addams founds Hull House to help city poor.
1892	Ellis Island opens as major entry station for European immigrants.
1913	Henry Ford sets up assembly line to mass produce automobiles.

Section 1

A New Industrial Revolution

Section 1 Focus Question

What conditions spurred the growth of industry? To begin answering this question,

- Find out why industry boomed.
- Learn about inventors and inventions.
- Explore a transportation revolution.

Section 1 Summary

After the Civil War, the United States experienced rapid industrial growth. Westward expansion, government policy, and new technology helped the nation become an industrial power.

Why Industry Boomed

As the nation expanded westward, industry grew. Enormous deposits of coal, iron, lead, and copper were now within reach. Government policy also helped to spur growth by giving generous land grants to railroads and businesses and by placing high tariffs on imports. Tariffs helped American industry by raising the price of foreign goods.

New technology also spurred industrial growth. Inventors developed the Bessemer process, a method to make stronger steel at a low cost. Steel replaced iron as the basic building material of cities and industry.

The oil industry developed refining methods to turn crude oil into lubricants for machines. "Black gold," as oil was called, later became gasoline to power engines and cars.

Railroads fueled the new Industrial Revolution. Trains transported goods and people to the West and raw materials to the

East. Big rail lines sought ways to limit competition and keep prices high. Many small farmers became angry over high rail rates to transport their goods, and many joined the Granger and Populist movements. ✓

Inventors and Inventions

In the late 1800s, Americans created a flood of new inventions. In 1897, more government **patents**, or documents giving someone the sole right to make and sell an invention, were issued than in the ten years before the Civil War.

At **Thomas Edison**'s "invention factory," scientists produced such inventions as the light bulb and motion picture camera. In 1882, Edison opened the nation's first electrical power plant. Soon plants all over the country provided power to homes, streetcars, and factories.

Inventions that improved communication prompted growth in business. Telegraphs transmitted messages from Europe more quickly. **Alexander Graham Bell**'s invention of the telephone in 1876 helped speed up the pace of business. The patent for the telephone was the most valuable patent ever issued. The typewriter improved office efficiency. African Americans such as Jan Matzeliger also contributed to the flood of inventions. ✓

A Transportation Revolution

Technology revolutionized transportation. The invention of the automobile ushered in an era of faster and faster transportation. Only 8,000 Americans owned automobiles in 1900. Then, an American manufacturer, **Henry Ford**, made the automobile affordable to millions by perfecting a system to mass produce cars. Ford introduced the **assembly line**, a manufacturing method in which a product is put together as it moves along a belt.

Another transportation revolution was taking place at this time. In 1903, **Wilbur and Orville Wright**'s gas-powered airplane took flight. By 1930, airplanes began to alter the world by making travel quicker and easier. ✓

Check Your Progress

1. How did government policy influence industrial growth?

____

____

____

2. How did Henry Ford make the automobile affordable to millions of people?

____

____

✓ Checkpoint

List three factors that influenced industrial growth.

____

____

____

✓ Checkpoint

Name three inventions that helped businesses to grow.

____

____

____

Vocabulary Builder

Reread the underlined sentence. Think about how airplanes affected travel. Based on this information, what do you think the word *alter* means?

Mark the Text

____

✓ Checkpoint

List two inventions that made transportation faster.

____

____

Section 1 Notetaking Study Guide

Question to Think About As you read Section 1 in your textbook and take notes, keep this question in mind: **What conditions spurred the growth of industry?**

► Use these charts to record key information from the section.

Factors Leading to the Industrial Boom

Factor	Effect
Westward expansion	• provided access to vast deposits of coal, ____, ____, and ____ • Pacific Northwest furnished ____ for ____
Government policies	• Congress gave ____ and other ____ to ____ and other ____. • kept ____ high, which made ____ expensive
Railroads	• Trains carried ____ and ____ west.

Inventions That Spurred Industry, Business, and Transportation

Invention	Impact
Bessemer process	• allowed people to make stronger steel at a lower cost • Steel replaced iron as the basic building material of industry.
Oil refining methods	Crude oil refined into ____ and ____
Electrical power plant	• ____ opened first one in ____ in ____ • allowed people to use inventions such as the ____, the ____, and the ____
Telegraph	• improved communication for ____
Underwater telegraph	• sped up communications with ____
Telephone	• invented by ____ in ____ • device that carried ____
Typewriter	• made office work ____ and ____
Automobile	• ushered in an era of ____ and ____ transportation
Assembly line	• introduced by ____ in ____ to mass produce ____
Gas-powered airplane	• first tested by ____ in ____ • later used by the ____ during ____

Refer to this page to answer the Chapter 14 Focus Question on page 232.

Section 2

Big Business and Organized Labor

Section 2 Focus Question

How did big business change the workplace and give rise to labor unions? To begin answering this question,

- Learn about new ways of doing business.
- Find out about growth in business.
- Explore changes in the workplace.
- Learn how workers organized.

Section 2 Summary

Without government regulation, big business grew out of control. A few barons accumulated incredible wealth while factory workers tried to form unions to improve poor working conditions.

New Ways of Doing Business

Entrepreneurs (ahn treh preh NYOORZ) led business expansion. An **entrepreneur** is someone who sets up a business to make a profit. These entrepreneurs needed capital, or money, to expand. To raise this capital, Americans adopted new ways of organizing business. Many businesses became **corporations**, or businesses owned by many investors. Corporations raise large amounts of capital by selling stock, or shares in a business. Stockholders receive a share of profits and pick directors to run the company.

Banks lent money to corporations and industries to spur faster growth. One banker, J. P. Morgan, became the most powerful force in the American economy by gaining control of key industries such as railroads and steel mills. ✓

Growth of Big Business

Congress seldom made laws to regulate business practices. This encouraged the growth of what came to be known as "big business." Entrepreneurs formed giant corporations and monopolies. A **monopoly** is a company that controls all or nearly all business in a particular industry.

Andrew Carnegie's companies controlled every step of making steel. The Carnegie Steel Company produced more steel than all the mills of England combined. **John D. Rockefeller** ended competition in the oil industry by creating the Standard Oil Trust. A **trust** is a group of corporations run by a single board of directors. He bought out his competitors and slashed prices to drive his rivals out of business. By 1900, trusts dominated many of the nation's industries.

Some Americans criticized big business practices as threats to **free enterprise**, the system in which privately owned businesses compete freely. Others praised big business for expanding the economy, creating jobs, and lowering prices.

Key Events

1869	Knights of Labor, a major labor union, is formed.
1889	Jane Addams founds Hull House to help city poor.
1892	Ellis Island opens as major entry station for European immigrants.
1913	Henry Ford sets up assembly line to mass produce automobiles.

✓ Checkpoint

Name two industries that J. P. Morgan controlled.

____

____

Vocabulary Builder

Mono comes from the Greek word meaning "one." *Poly* comes from the Greek word meaning "many." What do you think the word *monopoly* means?

____

____

____

✓ Checkpoint

Name the people who held monopolies in the steel and oil industries.

____

____

✓ Checkpoint

List three reasons used to justify the poor conditions of factories.

____

____

____

✓ Checkpoint

Name three issues that workers organized to change.

____

____

____

A new philosophy called Social Darwinism supported the trend toward trusts. Scientist Charles Darwin had said that, in nature, forms of life survived if they could adapt to change better than others. Social Darwinists applied this idea of "survival of the fittest" to human affairs. When applied to business, the "fittest" meant the entrepreneurs who beat out competition. ✓

Changes in the Workplace

Industry attracted millions of workers who toiled in dangerous conditions for low wages. Even young children worked in hazardous jobs. Employers did not have to pay employees if they were injured at work. Factory owners justified the harsh conditions by referring to Social Darwinism. The bad conditions of factories, they held, were necessary to cut costs, to increase production, and to ensure survival of the business.

An accident at a New York garment factory called attention to the dangers workers faced. In 1911, nearly 150 people, most of them young women, died in a fire at the Triangle Shirtwaist Factory. As a result, New York and other states began to pass laws protecting factory workers. ✓

Workers Organize

Although striking was illegal, workers attempted to organize against unsafe working conditions, low wages, and long hours. In 1869, workers in Philadelphia formed a union called the Knights of Labor. The union admitted both skilled and unskilled workers.

However, violent labor disputes undercut the union's successes. The American Federation of Labor replaced the Knights of Labor as the country's leading union. It admitted only skilled workers, who were difficult to replace. The AFL relied on collective bargaining to achieve its goals. In **collective bargaining**, unions negotiate with management for workers as a group.

In 1893, the nation plunged into an economic depression. Many business owners fired workers and cut wages. A wave of violent strikes swept the country. Federal troops were used to end some strikes, which often resulted in more violence. Most Americans sided with owners because they saw unions as radical and violent. ✓

Check Your Progress

1. What were the two differing views of big business?

____

____

____

____

2. Why did most Americans not favor unions?

____

____

Section 2 Notetaking Study Guide

Question to Think About As you read Section 2 in your textbook and take notes, keep this question in mind: **How did big business change the workplace and give rise to labor unions?**

▶ Use these organizers to record key information from the section.

Big Business	
Corporation	• businesses owned by investors • raised capital by ____________ • run by a ____________ • limited risk for ____________ • shareholders received ____________
Trust	• consisted of a group of corporations run by a ____________ • by 1900, dominated ____________ • used ____________ to justify efforts to limit competition
Monopoly	a company that controls ____________
Banks	• huge loans helped industry ____________ • J. Pierpont Morgan: most powerful force in ____________
Andrew Carnegie	• controlled steel industry • according to Carnegie's *Gospel of Wealth* philosophy, ____________ ____________
John D. Rockefeller	• used profits from his first ____________ to buy other oil companies • formed ____________, which ____________ ____________
Debate over big business	Arguments for: • lowered the price of goods • • Arguments against: • •

Workplace Conditions and Labor Unions	
Workplace	**Labor Unions**
Hours: long Pay: ____________ Conditions: ____________ Employers not required to ____________ ____________ for workplace injuries	Goals: safer working conditions, ____________, ____________ Early unions: • •

Refer to this page to answer the Chapter 14 Focus Question on page 232.

Key Events

1869 Knights of Labor, a major labor union, is formed.

1889 Jane Addams founds Hull House to help city poor.

1892 Ellis Island opens as major entry station for European immigrants.

1913 Henry Ford sets up assembly line to mass produce automobiles.

✓ Checkpoint

List three effects of urbanization.

____

____

____

Section 3

Cities Grow and Change

Section 3 Focus Question

What were the causes and effects of the rapid growth of cities? To begin answering this question,

- Learn about the rapid growth of cities.
- Find out about problems of urban life.
- Explore the excitement of city life.

Section 3 Summary

The Industrial Revolution reshaped American cities. Millions of people moved to cities in search of jobs. Cities and reformers battled the problems caused by such rapid growth while American urban dwellers discovered the excitement of city life.

Rapid Growth of Cities

The rate of urbanization during the late 1800s was astonishing. **Urbanization** is the rapid growth of city populations. Cities attracted industry, and industry attracted people. Farmers, immigrants, and African Americans from the South all migrated to cities in search of jobs and excitement.

Cities near waterways drew industry because they provided easy transport for goods. New York and San Francisco had excellent ocean harbors. Chicago rose on the shores of Lake Michigan. Technology also helped cities grow. Electric streetcars and subways made it easier for people to get around. Growing urban populations and public transportation gave rise to **suburbs**, or living areas on the outskirts of a city. Cities began to expand upward as well as outward. By 1900, skyscrapers towered over city streets.

Living patterns in cities also changed. The poor crowded into the old downtown sections of cities while the middle class lived in outlying row houses or apartments. The wealthy built fine homes on the cities' outskirts. ✓

Problems of Urban Life

Rapid urbanization created many problems. Fire was a constant threat to tightly packed neighborhoods. In downtown slums, the poor lived in crowded tenements. **Tenements** are buildings divided into many tiny apartments. Many apartments had no windows, heat, or indoor plumbing. As many as 10 people might live in a single room. Sanitation was perhaps the worst problem. Streets in slums were strewn with garbage, and outbreaks of cholera and other diseases were common. Babies ran the greatest risk. In one Chicago slum, half of all babies died before the age of one.

To improve urban life, cities set up police, fire, and sanitation departments. They paved streets and installed street lights while public health officials waged war on disease. Religious groups served the poor. Some set up hospitals and clinics, or places where people could receive medical treatment for little or no money, for people who could not afford a doctor. Others provided food and shelter to the homeless. Reformers like **Jane Addams** worked hard for poor city dwellers. She opened Hull House, one of America's first settlement houses. **Settlement houses** were centers offering help to the urban poor. Volunteers taught immigrants English and provided entertainment for young people and nurseries for children of working mothers. Addams and other settlement house leaders also pressured state legislative leaders to outlaw child labor. ✓

The Excitement of City Life

Despite hardships, cities offered attractions and excitement not available in the country. Newcomers were awed by electric lights, elevated railroads, and tall buildings that seemed to pierce the clouds.

Downtown shopping areas attracted hordes of people. Merchants developed a new type of store, the department store. These stores offered many types of goods in separate sections of the same store.

Long hours on the job made people value their free time. This strict division between work and play led to a new interest in leisure. To meet this need, cities provided a wealth of entertainment. Attractions included museums, orchestras, theatres, and circuses. City parks, zoos, and gardens allowed city dwellers to take a break from crowded city streets.

After the Civil War, professional sports teams began to spring up in cities. The most popular professional sport was baseball. Football gained popularity in American colleges. In 1891, James Naismith invented basketball. It quickly became a favorite winter sport. ✓

Check Your Progress

1. How did living patterns change in cities during the Industrial Revolution?

____

____

2. What services did settlement houses provide?

____

____

✓ Checkpoint

Name three problems created by urbanization.

____

____

____

Vocabulary Builder

The text states that people found leisure in a city's entertainment. Based on the context clues, write a definition of the word *leisure*.

____

____

✓ Checkpoint

List three attractions found in cities.

____

____

____

Section 3 Notetaking Study Guide

Question to Think About As you read Section 3 in your textbook and take notes, keep this section focus question in mind: **What were the causes and effects of the rapid growth of cities?**

► Use these charts to record key information from the section.

Growth of Cities		
Urbanization	**Expanding Cities**	**Living Patterns**
Urbanization: the rapid growth of ________ ________ Why people were attracted to cities: ________ ________ To meet the needs of shoppers, merchants developed ________, which ________ ________. Kinds of leisure activities cities offered: ________ ________ ________ ________	Public transportation: subways, ________, ________ Public transportation gave rise to new living areas called ________. ________ helped speed up the growth of suburbs. New types of buildings: ________ ________	Lived in oldest sections at cities' centers: ________ Lived away from city centers in row houses and apartments: middle class Lived in fine homes on outskirts of cities: ________

Urban Problems and Solutions	
Problems of Urban Life	**Solutions to Problems**
Fires endangered ________ ________. Tenement life was ________. Slum streets were ________ with ________. Disease was caused by ________.	Provided by cities: • • • Provided by religious groups: • • • • Provided by reformers: • •

Refer to this page to answer the Chapter 14 Focus Question on page 232.

Section 4
The New Immigrants

Section 4 Focus Question

How was the experience of immigrants both positive and negative? To begin answering this question,

- Learn why immigrants sought a fresh start in America.
- Explore how immigrants started a new life.
- Find out how immigrants became American.
- Learn about a new wave of nativism.

Section 4 Summary

Starting in the late 1800s, millions of immigrants came to America seeking freedom and opportunities. Immigrant labor was essential to the economy. Many immigrants wanted to assimilate to American culture.

A Fresh Start

The industrial age also changed the population. Some 25 million immigrants entered the country between 1865 and 1915. Some people emigrated from their homelands in search of employment or to escape political and religious persecution. Jews fled Russia after becoming the targets of government-sponsored **pogroms**, or violent attacks against Jews. A revolution in Mexico in 1910 pushed many political refugees into the United States.

The wave of "new immigrants" in the late 1800s came from southern and eastern Europe, as well as from Asia and the Pacific. Few of the new immigrants understood English or had experience living in a democracy. ✓

Starting a New Life

The passage to America was miserable. Most immigrants came to the United States crammed into the steerage of ships. **Steerage** consisted of large compartments that usually held cattle. After 1892, most people from Europe went through the receiving center on Ellis Island in New York. Asian immigrants entered through Angel Island in San Francisco Bay. About two thirds of immigrants settled in cities. Many immigrants settled near other people from the same country in ethnic neighborhoods. Here, they could speak their native languages and observe familiar holidays. ✓

Becoming American

Many newcomers to America clung to their traditional ways while trying to assimilate. **Assimilation** is the process of becoming part of another culture. Surrounded by English-speakers at school, children of immigrants learned the language more quickly and were more easily assimilated.

Key Events

1869	Knights of Labor, a major labor union, is formed.
1889	Jane Addams founds Hull House to help city poor.
1892	Ellis Island opens as major entry station for European immigrants.
1913	Henry Ford sets up assembly line to mass produce automobiles.

✓ Checkpoint

List three regions where the "new immigrants" came from.

____

____

____

✓ Checkpoint

About what fraction of immigrants settled in cities?

____

Vocabulary Strategy

Assimilate means "to make similar." If you assimilate, you become similar to something. How does the immigrant experience reflect this meaning?

____

____

____

Immigrant labor was essential to the new economy. Immigrants worked in steel mills, meat-packing plants, and garment factories. They helped build skyscrapers, railroads, subways, and bridges. With hard work and saving, immigrants slowly advanced economically.

Some Notable Immigrants

Immigrant	Place of Origin	Important Contribution
Alexander Graham Bell	Scotland	invented the telephone
Andrew Carnegie	Scotland	steel magnate; donated money to charities
Samuel Goldwyn & Louis Mayer	Eastern Europe	helped establish the motion picture industry in California
Arturo Toscanini	Italy	orchestra conductor
Leo Baekeland	Belgium	invented plastic

✓

✓ Checkpoint

Which immigrant invented the telephone?

____

A New Wave of Nativism

As immigration increased, a new wave of nativists sought to preserve the country for native-born Americans. Nativists charged that foreigners would never assimilate and also that they took jobs from Americans. Many Americans associated immigrants with anarchy, crime, and violence. An anarchist is a person who opposes all forms of government.

In the West, nativist feelings against Chinese drove many Chinese immigrants from mining camps and cities. The Chinese Exclusion Act of 1882 excluded, or kept out, Chinese laborers from the United States until it was repealed in 1943. In 1917, Congress passed a law that barred those who could not read their own language from immigrating to the United States. ✓

✓ Checkpoint

List two restrictions placed on immigration.

____

____

____

____

Check Your Progress

1. Why was it easier for children of immigrants to assimilate?

____

____

2. Why did nativists oppose immigration?

____

____

Section 4 Notetaking Study Guide

Question to Think About As you read Section 4 in your textbook and take notes, keep this section focus question in mind: **How was the experience of immigrants both positive and negative?**

▶ Fill in these charts to record key information from the section.

Reasons for Migration

- Employment opportunities
- ________ persecution: Russian Jews were the victims of ________.
- Political unrest: Many Mexicans were driven out of their homes because of ________.
- Most "new immigrants" came from southern Europe and ________. Smaller numbers came from ________ and the Pacific.

Starting New Lives

- Most immigrants were received at ________ and ________.
- About two thirds of immigrants settled in ________.
- Living in ethnic neighborhoods, immigrants could speak ________ and celebrate ________.

Becoming American

- Assimilation is the process of ________.
- Children of immigrants assimilated more quickly because ________ ________.
- Immigrants worked in ________, ________, ________, and ________. They helped build ________, ________, ________, and ________.
- Many immigrants advanced economically by ________.
- Immigrants who made major contributions: ________, ________, ________, ________, ________, ________.

A New Wave of Nativism

- Nativists sought to ________.
- Nativists charged that immigrants took away jobs from ________.
- Many Americans associated immigrants with ________, ________, and ________.
- The Chinese Exclusion Act of 1882 ________.
- In 1917, Congress passed a law that denied entry to immigrants who could not ________.

Refer to this page to answer the Chapter 14 Focus Question on page 232.

Section 5

Education and Culture

Section 5 Focus Question

What were the causes and effects of an expanded educational system? To begin answering this question,

- Learn about American education.
- Find out about new American writers.
- Explore the newspaper boom.

Section 5 Summary

Public education expanded during the economic boom. Compulsory education eventually became commonplace in all states. Better educated, Americans took more interest in reading. Newspapers vied for readers' attention with sensational headlines and colorful features.

Educating Americans

Before 1870, fewer than half of all American children went to school. Addressing the need for an educated workforce for the nation's growing industry, states improved public schools. In 1852, Massachusetts passed the first compulsory education law. **Compulsory education** is the requirement that children attend school up to a certain age. Southern states were more reluctant to pass compulsory education laws than states in the North or West. But by 1918, compulsory education became the norm in all states.

By 1900, there were 6,000 high schools in the country. Higher education also expanded. Private colleges for men and women opened, and states built universities that offered free or low-cost education.

Education for adults also improved. Wealthy people such as Andrew Carnegie gave money to build public libraries. These made speakers as well as books and magazines available to adults. The Chautauqua (shuh TAWK wuh) Society in New York, which began as a summer school for Bible teachers, was opened to the public. Middle class men and women of all ages turned out to hear lectures on a variety of subjects. ✓

New American Writers

As education became available to more people, reading habits changed. Americans began to read more books and magazines. In the 1880s, a new crop of American writers appeared. Many were **realists**, writers who try to show life as it is. Stephen Crane wrote about the hardships of city slums. Californian Jack London wrote about miners and sailors on the West Coast who put their lives at risk. Kate Chopin shocked readers by writing about an unhappily

Key Events

1869 Knights of Labor, a major labor union, is formed.

1889 Jane Addams founds Hull House to help city poor.

1892 Ellis Island opens as major entry station for European immigrants.

1913 Henry Ford sets up assembly line to mass produce automobiles.

Vocabulary Strategy

Reread the underlined sentence. What meaning would be lost if the word *compulsory* were replaced with the word *voluntary*?

✓ Checkpoint

Which states were reluctant to pass compulsory education laws?

married woman. Paul Laurence Dunbar was the first African American to make a living as a writer.

Mark Twain, the pen name of Samuel Clemens, was the most popular writer of the time. Twain made his stories, such as *Huckleberry Finn*, realistic by capturing the speech patterns of southerners living and working along the Mississippi River. Today, many critics consider *Huckleberry Finn* to be one of the greatest American novels. ✓

A Newspaper Boom

The number of American newspapers increased dramatically in the late 1800s. By 1900, half of the newspapers in the world were printed in the United States.

The spread of education was one cause of growth in the newspaper industry. As more Americans could read, they bought more newspapers and magazines. Urbanization was another reason for the newspaper boom. In small towns, news spread by word of mouth, but people in cities depended on newspapers to stay informed.

Immigrant **Joseph Pulitzer** created the first modern, mass-circulation newspaper. In 1883, he purchased the *New York World* and cut the price of the newspaper to make it more affordable.

Pulitzer added crowd-pleasing features to his newspaper, including color comics. The Yellow Kid, a tough but sweet slum boy, became the first popular American comic strip character. The *New York World* also became known for its sensational headlines. As a result, readership of the *New York World* skyrocketed, and other newspapers tried to follow suit.

Because of the Yellow Kid, critics of the *New York World* coined the term **yellow journalism** to describe the sensational reporting style of the *New York World* and other papers. ✓

Check Your Progress

1. Why did education become such an important issue in the late 1880s?

____

____

2. What caused the newspaper boom?

____

____

____

✓ Checkpoint

List three well-known writers of the time.

____

____

____

✓ Checkpoint

Name three ways in which Joseph Pulitzer changed the newspaper industry.

____

____

____

Section 5 Notetaking Study Guide

Question to Think About As you read Section 5 in your textbook and take notes, keep this section focus question in mind: **What were the causes and effects of an expanded educational system?**

► Use these organizers to record key information from the section.

Education and Culture

Better-Educated Americans

- States improved public schools because _____________________.
- States in the _______________ were more reluctant to pass compulsory education laws than states in the _______________ and West. Still, by _______________ every state required children to attend school.
- Elementary school students learned reading, _______________, and _______________.
- _______________ offered free or low-cost higher education.
- Wealthy individuals funded the building of __________ in cities and towns.
- The Chautauqua Society offered _____________________ and later began _____________________.

↓

Americans Read More Books and Magazines

What or Who People Read	Description or Accomplishment
Many bestsellers	low-priced paperbacks that told tales of the "Wild West" or "rags-to-riches" stories
Realists	
Stephen Crane	
Jack London	wrote about the lives of miners and sailors
Kate Chopin	
Paul Dunbar	
Mark Twain	

↓

A Newspaper Boom

By 1900, half the newspapers in the world were printed in the United States.

Causes:

- spread of education
- _______________

New York World

- first modern _______________ newspaper
- created by _______________, who cut prices so people could _______________ the paper
- known for _______________ and _______________
- term used to describe its reporting style: _______________

Refer to this page to answer the Chapter 14 Focus Question on page 232.

Chapter 14 Assessment

Directions: Circle the letter of the correct answer.

1. Which of the following created a trust in the oil industry?
A J. P. Morgan
B John D. Rockefeller
C Andrew Carnegie
D Joseph Pulitzer

2. Westward expansion was important to industrial growth because
A it provided new land on which to build factories.
B it created the need for more automobiles.
C it made raw materials readily available.
D it eased overcrowding in urban areas.

3. The sensational reporting style of the *New York World* and other newspapers became known as
A yellow journalism.
B trustbusting.
C Chautauqua journalism.
D realism.

4. Which of the following was *not* a result of urbanization?
A rise of the newspaper industry
B building of skyscrapers
C overcrowding in cities
D rise in the price of oil

Directions: Follow the steps to complete this task:

Decide whether the changes to cities were positive or negative.

Step 1: Recall information: In the chart, list ways rapid urbanization changed cities and the way people lived in them.

Changes to Cities	Effect on City Dwellers

Step 2: Analyze effects: which were positive? Which were negative?

____

____

Step 3: Explore consequences: Complete the topic sentence that follows. Then write two or three more sentences that support your topic sentence.

The rapid growth of cities led to ______________________________

____

____

____

Chapter 14 Notetaking Study Guide

Now you are ready to answer the Chapter 14 Focus Question: **How did industrialization increase the speed of change?**

► Fill in the following organizer to help you answer this question.

Industrial Growth

Caused by:

- Westward expansion: Industries gained access to natural resources, including ______, ______, ______, ______, and ______.
- Government policies: Congress gave ______ and other subsidies to ______ and other businesses. The government also kept high ______ on imports, making foreign goods ______.
- Technology: The ______ process made stronger ______ at a lower cost. ______ was increasingly used to fuel machines and became a valuable resource.
- Improvements in transportation: ______ carried people and goods to the West and raw materials to eastern ______.

Furthered by Inventions:

- light bulb
- electric power plant
- ______
- ______
- ______
- ______

Supported by labor from Immigration:

- The "new immigrants" came from ______.
- Many immigrants came to America in search of ______. Others wanted to escape religious persecution or ______ in their home countries.
- Many immigrants tried to maintain familiar traditions while trying to ______ to American culture.
- Immigrants worked in ______, ______, ______, and ______. They built ______, ______, and ______.

↓ ↓ ↓

The Growth of Cities

Problems of cities

- poor sanitation
-
-

Attractions and leisure activities:

- department stores
-
-
-

The Rise of Big Business

- Role of corporations and trusts: ______
- Conditions of factory work: ______
- Labor unions were formed to: ______

Improved Educational System

- Why education was needed: ______
- Better educated Americans took more interest in reading. This spurred a boom in ______.

Refer to this page to answer the Unit 6 Focus Question on page 261.

Chapter 15

Political Reform and the Progressive Era (1870–1920)

What You Will Learn

During the late 1800s and early 1900s, Americans organized in support of several different kinds of reform.

Chapter 15 Focus Question

As you read through the sections in this chapter, keep this question in mind: **How did society and politics change during the Progressive Era?**

Chapter Standards

History-Social Science 8.6.6, 8.11.3, 8.12.4, 8.12.5

Key Events

1890 Sherman Antitrust Act bars businesses from limiting competition.

1909 Reformers found the NAACP to promote rights of African Americans.

1920 Nineteenth Amendment guarantees women the right to vote.

Section 1

The Gilded Age and Progressive Reform

Section 1 Focus Question

How did reformers try to end government corruption and limit the influence of big business? To begin answering this question,

- Learn about reform during the Gilded Age.
- Find out about the Progressives' political reforms.
- Learn about the muckrakers.

Section 1 Summary

The Progressives supported various reforms aimed at ending government corruption and limiting the influence of big business.

Reform in the Gilded Age

The period after the Civil War was called the Gilded Age. It was a time of rapid economic growth. It was also a time of serious problems in society. One problem was the spoils system, which is the rewarding of political supporters with government jobs, a practice that started during Andrew Jackson's presidency. Many believed the spoils system encouraged corruption.

Support for reforming the spoils system grew when President James Garfield was assassinated by a disappointed office seeker. The Pendleton Act (1883) created the Civil Service Commission. The **civil service** is a system that includes most federal jobs in the executive branch. The system required that jobseekers be hired on merit instead of their political connections.

During the late 1800s, big businesses often bribed members of Congress to get favorable laws passed. The Constitution gave the federal government the power to regulate interstate commerce, or trade that crossed state lines. The Interstate Commerce Act (1887) prohibited pools and rebates. The Interstate Commerce Commis-

Vocabulary Builder

Gilded means "coated with a thin layer of gold paint." How was this appropriate for describing America after the Civil War?

____

____

✓ **Checkpoint**

List two laws that regulated big business.

✓ **Checkpoint**

List three reforms of state government.

✓ **Checkpoint**

Name the type of journalist who exposed corruption.

sion was set up to regulate railroads. The Sherman Antitrust Act (1890) was supposed to prohibit businesses from using trusts to destroy competition but it was hard to enforce. Instead the law was mainly used to limit the power of labor unions.

Corruption was a serious problem in city governments. Politicians called bosses demanded bribes from businesses that wanted work from the city. Immigrants often supported political bosses in exchange for favors. ✓

Progressives and Political Reform

The Progressive movement aimed to stop corruption and promote the public interest, or the good of all. The Wisconsin Idea was a set of reforms of state government. They included getting rid of political bosses and using commissions to solve problems. One important reform was the **primary**, or election in which voters, rather than party leaders, choose their party's candidate for an election.

There were other important political reforms to give more power to voters. One was the **recall**, a process by which people may vote to remove an elected official from office. Another reform was the **initiative**, a process that allows voters to put a bill before a state legislature. A third political reform was the **referendum**, a way for people to vote directly on a proposed law. Many reformers supported the Sixteenth and Seventeenth amendments. The Sixteenth Amendment (1913) gave Congress the power to pass a federal income tax. The Seventeenth Amendment (1913) required the direct election of U.S. senators by the people instead of state legislatures. ✓

The Muckrakers

The press played an important role in exposing corruption. **Muckraker** became a term for a crusading journalist.

Muckrakers	Exposed
Ida Tarbell	unfair business practices
Jacob Riis	city slums
Upton Sinclair	meatpacking industry

✓

Check Your Progress

1. What was the practice of rewarding political supporters with government jobs?

2. What were the two constitutional amendments supported by Progressive reformers, and what did each amendment do?

Section 1 Notetaking Study Guide

Question to Think About As you read Section 1 in your textbook and take notes, keep this section focus question in mind: **How did reformers try to end government corruption and limit the influence of big business?**

► Use this chart to record key information from the section. Some information has been filled in to get you started.

The Gilded Age and Progressive Reform

Reform in the Gilded Age

Two Political Concerns of the Gilded Age

- The wealthy were making themselves rich at the public's expense.
- There was widespread ________________ in government.

Reforming the Spoils System

- The spoils system ____________ political supporters with ____________.
- In 1883, the ________________ created the ________________, which filled jobs on the basis of merit.

Controlling Big Business

- In 1887, the Interstate Commerce Act forbade ________________ and set up the ________________ to oversee railroads.
- Although difficult to enforce, the Sherman Antitrust Act of 1890 was designed to ________________.

Corruption: A Serious Problem in City Government

- Politicians called ____________ controlled work locally and demanded ____________ from businesses.

Progressives and Political Reform

The Progressive Movement

- The ____________ Idea was a set of Progressive reforms proposed by Governor Robert LaFollette. These reforms included the creation of ____________, made up of experts, to solve problems.
- Some states instituted reforms to put more power in the hands of ____________. These included the recall, the ____________, and the ____________.

Constitutional Amendments

- The Sixteenth Amendment gave Congress the power to ________________.
- ________________ (1913) required the direct election of U.S. senators.

Muckrakers

- Muckraker became a term for a ________________.
- Muckrakers played an important role in exposing ____________ and other problems.
- Three well known muckrakers were ____________, ____________, and ____________

Refer to this page to answer the Chapter 15 Focus Question on page 246.

Section 2

The Progressive Presidents

Section 2 Focus Question

How did the Progressive Presidents extend reforms? To begin answering this question,

- Learn about Theodore Roosevelt, the first Progressive President.
- Find out about Roosevelt's Square Deal.
- Explore Taft and Wilson's accomplishments.

Key Events

1890	Sherman Antitrust Act bars businesses from limiting competition.
1909	Reformers found the NAACP to promote rights of African Americans.
1920	Nineteenth Amendment guarantees women the right to vote.

Section 2 Summary

The Progressive Presidents were Theodore Roosevelt, William Howard Taft, and Woodrow Wilson. New areas of reform included conservation of natural resources, consumer protection laws, and banking reform.

The First Progressive President

Theodore Roosevelt was the first Progressive President. A former war hero and governor, Vice President Roosevelt took office after the assassination of President McKinley.

Roosevelt was a **trustbuster**, a person who worked to destroy monopolies and trusts. He distinguished between "good trusts" that were fair and efficient, or acted in a way that minimized waste, and "bad trusts" that cheated the public and took advantage of workers. Roosevelt argued that the government must control bad trusts or break them up. In a case involving the Northern Securities trust, the Supreme Court used the Sherman Antitrust Act to break up a trust because it limited free trade. It was the first time the act had been used to break up trusts, not unions. Roosevelt used the decision to push for the breakup of other trusts. Roosevelt also forced mine owners to negotiate with striking coal miners. ✓

✓ Checkpoint

Why was the Northern Securities court case important?

The Square Deal

The Square Deal, Roosevelt's platform during the presidential election of 1904, promised that everyone, not just big businesses, would have the same opportunity to succeed. It helped him win an overwhelming victory.

Vocabulary Builder

Platform in this context means a set of policies that a politician or political party proposes.

Roosevelt was a strong advocate of **conservation**, or the protection of natural resources. He created the U.S. Forest Service to manage the nation's woodlands. He also created **national parks**, or natural areas protected and managed by the federal government.

Roosevelt also supported reforms to protect consumers from unsafe food and drugs. He was influenced by Upton Sinclair's book *The Jungle*, which exposed the meatpacking industry's unhealthy practices. Roosevelt made public a report exposing unhealthy conditions in meatpacking plants. As a result, Congress was forced to pass a law allowing closer inspections of meatpacking houses. Muckrakers also exposed companies for making false claims about medicines and adding harmful chemicals to food. In response, Congress passed the Pure Food and Drug Act, which required food and drug makers to list all ingredients on packages. ✓

✓ Checkpoint

List two causes Roosevelt supported.

____

____

Taft and Wilson

Roosevelt supported **William Howard Taft** for President in the election of 1908. Taft won easily. His approach differed from Roosevelt's. He was quiet and more cautious. Nevertheless, Taft supported many Progressive causes. He broke up more trusts than Roosevelt. He also favored a graduated income tax, approved new mine safety rules, and started to regulate child labor. However, Taft lost Progressive support by raising tariffs, which raised the price of consumer goods, and modifying some of Roosevelt's conservation policies.

In the election of 1912, Roosevelt ran against Taft for the Republican presidential nomination. Republican leaders sided with Taft and made him the nominee. Roosevelt then formed the Progressive, or Bull Moose, Party so he could run. Meanwhile, the Democrats nominated **Woodrow Wilson** as their candidate. A cautious reformer, Wilson was often criticized for being too rigid, or strict, and uncompromising. Wilson won the election of 1912 because Taft and Roosevelt split the Republican vote.

President Wilson created a program called the New Freedom. It sought to restore free competition among American corporations. The Federal Trade Commission (1914) helped restore competition by investigating and then stopping companies that used unfair trade practices. The Clayton Antitrust Act (1914) banned other business practices that harmed free competition. It also stopped antitrust laws from being used against labor unions. The Federal Reserve Act (1913) set up a system of federal banks and gave the government the power to change interest rates and control the money supply. ✓

✓ Checkpoint

List three parts of Wilson's New Freedom program.

____

____

____

Check Your Progress

1. How did President Roosevelt promote conservation?

____

____

2. Why did Woodrow Wilson win the election of 1912?

____

____

Section 2 Notetaking Study Guide

Question to Think About As you read Section 2 and take notes, keep this section focus question in mind: **How did the Progressive Presidents extend reforms?**

► Use this chart to record key information from the section. Some information has been filled in to get you started.

The Progressive Presidents
Theodore Roosevelt
• war hero, former governor, Vice President • became President in 1901 after ____________ • believed the government had to control or ____________ bad trusts • launched lawsuits against ____________ • Northern Securities: first time that ____________ ____________ • 1902 Pennsylvania coal miners strike: first time that ____________ ____________ • During the 1904 presidential campaign, Roosevelt promised Americans a Square Deal. By this, he meant ____________. • Conservation is ____________. • In 1905, Roosevelt created ____________ to conserve the nation's woodlands. He had ____________ of land set aside for ____________. • Roosevelt supported consumer protection reforms. The ____________ required food and drug makers to list all ingredients on packages.
William Howard Taft
• Roosevelt's secretary of war, won presidency in 1908 with Roosevelt's support • Unlike Roosevelt, Taft was ____________. • supported Progressive reforms: graduated ____________, new rules for mines, government workers, child labor • lost Progressive support because he ____________ and modified ____________ policies • Roosevelt broke with Taft and started the ____________. • In the presidential election of 1912, Roosevelt and Taft ____________, so Woodrow Wilson won.
Woodrow Wilson
• had served as a university president and a ____________ • was known as a brilliant scholar and a cautious reformer • His program to restore free competition was called ____________. It included the creation of the Federal Trade Commission (1914), the ____________, and the ____________.

Refer to this page to answer the Chapter 15 Focus Question on page 246.

Section 3
The Rights of Women

Section 3 Focus Question

How did women gain new rights? To begin answering this question,

- Learn about the women's suffrage movement.
- Find out about new opportunities for women.
- Learn about the temperance movement.

Section 3 Summary

After decades of effort, the movement for women's rights won the right to vote. New educational and career opportunities also opened for women.

Women Win the Vote

The Seneca Falls Convention of 1848 marked the start of an organized women's rights movement in the United States. After the Civil War, Elizabeth Cady Stanton and Susan B. Anthony organized the National Woman Suffrage Association. It pushed for a constitutional amendment to give women the right to vote.

In most states, leading politicians opposed women's suffrage. Still, the suffrage movement had its first successes in the late 1800s in four western states: Wyoming, Utah, Colorado, and Idaho. By giving women the right to vote, at least in local or state elections, these states recognized the contributions of pioneer women to the settlement of the West.

In the early 1900s, support for women's suffrage grew. One reason was that more women were beginning to work outside the home. Although women were paid less than men, wages gave them some power. Women wage earners believed that they deserved to be able to vote on laws that affected them.

A new generation of leaders took over after the deaths of Stanton and Anthony. **Carrie Chapman Catt** created a strategy for winning suffrage state by state. The plan coordinated the work of **suffragists,** or people who worked for women's right to vote, across the nation.

One by one, states in the West and Midwest began giving women the right to vote. Still, in some of these states, women could not vote in federal elections. More women joined the call for a federal amendment to allow them to vote in all elections. **Alice Paul** and other suffragists met with President Wilson on the matter. Wilson pledged his support for a constitutional amendment. The ratification of the Nineteenth Amendment gave women the right to vote in federal elections. ✓

Key Events

1890 Sherman Antitrust Act bars businesses from limiting competition.

1909 Reformers found the NAACP to promote rights of African Americans.

1920 Nineteenth Amendment guarantees women the right to vote.

Vocabulary Builder

A synonym is a word that is similar in meaning to another word. Which of the following words is a synonym for *coordinated*: organized, ruined, or finished?

____

✓ Checkpoint

Name the change that increased support for women's suffrage in the early 1900s.

____

____

____

New Opportunities for Women

Women also struggled for access to better jobs and educational opportunities. Starting with the first granting of a Ph.D. to a woman in the late 1870s, increasing numbers of women earned advanced degrees at graduate schools. By 1900, there were thousands of women doctors and lawyers.

During the late 1800s, many middle class women joined clubs. The earliest clubs were formed to help women improve their minds by, for instance, meeting to discuss books. Women's clubs gradually became more concerned with improving society. They raised money for libraries, schools, and parks, and pushed for laws to protect women and children, to ensure pure food and drugs, and to win the right to vote.

African American women also formed clubs. The National Association of Colored Women sought to end segregation and violence against African Americans. Its members also supported the women's suffrage movement.

Many women became reformers during the Progressive Era. Florence Kelley fought for safe working conditions and organized a boycott of manufacturers who used child labor. In time, she was made the chief factory inspector for Illinois. Some women entered the field of social work, helping poor city-dwellers. ✓

✓ Checkpoint

List three fields women entered.

____

____

____

The Crusade Against Alcohol

Women took a leading role in the temperance movement. The campaign against alcohol gained strength in the late 1800s.

The Woman's Christian Temperance Union was founded in 1874. Its president **Frances Willard** encouraged women to also support women's suffrage. Carry Nation was a more radical crusader for temperance. She gained publicity for the movement by attacking saloons, or places that sold liquor, with a hatchet.

After years of effort, temperance leaders persuaded Congress to pass the Eighteenth Amendment in 1917. The amendment enforced **prohibition**, a ban on the sale and consumption of alcohol. The amendment was ratified in 1919. ✓

✓ Checkpoint

Name two leaders of the temperance movement.

____

____

Check Your Progress

1. Where did women first gain the right to vote? Why?

____

____

____

2. How did the concerns of women's clubs change over time?

____

____

____

Section 3 Notetaking Study Guide

Question to Think About As you read Section 3 in your textbook and take notes, keep this section focus question in mind: **How did women gain new rights?**

► Use these charts to record key information from the section. Some information has been filled in to get you started.

Women's Suffrage	
Seneca Falls Convention (1848)	Importance: Marked the start of an organized women's rights movement in the United States.
National Woman Suffrage Association	Goal: Passage of ______________________________ ______________________________ Founders: ______________, ______________
Western states	By the late 1800s, women won voting rights in ______________, ______________, ______________, and ______________.
Reasons for increased support for women's suffrage	• More women ______________ and demanded ______________. • New leaders: ______________, ______________ • A detailed strategy to ______________
Nineteenth Amendment	Ratified: 1920 What it did: ______________________________

New Opportunities
Higher Education • Women began to earn advanced degrees. ***Clubs and Reform*** • At first women's clubs focused on advancing ______________. • The focus of many switched to social reforms: 1. raised money for ______________, ______________, and ______________. 2. pressed for laws to ______________, to ______________, and to ______________. • Racial barriers forced ______________ to form their own clubs.

Temperance	
Temperance	Campaign against ______________
Woman's Christian Temperance Union	Goal: ______________________________ Led by: ______________, ______________
Eighteenth Amendment	Ratified: ______________ What It Did: ______________________________

Refer to this page to answer the Chapter 15 Focus Question on page 246.

Section 4

Struggles for Justice

Section 4 Focus Question

What challenges faced minority groups? To begin answering this question,

- Learn how African Americans responded to discrimination.
- Explore how Mexican Americans lived.
- Find out about challenges faced by Asian Americans.
- Learn about prejudice facing religious minorities.

Key Events

1890	Sherman Antitrust Act bars businesses from limiting competition.
1909	Reformers found the NAACP to promote rights of African Americans.
1920	Nineteenth Amendment guarantees women the right to vote.

Section 4 Summary

African Americans and other groups faced discrimination with little support from Progressives.

African Americans

After the Civil War, African Americans faced discrimination in the North and South. They were denied housing in white areas and confined to the lowest paying jobs. Most white Progressives ignored the problems of African Americans. And President Wilson segregated workers in the federal civil service.

Booker T. Washington, a former slave, educator, and early leader in the struggle for African American rights, urged African Americans to learn trades and seek to move up gradually in society. Eventually, they would have the money and power to demand equality.

Washington founded the Tuskegee Institute in Alabama. The school trained African Americans in the industrial and agricultural skills they needed to get better jobs. Many white businessmen supported Washington's moderate approach.

The scholar **W.E.B. Du Bois** was the first African American to get a Ph.D. from Harvard. He had a different approach than Booker T. Washington. He urged blacks to fight discrimination rather than yield to it. Du Bois helped found the National Association for the Advancement of Colored People to fight for equal rights.

The African American woman Ida B. Wells tried to stop **lynching**, or the murder by a mob, of African Americans. She encouraged African Americans to protest lynching and to boycott white-owned stores and segregated streetcars.

Despite many obstacles, some African Americans succeeded. The scientist George Washington Carver discovered new uses for peanuts and other crops. Sarah Walker started a successful line of hair care products for African American women that made her the first American woman to make $1 million. Many black-owned businesses also served the African American community, and churches helped train new leaders. ✓

Vocabulary Builder

Reread the underlined sentence. One meaning of *discriminate* is "to treat differently." In the context of this sentence, does *discrimination* mean African Americans were treated better or worse than white Americans?

____

✓ Checkpoint

Name Ida B. Wells' main goal.

____

____

Mexican Americans

By 1900, about half a million Mexican Americans lived in the United States. They also faced legal segregation. Around 1910, famine and the Mexican Revolution forced many more Mexicans to settle in the United States. They first moved to the Southwest, then to the Midwest and Rocky Mountain region. Mexican Americans were confined to unskilled jobs and were paid less than Anglo workers.

Many Mexican Americans lived in barrios, or ethnic Mexican American neighborhoods, which helped preserve their language and culture. The largest barrio was in Los Angeles. In the barrio, mutualistas, or mutual aid groups, were formed. They helped provide insurance and legal advice and collected money to care for the sick and needy. ✓

✓ Checkpoint

Name three ways mutualistas helped residents of barrios.

____

____

____

Asian Americans

When the Chinese Exclusion Act of 1882 stopped Chinese immigration to the United States, employers on the West Coast hired workers from other parts of Asia, mainly the Philippines and Japan.

Many Japanese settled in California where they became successful farmers. When San Francisco forced all Asians into segregated schools, Japan protested the insult. Unions and other groups pressured President Roosevelt to limit Japanese immigration. A "Gentlemen's Agreement" was made. Japan agreed to stop workers from moving to the United States. In exchange, the American government allowed Japanese women whose husbands had already migrated to the United States to join them. ✓

✓ Checkpoint

List the terms of the "Gentlemen's Agreement" between Japan and the United States.

____

____

____

____

Religious Minorities

Religious minorities also faced prejudice. Nativist groups worked to restrict immigration of Roman Catholics and Jews. Both native-born and immigrant Catholics and Jews faced discrimination in housing and jobs.

To avoid prejudice in schools, Catholics set up church-sponsored schools. Jewish Americans founded the Anti-Defamation League to promote understanding and fight prejudice. (Defamation is the spreading of false or hateful information.) ✓

✓ Checkpoint

List two religious minorities that faced discrimination.

____

____

Check Your Progress

1. How did Washington's and Du Bois's views on ending discrimination differ?

____

____

____

2. What was one way that Mexican Americans preserved their language and culture?

____

Section 4 Notetaking Study Guide

Question to Think About As you read Section 4 in your textbook and take notes, keep this section focus question in mind: **What challenges faced minority groups?**

▶ Use this chart to record key information from the section. Some information has been filled in to get you started.

Struggles for Justice
African Americans
• Booker T. Washington founded the ________________. He advised African Americans to __learn trades__ and move up gradually in society.
• W.E.B. Du Bois helped found ________________________________. He urged African Americans to ________________.
• ______________ fought against lynching, or ________________.
Mexican Americans
• Before 1900, about __half a million__ Mexican Americans lived in the United States. Like ______________________, they faced legal ________. • In 1910, ______________ and ______________ swept Mexico. As a result, thousands of Mexicans fled into the United States. • Mexican Americans created barrios, or ________________________________. • Mexican immigrants and Mexican Americans formed ______________, or mutual aid groups. Members pooled money to pay for ______________ and ______________________. They also collected money for the sick and needy.
Asian Americans
• More than ______________ Japanese entered the United States in the early 1900s. • Most first went to ________________ to work on ______________. • In 1906, the city of ________________ forced Asian students to attend separate ______________. • This led to a compromise called the ______________ between the United States and Japan. Japan would stop any more ______________ from going to the United States. The United States, in exchange, allowed ____.
Religious Minorities
• ______________ groups worked to restrict immigration. Even ______________ and ________________ who were not immigrants faced discrimination in ______________ and ______________. • American Catholics set up ______________ schools. • American Jews set up the ________________________, which worked to fight ______________________, or prejudice against Jews.

Refer to this page to answer the Chapter 15 Focus Question on page 246.

Chapter 15 Assessment

Directions: Circle the letter of the correct answer.

1. Which did President Theodore Roosevelt strongly support?
   - **A** women's rights
   - **B** conservation
   - **C** banking reform
   - **D** African American rights

2. Women first won voting rights in several states in the
   - **A** Northeast.
   - **B** Midwest.
   - **C** South.
   - **D** West.

3. Which reformer urged African Americans to fight discrimination?
   - **A** Upton Sinclair
   - **B** Carry Nation
   - **C** W.E.B. Du Bois
   - **D** Booker T. Washington

Directions: Follow the steps to answer this question.

How did the reforms of the Wisconsin Idea help to achieve its goals?

Step 1: Recall information: What was the Wisconsin Idea and its goals?

The Wisconsin Idea	
Description	
Goals	• •

Step 2: Describe these reforms associated with the Wisconsin Idea.

The Wisconsin Idea Reforms	
Reform	**Description**
Primary	
Initiative	
Recall	
Referendum	

Step 3: Complete the topic sentence that follows. Then write two or three more sentences that support your topic sentence.

The Wisconsin Idea reforms ____

____

____

____

____

____

Chapter 15 Notetaking Study Guide

Now you are ready to answer the Chapter 15 Focus Question: **How did society and politics change during the Progressive Era?**

► Complete the following chart to help you answer this question. Use the notes that you took for each section.

Change in the Progressive Era	
The Gilded Age and Progressive Reform	
• ________________, or dishonesty in government, was widespread. • Critics said a key part of the problem was the ________________.	
Efforts to Control Big Business • • Interstate Commerce Commission •	**Political Reforms** • Wisconsin Idea • •
Progressive Presidents	
Theodore Roosevelt • In 1904, he campaigned on the promise of a ________________ for all Americans. • He also pressed for ________________, or the protection of natural resources. He had thousands of acres set aside to become ________________.	
William H. Taft • reputation: ________________ • Despite strong Progressive policy record, he lost Progressive support.	**Woodrow Wilson** • reputation: ________________ • Goal of New Freedom program: ________________
Rights of Women	
Two significant suffragist leaders: ________________ and ________________. •	The ________________ guaranteed women the right to vote.
Struggles for Justice	
Booker T. Washington • founded: ________________ • believed: ________________ ________________	**W.E.B. Du Bois** • helped found: ________________ • believed: ________________ ________________
Mexican Americans • Barrio: ________________ ________________	**Asian Americans** • Gentlemen's Agreement: ________________ ________________

Change in the Progressive Era

Chapter 16

The United States Looks Overseas

(1853–1915)

What You Will Learn

In the late 1800s, the United States began building an overseas empire and becoming more involved in foreign affairs.

Chapter Focus Question

As you read through the sections in this chapter, keep this question in mind: **How did a more powerful United States expand its role in the world?**

Section 1

Eyes on the Pacific

Section 1 Focus Question

How did the United States acquire new territory and expand trade in the Asia-Pacific region? To begin to answer this question,

- Learn how the United States looked overseas.
- Read about the expansionist mood in the United States.
- Find out how the United States gained footholds in the Pacific.
- Look at how foreign powers tried to carve up China.

Summary

By the late 1800s, the frontier had disappeared, and the United States began to look overseas for new opportunities for trade and raw materials.

The United States Looks Overseas

U.S. merchants in the mid-1800s wanted to trade with Japan, but Japan had shut itself off from the world. In 1853, Commodore **Matthew C. Perry** sailed to Japan, carrying a letter from the U.S. President calling for Japan to grant trade rights to Americans. Awed by the U.S. warships and guns, Japan signed a treaty opening itself up for trade. The technology and power of the United States had another effect. It caused Japan to transform itself into an industrial nation.

When Russia offered to sell Alaska to the United States in 1867, Secretary of State William Seward agreed. He saw Alaska as a stepping stone for trade with Asia and the Pacific. Many Americans who opposed Alaska's purchase changed their opinions when it was found to have valuable natural resources. ✓

Chapter Standards

History-Social Studies
Framework: Students trace the major trends in our foreign policy, culminating in our entry into World War I.

Key Events

1854	United States signs trade treaty with Japan.
1898	The Spanish-American War gives the United States an empire.
1904	The United States begins to build the Panama Canal.
1917	The United States enters World War I.

✓ Checkpoint

Name the U.S. naval officer who helped open up trade with Japan.

____

✓ Checkpoint

Name the foreign policy the United States pursued until the late 1800s.

____

Vocabulary Builder

The word *entrepreneur* comes from the old French word *entreprendre*, which means "to undertake." Using this information and the reading, what do you think the word *entrepreneur* means?

____

____

____

✓ Checkpoint

List the two nations Samoa was divided between in 1899.

____

____

✓ Checkpoint

Name the Chinese group that tried to expel foreigners from China.

____

The Expansionist Mood

Until the late 1800s, Americans had generally pursued a policy of **isolationism**. This is avoiding involvement in other countries' affairs. Meanwhile, the nations of Europe undertook a policy of **imperialism**. This is building empires by imposing political and economic control over peoples around the world. In the late 1800s, a new spirit of expansion gripped the nation as Americans looked beyond U.S. borders to increase trade, spread American ideas, and promote economic growth. ✓

Gaining Footholds in the Pacific

In the late 1800s, the United States, Britain, and Germany were all interested in Samoa, an island chain in the South Pacific. In 1889, the three countries came close to war over Samoa, but fighting was averted when a typhoon destroyed all but one warship. Ten years later, in 1899, Samoa was divided between Germany and the United States.

Expansionists eyed Hawaii because of its position in the Pacific. American missionaries arrived in Hawaii in 1820, and other Americans acquired land and established huge sugar plantations. Hawaiian Queen **Liliuokalani** advocated Hawaiian independence. When she replaced Hawaii's constitution in 1887, with one that increased her power and reduced the influence of American planters and entrepreneurs, they overthrew her. In 1898, the United States annexed Hawaii and made it a territory of the United States. ✓

Carving Up China

In the late 1800s, China was weak. European powers and Japan divided China into **spheres of influence**. These were areas of economic and political control. U.S. leaders feared that Americans would be shut out of trade with China. Secretary of State John Hay called for an "open door" policy in China that guaranteed equal trading rights to all nations.

In 1900, a Chinese secret society called the Boxers sought to expel foreigners. The United States and other countries sent troops to crush the rebellion. U.S. Secretary of State John Hay feared the Boxer Rebellion would be used as an excuse to seize more Chinese territory. He issued a second Open Door note, which repeated the principle of open trade and said that China should remain one country and not be broken up. ✓

Check Your Progress

1. What did Americans hope to do overseas in the late 1800s?

____

____

2. Why did expansionists find Hawaii attractive?

____

____

Section 1 Notetaking Study Guide

Question to Think About As you read Section 1 in your textbook and take notes, keep this section focus question in mind: **How did the United States acquire new territory and expand trade in the Asia-Pacific region?**

► Use this chart to record key information from the section.

The United States Looks Overseas

The Expansionist Mood

- European nations undertook a policy of imperialism. U.S. leaders feared that the United States would be shut out of ____________ and denied ____________.
- Supporters of expansion believed a strong ____________ was key to strong trade.
- Some believed that Americans had a ____________ duty to introduce ____________ ____________ and ____________ to people around the world.

U.S. Territories in the Pacific

Alaska
- Alaska was a ____________ colony purchased by the United States in the year ________.
- Some called the purchase ____________, but changed their minds when ____________________________.

Samoa
- The United States wanted to set up ____________ on Samoa.
- In 1899, Samoa was divided between ____________ and ____________.

Hawaii
- In 1893, American ____________ and ____________ overthrew ____________, with the help of ____________.
- In 1898, Hawaii became a ____________.

Foreign Trade

Japan
- For 250 years, Japan had shut itself off from the world.
- In 1853, ____________ presented the Japanese with a letter calling for ____________________________.
- The Japanese signed a treaty that ____________.

China
- In the late 1800s, European nations and Japan carved China into ____________.
- The first Open Door message called for ____________________________.
- In the spring of 1900, the Boxers began a rebellion to ____________.
- The second Open Door message ____________________________.

Refer to this page to answer the Chapter 16 Focus Question on page 260.

Key Events

1854 United States signs trade treaty with Japan.

1898 The Spanish-American War gives the United States an empire.

1904 The United States begins to build the Panama Canal.

1917 The United States enters World War I.

Vocabulary Builder

Intervene comes from the Latin words *inter* ("between") and *venere* ("to come"). Using these meanings and the context clues in the text, explain what some Americans wanted the United States to do in Cuba.

____

____

____

✓ Checkpoint

Name the U.S. ship that sank in Havana harbor in 1898.

____

Section 2

The Spanish-American War

Section 2 Focus Question

What were the causes and effects of the Spanish-American War? To begin to answer this question,

- Learn why war clouds loomed in the United States.
- Find out why the United States went to war.
- Explore how the United States governed its new territories.

Summary

The United States went to war in support of a rebellion of Cuba against Spanish rule. As a result, it gained new territories in both the Pacific and the Caribbean.

War Clouds Loom

Over the centuries, Cubans became discontented with Spain's harsh rule. After a Cuban uprising in 1895, the Spanish began a policy of **reconcentration**. This means moving large numbers of people into detention camps for military or political reasons. An estimated 200,000 people died as a result of poor conditions in the camps. Cuban exiles living in the United States urged the U.S. government to help the rebels.

Many Americans were sympathetic to the rebels and called on the U.S. government to oust the Spanish. Others thought the United States should intervene to safeguard American investments in Cuba. At the time, Americans had about $50 million invested in Cuban sugar and rice plantations, railroads, and iron mines. American trade with Cuba was worth about $100 million a year.

Some of the loudest cries for war came from the New York press. Two newspapers there engaged in a new style of reporting that become known as yellow journalism. The two papers tried to outdo each other in the use of sensational stories and headlines. Both papers focused on Cuba. Fed by horror stories from the press, American outrage intensified.

Early in 1898, fighting broke out in Havana, Cuba's capital. President William McKinley ordered the battleship *Maine* to Havana harbor to protect American lives and property. An explosion sank the *Maine* and killed 260 men. No one knows what caused the explosion, but the yellow press and the American public blamed Spain. ✓

The United States Goes to War

The United States declared war on Spain in April 1898. However, the first great battle of the Spanish-American War was not fought in Cuba, but in the Philippines, a Spanish colony in the Pacific. On May 1, U.S. warships sank the entire Spanish fleet near Manila without losing a single American ship or life. Soon, the United States found itself in control of the Philippines.

American forces arrived in Santiago, Cuba, in late June. One of the best-known fighting units was the Rough Riders, led by Theodore Roosevelt. In a battle off the coast of Cuba, U.S. ships destroyed the Spanish fleet. Spanish troops surrendered two weeks later.

After the Spanish surrendered, American troops invaded Puerto Rico, another Spanish possession in the Caribbean, and quickly brought the island under U.S. control. ✓

✓ Checkpoint

Name the site of the first battle of the Spanish-American War.

____

An American Empire

In December 1898, Spain and the United States signed a peace treaty. Under the agreement, Spain accepted Cuban independence and granted Puerto Rico, the Philippines, and the Pacific islands of Guam and Wake to the United States in return for $20 million. Many Americans believed that taking colonies violated the principles of the Declaration of Independence. Expansionists, however, welcomed the treaty because they felt it gave the United States important bases and provided new business opportunities. Also, they argued that Americans had a duty to spread the ideas of democracy to other parts of the world.

The United States did not give Cuba true independence. In 1902, Congress forced Cuba to add an amendment to its constitution that limited Cuba's power to make treaties and borrow money. It also gave the United States the right to intervene in Cuban affairs and maintain a naval base at Guantánamo Bay. In effect, it made Cuba a U.S. **protectorate**, or an independent country whose policies are controlled by an outside power.

The United States set up a government in Puerto Rico with a U.S.-appointed governor. Puerto Ricans, too, had limited control over their own affairs.

When the United States took control of the Philippines, Filipinos began a new revolt. Fighting continued until 1901, when the United States caught the Filipino independence leader. ✓

✓ Checkpoint

List four territories Spain turned over to the United States after the Spanish-American War.

____

____

____

____

Check Your Progress

1. How did the press influence public opinion about Cuba?

____

____

2. Why did some Americans object to the treaty that ended the Spanish-American war?

____

____

Section 2 Notetaking Study Guide

Question to Think About As you read Section 2 in your textbook and take notes, keep this section focus question in mind: **What were the causes and effects of the Spanish-American War?**

► Use this chart to record key information from the section.

The Spanish-American War	
Cause	**Effect**
Cubans rose up against Spanish rule in 1895.	Spain began a policy of reconcentration.
Many Americans were sympathetic toward Cuba. Others wanted to safeguard American investment in Cuba.	____________
• Yellow journalists ____________ • Americans blamed Spain for ____________	Americans called for the United States to declare war on Spain.
____________	The United States found itself in control of the Philippine Islands.
In a battle along the Cuban coast, U.S. ships destroyed the Spanish fleet.	____________
Spain and the United States signed a peace treaty.	• Spain accepted ____________ • Spain granted ____________ • The United States paid ____________
The United States forced Cuba to add the Platt Amendment to its constitution.	• limited Cuba's ____________ • gave the United States ____________ • allowed the United States ____________
The Foraker Act of 1900 was passed, setting up a government in Puerto Rico.	• gave Puerto Ricans ____________
Filipino rebels renewed their fight for independence.	• After three years of fighting, ____________ was captured and fighting ____________.

Refer to this page to answer the Chapter 16 Focus Question on page 260.

Section 3

The United States and Latin America

Section 3 Focus Question

How did the United States use the Monroe Doctrine to justify intervention in Latin America? To begin to answer this question,

- Learn about the plan to link the Atlantic and Pacific oceans.
- Find out about the construction of the Panama Canal.
- Explore Roosevelt's "Big Stick" policy.
- Examine the United States' relations with Mexico.

Summary

The United States intervened in Latin American conflicts. Building the Panama Canal was central to its goals in world trade and managing distant possessions.

Linking the Oceans

Ships travelling from the United States' West Coast to its territories in the Caribbean had to sail around the tip of South America. This was a dangerous journey that took more than two months. A canal across Central America linking the Atlantic and Pacific oceans would improve global shipping and make it easier for the United States to defend its new empire. The 50-mile-wide Isthmus of Panama was the ideal location. An **isthmus** is a narrow strip of land joining two larger areas of land.

In 1902, Panama was a <u>province</u> of Colombia. When negotiations with Colombia to build a canal hit difficulties, President Theodore Roosevelt secretly let Panamanians know that the United States would support Panama's independence from Colombia. The Panamanians revolted on November 3, 1903. U.S. gunboats waited nearby to provide support for the rebels. The United States immediately recognized the independent Republic of Panama. Three days later, Panama and the United States signed a treaty. It gave the United States permanent use and control of a 10-mile-wide zone across the Isthmus of Panama in exchange for $10 million plus $250,000 a year in rent. ✓

The Panama Canal

In 1904, the U.S. government began construction of the canal. President Roosevelt urged the engineers to "Make the dirt fly!" The first obstacle was controlling yellow fever and malaria, which were widespread in Panama. After doctors figured out that these diseases were carried by mosquitoes, workers cleared brush and drained swamps where mosquitoes lived. By 1906, yellow fever was nearly wiped out, and malaria was reduced in Panama.

Key Events

1854	United States signs trade treaty with Japan.
1898	The Spanish-American War gives the United States an empire.
1904	The United States begins to build the Panama Canal.
1917	The United States enters World War I.

Vocabulary Builder

Use context clues to define *province*. How does a province differ from a colony?

____

____

____

✓ Checkpoint

Name the two bodies of water that the United States wanted to link by a canal.

____

____

✓ Checkpoint

List the three major tasks involved in constructing the Panama Canal.

____

____

____

Building the Panama Canal	
Major Tasks of Construction	**Conditions**
• Cut through a mountain • Dam a river • Erect the canal's giant locks	• Tropical sun • Drenching rainstorms • Constant mudslides

Despite unexpected costs and delays, the canal opened on August 15, 1914. ✓

Wielding a "Big Stick" in Latin America

Roosevelt was fond of saying, "Speak softly and carry a big stick; you will go far." He wanted the world to know that if diplomacy failed, the United States would not hesitate to use force. Roosevelt applied his "big stick" policy in Latin America, which he saw as the United States' back yard.

In 1904, Roosevelt announced a policy known as the Roosevelt Corollary to the Monroe Doctrine. A **corollary** is a logical extension of a doctrine or proposition. Roosevelt stated that when neighbors of the United States got into disputes with foreign powers, the United States had the right to act as a police power to restore order.

✓ Checkpoint

Name the earlier policy that the Roosevelt Corollary extended.

____

William Howard Taft, who followed Roosevelt as President, preferred **dollar diplomacy**. This was a policy based on the idea that economic ties were the best way to expand American influence. Responding to Taft's urging, American bankers and business leaders invested heavily in Asia and Latin America. ✓

Relations With Mexico

Woodrow Wilson, who became President in 1913, argued that the United States should aim to support and nurture democracy throughout the world. Wilson's ideas were first tested in Mexico. The country was in the middle of a violent revolution following the overthrow of a longtime dictator. Wilson followed a policy he called "watchful waiting," hoping that Mexico would develop a democratic government. However, the United States twice became drawn into conflict with Mexico, bringing the two countries close to war. ✓

✓ Checkpoint

Name Wilson's foreign policy goal.

____

____

Check Your Progress

1. Why did Roosevelt want to build the Panama Canal?

____

____

2. What was meant by Roosevelt's "big stick" policy?

____

____

Section 3 Notetaking Study Guide

Question to Think About As you read Section 3 in your textbook and take notes, keep this section focus question in mind: **How did the United States use the Monroe Doctrine to justify intervention in Latin America?**

► Use this chart to record key information from the section. Some of the information has been filled in to get you started.

The United States and Latin America

The United States and Panama

- In 1902, the United States wanted to build a canal across Panama linking the ____________ and ____________ oceans.
- After helping Panama win its independence from Colombia, the United States and Panama signed a treaty that gave the United States ______________________ ______________________.
  In return, the United States paid Panama ______________________.
- Construction on the ______________ began in 1904. It was completed in ________.

Roosevelt's Foreign Policy

- Roosevelt wanted the world to know that the United States ______________________ ______________________.
- In 1904, European nations considered ______________________ in the Dominican Republic. Roosevelt wanted to prevent this. He announced a new policy that became known as the ______________ to the ______________.
  It stated that the United States had the right to ______________________ ______________________.

Taft's Dollar Diplomacy

- Dollar diplomacy was based on the idea that ______________ were the best way to expand American influence.
- As a result, American bankers and business leaders ______________________ ______________________.
- Dollar diplomacy led to U.S. military intervention in ____________, ________, and ____________.

Woodrow Wilson's Foreign Policy

- Wilson believed the United States had to compete with other nations for ________, ____________, and ____________. He also believed that U.S. foreign policy should ______________________.
- In 1914, Wilson intervened in Mexico after ______________________.
- In 1916, the United States was drawn into Mexican affairs again when ______________________. The United States responded by ______________________.

Refer to this page to answer the Chapter 16 Focus Question on page 260.

Section 4
World War I

Key Events

1854 United States signs trade treaty with Japan.

1898 The Spanish-American War gives the United States an empire.

1904 The United States begins to build the Panama Canal.

1917 The United States enters World War I.

Vocabulary Builder

Alliance comes from the Latin word *alligare*, which means "to bind to." What do you think it means when a group of nations forms an alliance?

____

____

____

✓ Checkpoint

Name the event that triggered World War I.

____

____

Section 4 Focus Question

How did the United States get involved in World War I and what was the outcome? To begin to answer this question,

- Find out about the war in Europe.
- Learn how the United States entered the war.
- Read about Americans at war.
- Find out about the search for peace.

Summary

In 1914, tensions in Europe erupted into the largest war the world had seen. After initial reluctance, Americans entered this war and were instrumental in a peace plan.

War in Europe

World War I had many causes. One was a competition among the nations of Europe for territory and trade in Africa, Asia, and the Pacific. A surge of nationalism, or pride in one's own nation or ethnic group, boosted tensions. France wanted to reclaim territory it had lost to Germany in 1870. Groups in the Balkan region wanted to break free from Austria-Hungary. Russia encouraged these Balkan nationalists. To protect themselves, European nations made defensive alliances with one another. These alliances meant that any conflict between two powers would quickly involve others. An arms race in Europe also contributed to the outbreak of war.

The event that set off the war was the assassination of the heir to Austria-Hungarian throne in 1914. The conflict that followed drew one country after another into the war. Britain, France, and Russia fought on one side and were known as the Allies, and Germany and Austria-Hungary fought on the other side and were called the Central Powers.

Fighting took place mainly on two fronts, or zones of battle. On the western front, Britain, France, and Italy faced Germany and Austria-Hungary. On the eastern front, the Central Powers faced Russia. Both fronts settled into stalemates and **trench warfare**, in which soldiers took shelter in opposing lines of ditches. New technology, such as airplanes, tanks, and poison gas, raised the death toll. ✓

The United States Enters the War

President Wilson said the United States should stay out of the war, and most Americans agreed. Both the Allies and the Central

Powers sought help from the United States with its vast industrial capacity. However, most U.S. trade was with the Allies because of a British blockade of German ports.

The German navy had a powerful weapon—submarines, or U-boats. In May 1915, a U-boat sank the British passenger ship *Lusitania*, killing nearly 1,200 people, 124 of them Americans. After U.S. protests, Germany stopped attacking passenger liners. However, Germany later resumed attacks. After U-boats sank four U.S. merchant ships, Wilson finally asked Congress to declare war on Germany in April 1917.

At the start of the war, the United States had a relatively small army of 125,000 men. By the war's end, almost four million Americans had served in uniform. American factories quickly converted to produce weapons and supplies. At home, many people conserved food and grew "victory gardens." Americans bought Liberty Bonds to help pay for the war. ✓

✓ Checkpoint

Name the actions that finally led the United States to enter the war.

____

____

Americans at War

When U.S. troops reached France in June 1917, things looked bad for the Allies. Russia had withdrawn after a March 1917 revolution, and the Germans were just 50 miles from Paris. In intense combat, the Allies pushed the Germans back. The German army was running out of supplies and troops. German military and political leaders decided the cause was lost and agreed to an armistice, or halt in fighting. It took effect on November 11, 1918. The Central Powers had lost the war. ✓

✓ Checkpoint

Name the event that took place on November 11, 1918.

____

____

Searching for Peace

Wilson proposed a peace settlement known as the Fourteen Points. Wilson called for nations to end secret treaties, agree to freedom of the seas, reduce arms, and settle colonial claims. Most important to Wilson was a proposal for an international organization to help nations settle disputes peacefully, called the League of Nations. Europeans, however, wanted to punish Germany. In the end, Wilson compromised on many issues in order to keep the League of Nations. The Treaty of Versailles (vuhr SĪ) took away territory on German borders, stripped Germany of colonies, and made it pay huge **reparations**, or war damages.

The Versailles Treaty created bitterness in Germany. In the United States, the Senate did not ratify it. The Senate also refused to let the United States join the League of Nations. ✓

✓ Checkpoint

Name the organization that Wilson wanted to establish after the war.

____

____

Check Your Progress

1. What were the four main causes of World War I?

____

____

2. What was the League of Nations?

____

____

Section 4 Notetaking Study Guide

Question to Think About As you read Section 4 in your textbook and take notes, keep this section focus question in mind: **How did the United States become involved in World War I and what was the outcome?**

► Use this chart to record key information from the section.

World War I

Causes of World War I

1. Imperial Rivalries: great powers of Europe competed for territory.
2. ____________________: pride in one's nation or ethnic group
3. The ____________________ System: to protect themselves, European nations ____.
4. ____________________: nations built up ____________________________________.

Event that set off the war: ____
____

Alliances During the War

- Allies: ____
- Central Powers: ____

The Deadliest War

- Main Fronts: 1. ____________________, 2. ____________________
- New technology: improved machine guns, ____________________, ____________________, ____________________, and ____________________.
- Stalemates led to ____________________________________.

The United States Enters the War

- Why the United States entered the war: ____________________________ ____
- American factories ____.
- Americans at home supported the war by ____________________________, ____________________________, and ____________________.
- U.S. Marines cleared the Germans from ____________________, which helped prevent the Germans from reaching ____________________. Then, an Allied offensive ____.
- Armistice declared on ____________________________________.

Wilson and the Peace

- Wilson's plan was called ____________________________. In it, Wilson called for ____ ____.
- Treaty of Versailles punished Germany by ____________________________ ____
- The U.S. Senate ____________________________________ the Treaty of Versailles.

Refer to this page to answer the Chapter 16 Focus Question on page 260.

Chapter 16 Assessment

Directions: Circle the letter of the correct answer.

1. Which of the following territories did the United States purchase from Russia?
   - A Hawaii
   - B Samoa
   - C Guam
   - D Alaska

2. Why did some Americans object to the United States taking new territories in the Spanish-American War?
   - A They thought it would cost too much to maintain the territories.
   - B They believed it violated the principles of the Declaration of Independence.
   - C They feared it would worsen the United States's relationship with Spain.
   - D They believed the United States should follow a policy of isolationism.

3. Why did so many countries enter World War I?
   - A Nations were bound by defensive alliances.
   - B There were many assassinations.
   - C All of Europe wanted to defeat Germany.
   - D They were outraged by U-boat attacks.

Directions: Follow the steps to complete this task:

Compare Theodore Roosevelt's and William Howard Taft's policies toward Latin America.

Step 1: Recall information. Record the main ideas about each President's policies.

President	Policy/Main Idea
• Roosevelt	• •
• Taft	•

Step 2: Compare: Describe the ways each President's policies were alike and different.

How Their Policies Were Alike	How Their Policies Were Different

Step 3: Complete the topic sentence that follows. Then write two or three more sentences that support your topic sentence.

Theodore Roosevelt and William Howard Taft's policies toward Latin America were

____

____

____

____

Chapter 16 Notetaking Study Guide

Now you are ready to answer the Chapter 16 Focus Question: **How did a more powerful United States expand its role in the world?**

► Complete the following chart to help you answer this question. Use the notes that you took for each section.

The United States Looks Overseas	
Commodore Perry's mission to Japan	• Opened up ____________ with Japan. • Effect on Japan: set out to transform its feudal society • into an industrial nation
The purchase of Alaska and the annexation of Hawaii	• Secretary of State Seward saw Alaska as a stepping stone for trade with ____________ and the ____________. • Why expansionists were interested in Hawaii: ____________ ____________ • How Hawaii became a U.S. territory: ____________ ____________
Open Door Policy in China	• The first Open Door policy: ____________ ____________ • The second Open Door policy: ____________ ____________
Spanish-American War	• The United States intervened in the conflict in Cuba to protect ____________. • Terms of the treaty ending the war: ____________ ____________
Panama Canal	• The United States gained access to the Isthmus of Panama after helping Panama gain its independence from ____________. • The canal linked the ____________ and ____________ oceans.
Foreign relations under Theodore Roosevelt	• Roosevelt's Big Stick Policy: ____________ ____________ • The Roosevelt Corollary: ____________ ____________
Foreign relations under Taft	• Taft's policy was called ____________. • What it was: ____________ ____________
World War I	• Four Causes: ____________ ____________ • Why the U.S. entered the war: ____________ ____________ • Result of the Treaty of Versailles: ____________ ____________

Refer to this page to answer the Unit 6 Focus Question on page 261.

Unit 6 Pulling It Together Activity

What You Have Learned

Chapter 13 Miners and railroad builders led to settlement of the West. Native Americans struggled to maintain their way of life. Western farmers faced many challenges.

Chapter 14 In the late 1800s, industrialization caused urban growth, altered the way business was run, and prompted reforms in education. A new wave of immigration to America occurred during this period.

Chapter 15 During the late 1800s and early 1900s, Americans organized to press for reforms in many areas of government and society.

Chapter 16 In the late 1800s, the United States began building an overseas empire and becoming more involved in foreign affairs.

Think Like a Historian

Read the Unit 6 Focus Question: **How did the industrialization of the United States change the economy, society, and politics of the nation?**

▶ Use the organizers on this page and the next to collect information to answer this question.

What are some developments made during the industrialization of the United States? Some of them are listed in this chart. Review your section and chapter notes. Then complete the chart.

Growth of U.S. Industry		
Inventions	**Transportation**	**Other Industries**
• phonograph	•	• cattle
• camera	•	•
•	•	•
•		•
•		
•		

What aspects of the industrialization of the United States caused changes in territorial expansion, growth of cities, and the Progressive movement and labor unions? The organizer below gives you a part of the answer. Review your section and chapter notes. Then fill in the rest of the organizer.

Industrialization's Impact on the Nation

Causes	Effect
• raw materials needed for industry •	Territorial expansion
• Factories needed workers. • • •	Growth of big cities
• • •	Progressive movement and labor unions

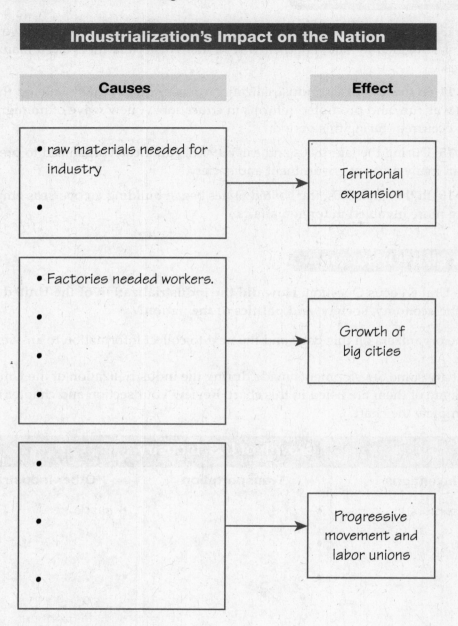

Linking Past to Present: The United States in the Modern World

What You Will Learn

Since the early 1900s, immigrants, ethnic minorities, women, children, and workers have all witnessed major changes to social and economic conditions in the United States.

Epilogue Focus Question

As you read the epilogue, keep this question in mind: **How have society and the economy changed over the last century?**

Chapter Standards

History-Social Studies
Framework: Students examine the transformation of the social conditions in the United States from 1914 to the present.

Summary 1

Summary 1 Focus Questions

- How have immigrants contributed to the diversity of the United States?
- What population trends have changed the face of America?

Summary

Immigration patterns, migration within the United States, the rise of the middle class, and the baby boom have changed modern American society and increased cultural diversity.

Nation of Immigrants

Throughout U.S. history, immigration has increased **diversity**, or differences. A wave of immigration in the early 1800s drew millions of immigrants to the United States. Between the 1880s and 1920s, millions of immigrants from southern and eastern Europe settled on the East Coast of the United States. At the same time, Asian immigrants settled in the American West.

As immigration increased, so did anti-immigrant feelings. By the early 1900s, Congress had passed laws ending most Asian immigration. In the 1920s, laws were passed restricting most other immigration.

Immigration continued from the Americas, and in the early 1900s, many Mexicans immigrated to the United States. They typically settled in barrios, or Latino neighborhoods in the cities in the American Southwest. Ethnic neighborhoods gave immigrants a sense of security and belonging. Immigrants became proprietors of Mexican American businesses. In San Francisco's Chinatown and other Asian neighborhoods, immigrants set up **benevolent associations,** or groups that looked after the welfare of their members and their community. The associations also helped recent immigrants.

In 1965, Congress ended most limits on immigration. Since then, immigrants from around the world have come to the United

Vocabulary Builder

Which of the following words is opposite in meaning to *restricting*: challenging, expanding, or abandoning?

____

States in search of greater opportunity. They have arrived at a faster rate than at any time since the early 1900s.

Most immigrants still settle in ethnic neighborhoods. For instance, since the 1960s many immigrants fleeing political unrest in Cuba have settled in Miami's Little Havana neighborhood. In more recent times, immigrants from Eastern Europe, Southeast Asia, Central America, the Middle East, and Southern Asia have established ethnic neighborhoods in American cities. While recent immigrants often face hardships, many have gone on to become leaders in American business, culture, government, and the military.

Today, immigrants from every corner of the globe flock to the United States. Rather than melting away our differences, the American experience has led us to accept differences. This has greatly enriched American culture. ✓

✓ Checkpoint

Name the region in which most Mexican immigrants first settled.

____

A Changing Population

The "second Industrial Revolution" led many immigrants and farmers to cities, where there were better-paying jobs. New city dwellers enjoyed the benefits of city life such as sporting events and department stores. New means of transportation—buses, subways, and streetcars—developed. For the first half of the twentieth century, cities were vibrant centers of economic growth.

In the middle of the 20th century, many middle-class city-dwellers began moving to suburbs on the outskirts of big cities. **Satellite cities**—or smaller cities located near large ones—developed. The GI Bill of Rights helped spur this middle class growth. In addition to helping World War II veterans set up farms and businesses, the GI Bill provided loans for veterans to attend college. A better education led to higher paying jobs, which in turn paid for new houses in the suburbs, as well as automobiles. By 1960, nine out of ten people living in the suburbs had an automobile. The increase in automobiles prompted the federal government to build thousands of miles of highways.

Economic prosperity led to increased confidence in the future, which in turn led to a **baby boom**, or soaring birth rate. As these "baby-boomers" became teenagers, a new youth culture grew. New television shows appeared, and rock-and-roll music became the sound of the baby boomer generation. Today the baby boomers are growing older. This "graying" of America presents new challenges, such as how to care for the increasing numbers of elderly Americans. ✓

✓ Checkpoint

Name the legislation that helped World War II veterans start businesses and go to college.

____

Check Your Progress

1. Why did immigrants settle in ethnic neighborhoods?

____

____

2. Name two results of economic growth after World War II.

____

____

Faces of America Notetaking Study Guide

Keep in mind the Summary 1 Focus Questions as you read about immigration and the changing face of America in your textbook and take notes.

► Complete these charts to help you record key facts.

Immigration	
Early 1800s	• Waves of immigration brought millions to the United States.
1880s-1920s	• Millions came from __________ and __________ Europe to the _____ coast of the United States. • __________ crossed the Pacific Ocean and settled in the American __________.
After 1965	• New laws made it easier for ______________ to enter the country. • Since then, immigrants have been arriving ________ than at any time since the early 1990s.

Effects of Immigration

Anti-Immigration Feeling

- Early 1900s: Most Asian immigration was banned.
- 1920s: ____

Ethnic Neighborhoods

- Unrest drove Mexicans to the ________ of the Southwest.
- San Francisco had the largest ________ neighborhood in America.
- Many immigrants became ____________ of businesses.
- ______________________ looked after the welfare of their members.

Growth of Middle Class

Ethnic Neighborhoods

- People flooded the cities because there were jobs there.
- The activity in cities created a thriving ______________ in America.
- The ____________ helped veterans start businesses and go to college.
- With growing families and icomes, people left the city for the ________.
- During the 1950s, __________ became a key part of middle-class life.
- Increased prosperity let to a ________.
- A new culture oriented toward ________ was created.
- By the early 2000s the U.S. __________ was aging.

Refer to this question to answer the Epilogue Focus Question on page 273.

Summary 2

Summary 2 Focus Questions

- What factors have affected the American economy?
- How have new technologies changed the American workplace?
- How has the Civil Rights movement developed?

Summary

Since the Great Depression, the federal government has been involved in controlling the economy. Unions and child labor reforms have helped many workers. Changes in the American economy have both benefited and challenged Americans.

Transforming the American Economy

The Industrial Revolution transformed the United States from a farming economy into a manufacturing economy. By 1929, American creativity had helped the United States become the world's mightiest industrial economy. Despite this time of great prosperity, the United States suffered a downturn for the whole of the 1930s that left tens of millions of people jobless and many homeless.

The Great Depression of the 1930s was much more drastic than earlier economic downturns. President Franklin Delano Roosevelt, who believed that the government should help repair the economy, helped enact a series of programs called the New Deal. Since then, the U.S. government has taken a larger role in regulating the economy.

The hardships of the Great Depression gave the union movement a boost. By the 1950s, American factory workers gained union recognition. The struggle then turned to agricultural workers, many of whom were Latinos. One of these workers, César Chávez, led a campaign for unions that resulted in the founding of the United Farm Workers.

Until the 1930s, children often worked long hours in unsafe factories. In 1916, Congress banned child-made goods from interstate commerce, but the Supreme Court struck down the law. In 1938, the Fair Labor Standards Act put real limits on child labor. Today, child labor remains a problem in industries that hire migrant farm workers. Also, some companies still import goods made by child workers. ✓

✓ Checkpoint

Name the act that put real limits on child labor.

____

The Changing American Workplace

By 1915, heavy industry dominated the U.S. economy. Later, new technologies and increasing prosperity led manufacturers to produce mostly consumer goods. In the late 1940s, electronics manufacturing grew, led by radio and television.

In recent years, the American economy has shifted from manufacturing to the production of **services**. Services are economic actions that one person performs for another. Today, the United States is the world's leading producer of services.

Since the 1980s, computers have had a strong influence on the U.S. economy. Our times are called the "Information Age" because many of the jobs created by this new industry involve the storage, use, and transfer of information. The economic impact of computers includes new careers, more workers working at home, a rise in service jobs, and less demand for unskilled workers.

The benefits of new technology have not reached all Americans. Parts of New England and the Midwest, which used to be dominated by industrial factories, are now called the Rust Belt because of all the aging and abandoned factories. Factory jobs also have declined because workers in other countries work for less money. Many senior citizens, Native Americans, and inner-city residents struggle with poverty. ☑

The Era of Civil Rights

After the end of slavery, African Americans struggled with segregation, especially in the South. After 1910, African Americans began moving to northern and western cities in what was called the Great Migration. However, job and housing discrimination in the North forced African Americans to live in **ghettos**, or poor sections of the city.

After World War II, African Americans began to push for equal rights through the courts and by holding political demonstrations. One major breakthrough, *Brown* v. *Board of Education of Topeka* (1954), ended segregation in schools.

Change did not come easily, but another turning point came in 1955 when Rosa Parks and the Reverend Martin Luther King, Jr., led the Montgomery Bus Boycott. King, a leader of the Civil Rights movement, supported nonviolent protest. But by the 1960s, some African Americans rejected King's nonviolence and adopted a more confrontational approach. They demanded more rights and more power immediately.

In the 1960s, Congress passed civil rights laws to help end racial segregation and discrimination. For instance, the Voting Rights Act of 1965 protected African Americans' right to vote. By 2000, there were 39 members of the Congressional Black Caucus. Despite advances, many African Americans still live in urban slums. ☑

Check Your Progress

1. How has the U.S. government changed since the New Deal?

____

____

2. What kind of protest did Martin Luther King support?

____

✓ Checkpoint

Recall the name given to our times.

____

Vocabulary Builder

The text in the bracketed paragraph states that by the 1960s, some African Americans rejected nonviolence for a more confrontational approach. Based on context clues, write a definition of *confrontational*.

____

____

____

✓ Checkpoint

Name the places African Americans went during the Great Migration.

____

____

Economics, Workplace, and Civil Rights Notetaking Study Guide

Keep in mind the Summary 2 Focus Questions as you read about changes in economics and the workplace, and civil rights in your textbook and take notes.

► Use these charts to help you record key facts.

Transforming the American Economy

The Industrial Revolution: The United States went from a farming economy to a ______________________ economy.

The Great Depression: For the whole of the __________s, the United States suffered a drastic ______________ setback. Through Roosevelt's ______________________, the federal government began a new relationship with citizens.

The Union Movement: By the __________s, American ______________ workers had union recognition. The struggle then turned to ____________________ workers. ____________________ started a union for these workers and led them on strikes.

Child Labor: Until the __________s, children often worked long hours in dangerous factories. The ______________________ finally put real limits on child labor.

The Changing American Workplace

Changes in the U.S. Economy: By the year 1915, heavy industry dominated the U. S. economy. Later, the focus changed to ______________ goods. Today, the United States is the world's leading producer of ______________.

The Impact of the Computer: By the __________s, computers led to new jobs that involved the storage, ______________, and ____________ of information. As a result, economists refer to our times as the "______________________."

Industries in Decline: Parts of New England and the ______________ are now called the ______________ because of their aging and abandoned ____________. Today, there are fewer jobs for ____________ workers.

Era of Civil Rights

Segregation and the Great Migration: African Americans moved from the __________ to the __________ and the __________ in what is known as the Great Migration. Even in these areas, they encountered housing ______________, which forced them to live in ______________.

The Civil Rights Movement: A Supreme Court ruling in the case of ______________________ outlawed ______________________ in public schools. A young minister named ______________________ encouraged ______________ protests. But by the 1960s, some African Americans were ______________ more immediate change. The ______________________ of 1965 protected African Americans who wanted to register to vote.

Refer to this question to answer the Epilogue Focus Question on page 273.

Summary 3

Summary 3 Focus Questions

- How have opportunities grown for women and minorities?
- How are Californians empowered to bring about political change?

Summary

There have been expanding opportunities for women, Latinos, and Asian Americans, but these groups still face challenges. Democratic reforms in California aim to "return government to the people."

Expanding Opportunities

American women first organized to fight for the right to vote in the mid-1800s. It took many years of effort, but in 1920, the Nineteenth Amendment finally granted women the right to vote in national elections.

Women now work in a wide variety of occupations, including management and professional jobs such as doctors and lawyers. Women also hold important posts in state and federal government. Despite such advances, there is still a long way to go before women reach full equality. For instance, on average, women still earn less than 75 percent of what men earn.

The largest ethnic group in the United States today consists of Americans whose ancestors came from Mexico or the Spanish-speaking countries of Central America, South America, and the Caribbean. These immigrants' experience coming to the United States has varied widely. Like other Americans, many unskilled Latinos have difficulty adjusting to American society.

As Americans, Latinos have helped pioneer an end to school segregation. In 1946, the court case *Mendez* v. *Westminister* declared it unconstitutional to segregate Latinos in public schools. Rulings such as these have helped Latinos make great advances. In more recent years, Latinos have held important government positions and have become business leaders.

Another group, Asian Americans, have also made substantial contributions to the growth of the nation. For instance, Chinese immigrants played a key role in building the transcontinental railroad in the late 1800s.

Such achievements have not exempted Asian Americans from the struggle to find acceptance. In 1882 and 1907, Congress passed "exclusion" laws prohibiting further immigration from China and Japan. Then, in 1942, the United States forced over 100,000 Japanese Americans into internment camps. Congress has since apologized for the internments and partially <u>compensated</u> the survivors, and the last of the Asian "exclusion" laws was repealed in 1952.

Vocabulary Builder

Which is a synonym for the underlined word: *slowed*, *paid*, or *began?*

____

✓ Checkpoint

Name the largest and the fastest growing ethnic groups in the United States today.

Largest: ____________________

Fastest growing: ______________

✓ Checkpoint

List two reforms that allow California citizens to participate in democracy.

____

____

Since then, Asians have come to the United States in increasing numbers. They are the fastest-growing ethnic group today. At present, there are more than 10 million Asian Americans living in the United States. They bring diversity to the United States by speaking many different languages and practicing a number of different religions. ✓

California: Democracy In Action

During the early 1900s in California, reformers called Progressives tried to reduce the influence of powerful interest groups in state government and "return government to the people." This tradition of Progressive reform gave California citizens rights that citizens of many other states do not have. In addition to voting and demonstrating, California citizens can participate in democracy through **recall** laws and the right of **initiative**.

Recall	Initiative
Purpose: to remove an elected official	**Purpose:** to directly propose laws
Step I: Petition	
The process begins with a formal written request, signed by a group of people, for a vote by ballot.	
Step II: Ballot	
Ballot contains: **Part 1:** vote yes or no for recall **Part 2:** contains names of replacement candidates	**Ballot contains:** a proposition, or proposed law
Process of enactment: The recall measure in Part 1 must pass by a majority. Then, the candidate with the most votes in Part 2 takes office.	**Process of enactment:** If a majority of voters approve the proposition, it becomes state law.

✓

Check Your Progress

1. What reform movement influenced California's democratic reforms?

____

2. What did the Nineteenth Amendment do?

____

Opportunities and California Democracy Notetaking Study Guide

Keep in mind the Summary 3 Focus Questions as you read about expanding opportunities and California's democracy in your textbook and take notes.

► Use these organizers to help you record key facts.

Expanding Opportunities

Women

- What Nineteenth Amendment did: gave women the right to vote in national elections
- Women now hold many important positions, but make, on average, less than ______ of what men make.

Latinos

- What *Mendez v. Westminister* declared: ______
- Latinos without ______ skills find the transition to the United States the most difficult.

Asian Americans

- Laws passed in 1882 and 1907: ______
- Events in 1942: ______
- Government actions since then: ______

California: Democracy in Action

The tradition of ______ reform gave California citizens rights that citizens of many other states don't have.

Recall

- Purpose: to remove elected officials
- Step I: ______
- Step II: recall ballot
  - Part 1: ______
  - Part 2: ______
- Process of enactment: ______

Initiative

- Purpose: ______
- Step I: ______
- Step II: ______
  - contains: ______
- Process of enactment: ______

Refer to this question to answer the Epilogue Focus Question on page 273.

Epilogue Assessment

Directions: Circle the letter of the correct answer.

1. Which most contributed to the economic prosperity of the 1950s and 1960s?
- **A** increased agriculture
- **B** growth of the service economy
- **C** spread of computers
- **D** the GI Bill of Rights

2. Which was a result of the New Deal?
- **A** increased economic regulation by government
- **B** the Great Migration
- **C** the Baby Boom
- **D** increased immigration from southern Europe

3. Where is today's fastest growing immigrant group from?
- **A** Europe
- **B** Asia
- **C** Africa
- **D** South America

4. How do economists refer to today's technologically influenced society?
- **A** the initiative
- **B** the New Deal
- **C** the Information Age
- **D** Suburbanization

Directions: Follow the steps to answer this question:

How and why have immigration patterns changed?

Step 1: Recall information: List the main sources of immigration to the United States in the early 1900s and why immigration slowed.

Immigration in the Early 1900s	
Main sources	
Why immigration slowed	

Step 2: Recall information. List the main sources of immigration today and why it began to increase.

Immigration Today	
Main sources	
Why immigration began to increase again	

Step 3: Complete the topic sentence that follows. Then write two or three more sentences that explain the main reason for the changes in immigration patterns.

The main sources of immigration in the early 1900s and today are ______________

____

____

____

____

Epilogue Notetaking Study Guide

Now you are ready to answer the Epilogue Focus Question: **How have society and the economy changed over the last century?**

► Fill in the following organizers to help you answer this question. Use the notes that you took for each section.

Immigration
• Major sources of immigrants in the late 19th and early 20th centuries: southern Europe, ______, ______ • ______ feeling led to laws restricting immigration for more than 40 years. • Acceptance of differences has enriched American ______.

Transforming the American Economy	The Changing American Workplace	The Era of Civil Rights
• ______ had helped the United States to develop the world's mightiest industrial economy. • During the ______ ______, President Roosevelt helped enact the ______ to help the economy.	• The United States economy has moved from ______ and electronics to the production of ______. • The impact of computers has created the "______ Age."	• The movement of African Americans to the North and West was called the ______. • In 1954, the U.S. Supreme Court outlawed ______. • The ______ of 1965 protected African Americans' right to vote.

Opportunities		
Women	**Latinos**	**Asian Americans**
• The ______ Amendment guaranteed women the right to vote. • Women have many more job ______ but on average earn less than men.	• *Mendez v. Westminister* outlawed ______ based on national origin. • Latinos make up the largest ______ in the United States.	• Congress ______ Asian "exclusion" laws. • Asian Americans are the ______ ethnic group in the United States.
California		
• California's tradition of ______ reform is reflected in special rights. • Californians have the power of ______, a way for removing elected officials. The ______ is a way for citizens to propose laws.		

Ideas to Build On: Grade 6 Review

The Beginnings of Humankind

Chapter 1: Early People

Section 1: Studying the Distant Past

- Archaeologists study prehistoric times by examining things that early peoples left behind.
- The study of fossils has helped archaeologists learn about the lives of the earliest humans.
- Archaeological studies suggest that the earliest humans lived in Africa millions of years ago.

Section 2: Hunter-Gatherer Societies

- Hunter-gatherer societies moved from place to place, hunting small animals and gathering plants for food.
- The development of tools and the use of fire helped the people in hunter-gatherer societies improve their lives.
- Modern humans developed the ability to use language, which helped them to survive.

Section 3: Populating the Earth

- By about 12,500 years ago, modern humans had spread to many regions of the world, including Africa, Asia, Europe, Australia, North America, and South America.
- Modern humans adapted to Ice Age conditions by building shelters and making warm clothing.
- By forming larger groups, modern humans adapted in order to better hunt and defend themselves.

Chapter 2: The Beginning of Civilization

Section 1: Early Agriculture

- Over a long time, hunter-gatherers domesticated plants and animals, and most groups became farmers.
- Although the Middle East was the first center of agriculture, farming appeared in several other parts of the world.
- Permanent farming settlements developed, and surplus food allowed some people to become craftsworkers.

Section 2: Cities and Civilizations

- Some farming villages grew into cities with large populations and large land areas.
- Wealth from farming and trade created powerful cities that gave rise to civilizations.
- The shared features of most civilizations are cities, a well-organized government, an established religion, job specialization, social classes, a developed culture, and a system of writing.

Section 3: The Maya Civilization

- Unlike river valley civilizations, the Maya civilization arose in the rain forests of Mesoamerica.
- The Maya lived in separate, independent cities, but their civilization shared many of the features of other civilizations.
- Maya achievements included a system of writing, knowledge of astronomy and mathematics, and highly developed arts and architecture.

The Ancient Middle East

Chapter 3: Ancient Mesopotamia

Section 1: The Fertile Crescent

- As people began to farm the fertile soil near the Tigris and Euphrates rivers, new methods of farming began to develop.
- Eventually, cities emerged and became powerful centers of trade and government.

Section 2: The Civilization of Sumer

- With the growth of cities, government became more important, and different social classes emerged.
- Writing may have begun at religious structures, such as temples and ziggurats, to keep records of goods that were received.
- Learning in math and science also became important.

Section 3: The Development of Writing

- Writing began in Sumer as a way to keep track of goods in the temple.
- Writing began with pictographs. Then some symbols began to be used to represent syllables. Eventually some symbols began to represent individual sounds.
- Our modern alphabet descended from an alphabet that began in the Middle East.

Section 4: The First Empires

- As civilization advanced, strong rulers united city-states into empires.
- Sargon the Great created Mesopotamia's first empire.
- Hammurabi united the Babylonian Empire. He also created a written law for his people.

Chapter 4: Ancient Egypt

Section 1: The Nile River Valley

- Egypt and Nubia rose in the valley of the Nile River, which flows from central Africa to the Mediterranean Sea.
- Early farmers grew crops in the fertile "Black Land" of the Nile Valley, but no crops could grow in the deadly "Red Land" of the Sahara.
- Around 3000 B.C., Upper Egypt and Lower Egypt were united into one kingdom.

Section 2: Egypt Under the Pharaohs

- Pharaohs based their authority on Egyptian religious beliefs. The pharaoh was believed to be a god.
- A strong government carried out the pharaoh's orders and provided for the needs of the people.

Section 3: Egypt and Nubia

- Egypt traded with lands around the Mediterranean Sea and in Africa.
- At first, Egypt gained control over Nubia. Later, Nubia, called Kush by the Egyptians, conquered Egypt.

Section 4: Life and Death in Ancient Egypt

- The ancient Egyptians believed in many gods and goddesses.
- The Egyptians believed in an afterlife and carefully preserved the bodies of their dead.

Section 5: Art, Architecture, and Learning in Egypt

- Egyptian architects built huge pyramid tombs and temples for the worship of gods.
- Paintings and statues in tombs were meant to provide for the dead in the afterlife.

Chapter 5: The Ancient Hebrews and Judaism

Section 1: The Orgins of Judaism

- According to the Torah, ancient Hebrews left Mesopotamia for Canaan under the leadership of the patriarchs.
- Centuries after the Israelites entered Egypt, Moses led them out of slavery.
- The Israelites received many commandments in the wilderness.
- Then the Israelites began the conquest of Canaan.

Section 2: The Beliefs of Judaism

- The commandments that were received at the time of Moses make up the first part of the Hebrew Bible.
- Other religious writings and traditions continue to guide Jews today.

Section 3: The Spread of Judaism

- After reaching Canaan, the Israelites were led first by judges, and then by kings.
- After the kingdom weakened, many people were taken captive into other lands. This was the beginning of the Diaspora.
- Many Jews were able to return to Jerusalem from Babylon and Persia. However, many centuries later, Roman officials again drove many Jews away from Jerusalem.
- Today Jews live all over the world. Judaism has affected many religions and cultures.

Ancient India

Chapter 6: The Early Civilizations of India

Section 1: The Geography of South Asia

- Natural barriers strongly influenced the development of civilization in South Asia.
- The Indus River valley supported the growth of early civilization on the Indian subcontinent.
- Early agriculture in South Asia depended on the rains of the summer monsoon.

Section 2: The Indus Valley Civilization

- Studies of archaeological sites have provided information about the Indus Valley civilization.
- This civilization demonstrated central planning, as well as an extensive trade network.
- The reason for its decline is one of several mysteries surrounding the Indus Valley civilization.

Section 3: India's Vedic Age

- The emergence of the Indo-Aryans marked the beginning of India's Vedic age.
- The Indo-Aryans were a nomadic people who composed an oral literature called the Vedas.
- The caste system was a social structure that had a strong impact on Aryan society.

Chapter 7: Hinduism

Section 1: The Origins of Hinduism

- Hinduism evolved from Brahmanism into the major religion of India.
- Hinduism continues to change over time.

Section 2: The Beliefs of Hinduism

- The four main goals that Hindus want to achieve during their lifetimes are pleasure, success, an ethical and moral life, and release from life.
- Hindus believe that there are three different paths to becoming one with God: the way of knowledge, the way of works, and the way of devotion.

Section 3: The Spread of Hinduism

- Today, Hinduism is the third-largest religion in the world.
- Hinduism has spread to many places outside India, including the United States.

Chapter 8: The Development of Buddhism

Section 1: The Origins of Buddhism

- When Siddhartha Gautama saw people's suffering and sadness, he began to search for truth.
- Siddhartha studied with Hindu gurus and later joined a group of ascetics in his search for enlightenment.
- After achieving enlightenment, the Buddha spent his life teaching others what he had learned.

Section 2: The Beliefs of Buddhism

- The teachings of the Buddha formed the basis of Buddhism. He advised following a Middle Way between pleasure and self-denial.
- The Buddha described the Four Noble Truths and the Eightfold Path that leads to nirvana.
- Some Buddhists join religious communities and become monks or nuns, but anyone may study Buddhist texts.

Section 3: The Spread of Buddhism

- After the Buddha's death, missionaries spread his teachings from India to many parts of Asia.
- Two major schools of Buddhism developed, Theravada and Mahayana. But as Buddhism reached other countries, it declined in India.
- Today, many people besides Buddhists respect the Buddha's moral teachings. Buddhism has also influenced art and literature throughout the world.

Chapter 9: India's Empires and Achievements

Section 1: The Maurya Empire

- Chandragupta conquered many kingdoms to create India's first empire.
- Chandragupta established a bureaucracy to govern the regions and provinces of his empire.
- A spy network kept the emperor informed of dangers.

Section 2: Asoka's Rule of Tolerance

- Chandragupta's grandson Asoka came to power during a time of conflict.
- After he had conquered Kalinga, Asoka converted to Buddhism.
- During the rest of his reign, Asoka practiced tolerance and worked for the welfare of his people.

Section 3: India's Classical Age

- The Gupta Empire was founded by Chandra Gupta. It arose during a time of increased learning and culture.
- The classical age saw growth in arts, entertainment, and science.

Ancient China

Chapter 10: The Rise of Civilization in China

Section 1: The Middle Kingdom

- Geographic features such as mountains, deserts, and forests made the transport of goods and ideas difficult in ancient China.
- China's earliest civilization arose in the Huang He valley.
- China's location and natural barriers isolated the area from other early civilizations.

Section 2: China's First Dynasties

- The ruler Yu became the founder of China's first dynasty, the Xia.
- China's first historical dynasty, the Shang, lasted about 600 years.
- During the Shang Dynasty, China expanded its territory and developed a system of writing.

Section 3: China Under the Zhou Dynasty

- A group known as the Zhou gained control of China from the Shang about 1050 B.C.
- The Zhou kingdom grew very large and became difficult for one ruler to control. Zhou kings asked family members to rule different parts of the kingdom.
- Conflicts between the rulers of individual states marked the end of the Zhou Dynasty.

Chapter 11: Chinese Society and Thought

Section 1: Family and Religion

- Loyalty to one's family was one of the most important values in ancient China.
- A person's age and sex often determined his or her status in a family in ancient China.
- Religious views in ancient China focused on a belief in spirits. The worship of the spirits of ancestors was important in Chinese religion.

Section 2: The Teachings of Confucius

- Chinese thinkers such as Hanfeizi and Mo-zi proposed solutions to the state of anarchy in China during the Era of the Warring States.
- A Chinese thinker named Confucius suggested that China could restore order by returning to traditional values.
- Important Confucian ideas, such as the five key relationships, had a strong impact on Chinese society.

Section 3: Daoism and Buddhism in China

- The philosophy of Daoism encouraged people of ancient China to lead simple lives that worked in harmony with the way of nature.
- After Buddhism spread from India to China in the first century A.D., the Chinese shaped these ideas into their own sects.
- Important ideas of Confucianism, Daoism, and Buddhism were mixed and borrowed in China.

Chapter 12: Growth of the Chinese Empire

Section 1: Shi Huangdi Unites China

- Qin armies united China and founded a new dynasty.
- The powerful Qin ruler Shi Huangdi succeeded in expanding and unifying China into one people under one government.

Section 2: Expansion Under the Han Dynasty

- The Han Dynasty built upon Shi Huangdi's foundations to create one of the most successful dynasties in Chinese history.
- An imperial bureaucratic state and expansion of the empire were important contributions of the Han Dynasty.

Section 3: Han Society and Achievements

- Confucian teachings helped create a strong economy in Han society.
- Many achievements in technology, arts, and science resulted from a prosperous Han society.

Ancient Greece

Chapter 13: The Ancient Greeks

Section 1: The Aegean World

- The Peloponnesian Peninsula and surrounding islands became home to early Greek-speaking people.
- The earliest people of Greece developed independent settlements that were often known for trade and sea travel.

Section 2: The Rise of City-States

- Because Greece's steep hillsides made travel by land difficult, ancient Greece was politically divided into city-states.
- The Greek city-states shared much culture but had differences in the way they were governed.

Section 3: Daily Life in Ancient Greece

- City-states of ancient Greece were often governed by wealthy landowners called aristocrats.
- Although they had little direct say in government, Greek women contributed to the culture and economy of their family and community in many ways.
- Culture, the arts, and learning flourished.

Section 4: Trade and Expansion

- The population of many Greek city-states eventually grew so great that the land could not support them.
- Some city-states began wars of conquest, while others became more dependent on trade or founded colonies in other regions.

Chapter 14: Athens and Sparta

Section 1: Political Changes in Greece

- Early Greek city-states were often controlled by governments called oligarchies, in which small groups of aristocrats held power.
- Tyrannies, or governments run by one strong ruler, replaced some Greek oligarchies.
- In Athens, citizens began to take a more active role in government, as the city-state moved toward democracy.

Section 2: Democracy in Athens

- Leaders such as Cleisthenes and Pericles carried out reforms that aided the development of Athenian democracy.
- Athens' democratic government included a large assembly, a 500-member council, and a court system with citizen juries.
- Athens used a system of government called direct democracy, in which citizens take part directly in government decision making.

Section 3: Oligarchy in Sparta

- The city-state Sparta featured an oligarchical government led by two kings.
- To overcome their population problems, Spartans carried out conquests of areas such as Messenia.
- The society of Sparta was based on military discipline and did not value growth and change.

Chapter 15: Greek Religion, Arts, and Learning

Section 1: Greek Mythology and Religion

- The people of ancient Greece worshiped many gods, who they believed influenced the world around them.
- Greek religious practices were based upon Greek mythology and the epics of Homer.
- People in ancient Greece practiced their religion in many ways, such as building temples and participating in festivals.

Section 2: Greek Art and Literature

- Greek artists became known for the beauty of their work. Ancient Greek architecture continues to influence architects today.
- Lyric poetry and drama were important parts of the literature of ancient Greece.
- The Greeks enjoyed collections of fables, such as those of Aesop.

Section 3: Greek Learning

- Greek philosophers, such as Socrates and Plato, used reason to help them determine what is real and true.
- Historians in ancient Greece began to examine why historical events took place in addition to recording the events themselves.
- Greek scholars made important advances in the natural sciences, mathematics, and medicine.

Chapter 16: Greece and Persia

Section 1: The Persian Empire

- The rulers of the Persian Empire set up an efficient political organization.
- The Persian Empire balanced local self-government with central government in order to govern their vast territory.

Section 2: The Persian Wars

- The Persian king Darius intended to conquer all of Greece.
- The Athenians and Spartans worked together to defend themselves against the Persians.

Section 3: The Peloponnesian War

- Athens and its allies formed the Delian League. Sparta formed the Peloponnesian League with its allies.
- Although together they defeated the Persians, Athens and Sparta fought against each other in the 27-year-long Peloponnesian War.

Section 4: The Empire of Alexander the Great

- The Greek city-states were finally united under one rule by Alexander the Great.
- Alexander the Great's conquests spread Greek culture east toward India and south into Egypt.

Ancient Rome

Chapter 17: The Roman Republic

Section 1: On the Banks of the Tiber

- Rome was settled along the Tiber River in the Italian Peninsula during the 500s B.C.
- Romans developed myths to explain the city's founding.
- The location of Rome allowed the settlement to grow. It provided natural defenses, nearby farmland, and access to key trade routes.

Section 2: Rise of the Roman Republic
- The earliest rulers of Rome were kings. Etruscan rule introduced new trade goods, ideas, and customs to Rome.
- After becoming tired of Etruscan rule, the Romans overthrew the third Etruscan king. They then established the Roman Republic.
- Roman society included two social classes. Struggles between these classes led Rome to move toward a more democratic form of government.

Section 3: The Government of the Republic
- The government of the Roman Republic had three branches. These branches represented monarchy, oligarchy, and democracy.
- The Roman constitution was a series of laws and practices that formed the basis of government in Rome.
- A system of checks and balances and the rule of law were among the important principles of the Roman constitution.

Section 4: Roman Society
- Roman society placed much importance on traditions, such as family relationships.
- The relationships between patrons and clients also helped form the social structure of Rome.
- Roman society valued traits such as gravitas and civic virtue. Religion in ancient Rome involved the worship of many gods, both in public and at home.

Chapter 18: The Roman Empire

Section 1: The Conquest of an Empire
- Rome's military strength, as well as diplomacy, helped the empire succeed.
- Rome fought against Carthage in three wars know as the Punic Wars.
- Social problems led to the downfall of Rome.

Section 2: The Pax Romana
- Julius Caesar ruled Rome as "dictator for life" until his assassination in 44 B.C.
- Caesar's adopted son Octavian ruled the Roman Empire during a long period of peace and prosperity.

Section 3: Commerce and Culture
- Economic growth and colonization helped the Roman Empire expand during the Pax Romana.
- Greco-Roman culture spread throughout the Roman Empire as the empire expanded.

Chapter 19: Christianity

Section 1: The Origins of Christianity
- During the Roman occupation of Jerusalem, a Jewish teacher named Jesus became popular.
- Jesus was crucified, but his followers believed that he was resurrected.

Section 2: The Beliefs of Christianity
- Christians follow the teachings of the early church, as they were recorded in the New Testament.
- Christians believe that Jesus is God and that he died so people could be forgiven for their sins.

Section 3: The Spread of Christianity
- Apostles such as Peter and Paul helped spread the new faith across the Roman Empire.
- In spite of persecution, the faith continued to grow.
- Today there are many branches of Christianity.

Section 1: Roman Arts and Engineering

- Roman art and architecture were modeled on Greek works.
- New types of roads, water systems, and advances in science, medicine and technology improved the Romans' daily life.

Section 2: Literature, Language, and Law

- Rome's legacy of literature was based on both Greek and Latin models.
- Roman government and law influenced modern political and legal systems.

Section 3: The Decline of the Roman Empire

- Many internal problems contributed to the fall of the Roman Empire.
- Attacks by invaders further weakened the empire.

Ideas to Build On: Grade 7 Review

Rome and Byzantium

Chapter 1: The Roman Empire

Section 1: Uncovering the Remote Past

- Historians find evidence about the past in myths, primary sources, secondary sources, and material culture.
- Romans have left historians with a wealth of documents and artifacts to interpret. Pompeii offers an especially rich variety of material culture.
- Historians are always questioning their views of the past.

Section 2: The Empire at Its Height

- The Roman Republic lasted from 510 B.C. until 31 B.C., when Octavian became the first emperor of Rome.
- During the Pax Romana, the Roman Empire expanded to include Western Europe and most of the region bordering the Mediterranean Sea.
- By the third century, the Roman Empire had become too large to rule easily.

Section 3: The Western Empire Collapses

- The Roman Empire had many social and economic weaknesses.
- The Huns and the Goths threatened the Roman Empire.
- The Western Empire came under the power of the Franks and Germanic rulers.

Section 4: The Lasting Contributions of Rome

- Many countries have legal systems based on Roman law and speak languages based on Latin.
- A large network of roads helped unify the empire. Public water and sewer systems were very sophisticated.
- At first, Christianity was a persecuted religion. Later, Christianity helped to unify the empire.

Chapter 2: The Byzantine Empire

Section 1: The Survival of the Eastern Empire

- Power in the Roman Empire shifted to the East under the emperor Constantine.
- Constantinople's location made it the center of trade in the East and made it easier to defend.
- Justinian enlarged the Byzantine Empire and transformed the city of Constantinople.

Section 2: The Division of the Christian Church

- The Eastern Church, ruled by patriarchs, was well organized.
- The Byzantine emperor controlled the Eastern Church. The pope in Rome controlled the Western Church and had political influence in Western Europe.
- The Eastern and Western Christian civilizations moved apart because of political, cultural, and religious differences.

Section 3: Byzantine Civilization

- Constantinople was a cultural and political center. Byzantine civilization made important contributions to law, art, and architecture.
- The Byzantine Empire spread its culture and religion to the peoples of Eastern Europe.
- The Byzantine Empire shrank and eventually fell because of attacks from the outside and struggles from within.

Islamic Civilization

Chapter 3: Islam

Section 1: The Origins of Islam

- Islam arose in Arabia, a harsh land where people lived according to tribal culture.
- Muhammad, the founder of Islam and a political and military leader, united most of Arabia under Muslim rule.

Section 2: The Beliefs of Islam

- Islam's most sacred texts, the Qur'an and the Sunnah, are believed to contain the word of God and the practices of Muhammad.
- One God, the individual soul, and the afterlife form the core beliefs of Islam.
- Muslims have religious duties called the Five Pillars: declaration of faith, prayer, alms-giving, fasting, and pilgrimage.

Section 3: The Spread of Islam

- In three phases, Islam was spread as far as Europe, Africa, and Asia by military conquest and peaceful conversion.
- Islam is the second-largest religion today, with two main groups, the Sunnis and the Shiites.

Chapter 4: The Islamic World

Section 1: The Expansion of Muslim Rule

- The caliphate reached it maximum geographic extent under the Umayyads, who established the first Islamic dynasty.
- The Abbasid Dynasty oversaw the golden age of Muslim civilization as well as the breakup of the caliphate.

Section 2: Muslims' Daily Life

- Islamic law, or the Sharia, was developed from the Qur'an and the Sunnah. It detailed rules of personal conduct in Muslim society.
- Social class, gender roles, and education gave order to Islamic society.

Section 3: The Growth of Cities and Trade

- The Islamic world had many large, highly developed cities with strong economies.
- Traders traveled over land and by sea across the Islamic world and beyond, spreading goods, ideas, and inventions.

Section 4: Islamic Achievements

- The Muslim empire valued learning. Muslim scholars' work in philosophy, medicine, science, mathematics, and geography influenced future civilizations.
- Muslim art, architecture, and calligraphy are noted for their use of patterns and the absence of human forms.
- The folk tales and poetry of the Muslim world were based on an oral tradition.

Civilizations in Sub-Saharan Africa

Chapter 5: The Rise of West African Empires

Section 1: Sub-Saharan Africa

- The Sahara acted as a barrier between Mediterranean and West African peoples.
- South of the Sahara, the landscape shifts from the dry Sahel to grasslands to rain forests.
- West Africa's resources included minerals, plants, animals, and people.

Section 2: Ghana

- Ghana was founded by the Soninke people in the western Sudan.
- Traders from North Africa crossed the Sahara to exchange salt for Ghana's gold.
- The Muslim Almoravids invaded Ghana and controlled it for a decade. Ghana never regained its previous power.

Section 3: The Rise of Mali

- After the fall of Ghana, Mali became a powerful empire in West Africa.
- Mali had a rich trade with countries in North Africa.
- The religion of Islam was an important influence in Mali.

Chapter 6: West African Civilization

Section 1: The Growth of Islam in West Africa

- The Songhai Empire expanded under Muslim rulers. It was the largest empire in West Africa.
- Timbuktu was a center of Islamic scholarship.
- Arabic became the language of law, learning, and business.

Section 2: West African Society

- West African societies were organized according to complex systems of kinship and class.
- Slaves made up the lowest caste in West Africa. However, slaves had some important rights.
- Trade was a central part of life in both villages and cities.

Section 3: Storytelling and the Arts of West Africa

- West Africans passed on their history and morals through an oral tradition.
- Music, dance, and sculpture played key roles in transmitting West African culture.
- West African cultures from the past have influenced modern African, European, and American societies.

Chapter 7: The Mayas

Section 1: The Rise of the Mayas

- Maya civilization thrived in the southern lowlands of Mesoamerica.
- For hundreds of years, Classic Maya civilization had a rich and vibrant culture.
- Warfare, food shortages, disease, and other factors contributed to the decline of Maya civilization.

Section 2: Maya Society

- Maya society was roughly divided into two groups, nobles and commoners.
- The extended family was the basic unit of Maya society.
- The king's authority was based on alliances, military power, and the favor of the gods.

Section 3: Maya Achievements

- Maya writing used a complex system of 800 glyphs.
- The Mayas were sophisticated astronomers and mathematicians.
- Maya buildings were impressive examples of architecture that were covered in elaborate, painted sculptures.

Chapter 8: The Incas

Section 1: The Rise of the Incas

- The peoples of the central Andes adapted to the harsh terrain by developing terrace farming and breeding hardy animals.
- The Inca Empire had its birth in southern Peru in the valley of Cuzco.
- The Inca Empire grew quickly to cover a vast region that included millions of people.

Section 2: Inca Society

- Inca society was organized according to a strict hierarchy. Each person's role was defined by the state.
- All property in the Inca Empire was communal. There were few extremely wealthy or poor Incas.
- The Incas worshiped many gods and believed the Sapa Inca was a descendant of a god.

Section 3: Inca Achievements

- The Inca government was highly organized and efficient.
- The Inca people obeyed strict rules but were guaranteed food, clothing, and shelter.
- The Incas built sophisticated roads and buildings. They also excelled at metalwork and textile weaving.

Chapter 9: The Aztecs

Section 1: The Rise of the Aztecs

- The Valley of Mexico offered fertile land and a mild climate.
- The Aztecs founded Tenochtitlán on an island that provided good farmland, easy travel, and safety from attack.
- The Aztecs established a large empire in Mexico.

Section 2: Aztec Society

- Aztec society was divided into two main classes: nobles and commoners.
- The Aztec government depended on tribute from conquered states.
- The Aztecs practiced human sacrifice to appease the gods and to control their subjects.

Section 3: Aztec Achievements

- Tenochtitlán was a thriving city with impressive public and private buildings.
- The Aztecs created works of art using precious metals, colorful stones, and feathers.
- The Aztecs highly respected orators for their ability to recite stories, poems, and legends.

Civilizations in East Asia

Chapter 10: China's Golden Age

Section 1: The Tang and Song Dynasties

- From their capital at Chang'an, the Tang expanded China's borders, strengthened the government, and promoted the arts.
- The Song era was one of good government. Scholar-officials rose to the top of society.
- After a barbarian invasion from the north, the Song moved south and prospered.

Section 2: Religion and Thought in China's Golden Age

- Daoism, a philosophy of following the way of nature, became a religion by the Tang era.
- Pure Land and Chan Buddhism were popular in China. Some Daoists and Confucianists strongly opposed Buddhism.
- Confucian philosophy and religion stressed the importance of social order.

Section 3: Advances in Farming, Technology, and Trade

- Improved farming techniques enabled the population to double quickly, but changes in land tenure made some farmers poor.
- Technological inventions led to increased literacy and expanded overseas trade.
- Advances in farm production, transportation, and a money economy led to growth in trade and industry.

Chapter 11: China Under the Mongols and the Ming

Section 1: The Mongol Ascendancy

- The Mongols, united under Genghis Khan, conquered a vast portion of Asia.
- Genghis Khan established the Yuan Dynasty in China and encouraged foreigners to come there.
- Marco Polo spent seventeen years in China and shared his knowledge of China with Europe on his return.

Section 2: The Ming Dynasty

- The Ming Dynasty restored centralized rule to China. China saw itself as the center of the world.
- China launched huge maritime expeditions that reached west to India, the Middle East, and Africa.
- China withdrew from official contact with other nations, though foreign trade continued to thrive.

Section 3: China's Influence on the World

- Confucianism and Buddhism spread from China to influence Korea, Vietnam, and Japan.
- Chinese inventions such as paper, gunpowder, and the magnetic compass changed life in European countries.

Chapter 12: The Rise of Japan

Section 1: Land of the Rising Sun

- Japan consists of a chain of islands with a wide range of climates.
- People from the Asian mainland settled Japan over time.
- Japan adapted the Chinese writing system to its own language. It also embraced Buddhism when that religion arrived from Korea.

Section 2: The Age of Emperors

- Local clans and their leaders controlled early Japan.
- The Yamato clan gained power over Japan through wars and marriage alliances.
- Prince Shotoku introduced Japan's first constitution. He borrowed heavily from China to create a strong, centralized government.

Section 3: The Development of Feudalism

- Japanese ruling society was based on rank, not merit. The court moved to Kyoto to avoid increasingly powerful Buddhists.
- After a long war, Minamoto Yoritomo became the first shogun of Japan.
- Feudalism emerged in Japan. Samurai served daimyo, who ruled like minor kings.

Section 4: Japan Under the Shoguns

- Samurai followed a strict code of honor in which loyalty to the lord was most important.
- Japan repelled two Mongol invasions with help from what they called a *kamikaze,* or divine wind.
- Tokugawa Ieyasu ended a long period of instability. He established his capital at Edo.

Chapter 13: Japan's Golden Age

Section 1: Japan's Cultural Flowering
- The development of a simpler form of writing made composing poetry, journals, and other literature easier.
- Women writers produced some of the most important literature of the Heian period.
- Buddhism influenced painting, sculpture, and architecture.

Section 2: The Development of Japanese Buddhism
- Buddhism became widely practiced in Japan by the Heian period. At the same time, the practice of Shinto continued.
- Some Buddhist sects emphasized prayers, ritual, and separation from society as essential to enlightenment.
- Other forms emphasized individual effort. Buddhism became increasingly popular.

Section 3: Japanese Society
- The basis of Japanese society was the clan. The welfare of the group was more important than individual needs.
- Buddhism and Confucianism emphasized ideas of harmony and unity. They viewed women as inferior.
- The economy grew because of increased numbers of artisans and merchants and through expanded trade.

In the Middle Ages

Chapter 14: A New Civilization in Europe

Section 1: Europe in the Early Middle Ages
- Europe, which has a varied topography, is part of the Eurasian landmass.
- The Middle Ages is the period from 500 to 1500, after the Roman Empire and before the Modern Age.
- Charlemagne built an empire that covered most of central and western Europe.

Section 2: The Spread of Christianity in Europe
- The rise of monasteries and religious orders strengthened Christianity.
- Missionaries carried Christian beliefs throughout Europe.
- Eventually, most peoples of Europe were united under one Christian faith.

Section 3: The Development of European Feudalism
- Various groups of invaders entered western Europe between 800 and 1000.
- Outside attacks and a weak central government caused the feudal system to develop.
- The manor formed the economic foundation of European feudalism.

Chapter 15: Medieval Conflicts and Crusades

Section 1: Popes and Rulers
- Charlemagne established a Christian kingdom with close ties to the Church.
- Pope Leo III crowned Charlemagne emperor, but this practice later caused problems.
- A power struggle between Henry IV and Pope Gregory VII revealed conflicts between the pope and emperor in the Holy Roman Empire.

Section 2: Kings, Nobles, and the Magna Carta
- In 1066, the Normans conquered Anglo-Saxon England and transformed English life and the English language.
- The Magna Carta and English law limited royal power and guaranteed basic rights.
- Parliament was formed to advise the king and limit his power.

Section 3: Religious Crusades

- European Christians launched the Crusades to capture the Holy Land from the Muslims.
- The religious fervor of the Crusades led to the persecution of Muslims, heretics, and Jews.

Section 4: Christians and Muslims in Spain

- Muslim Spain had a highly advanced civilization.
- The Reconquista ended Muslim rule in Spain and brought the growth of Christian kingdoms.
- Spanish Muslims and Jews were persecuted during the Reconquista.

Chapter 16: A Changing Medieval World

Section 1: The Revival of Trade and Towns

- Farming innovations led to an increase in the food supply, which led to population growth.
- Increases in trade resulted from increases in population and wealth. A banking system and the growth of towns followed.

Section 2: An Age of Faith

- Europeans joined mendicant religious orders and built Gothic cathedrals as expressions of religious devotion.
- Universities developed from cathedral schools. Trade gave scholars access to ancient texts.

Section 3: The Breakdown of Medieval Society

- Famine and the Hundred Years' War struck medieval Europe. New weapons ended feudal-style warfare.
- The bubonic plague spread along trade routes. A huge loss of life and dramatic social changes followed.

Early Modern Europe

Chapter 17: The Renaissance

Section 1: The Origins of the Renaissance

- Economic and social changes began to break down the feudal order.
- Secular learning began to weaken Church control over education.
- These trends gave rise to the Renaissance, which began in prosperous Italian city-states.

Section 2: New Ways of Viewing the World

- Renaissance thinkers revived the classical ideas of ancient Greece and Rome.
- This "new learning" helped produce three new viewpoints: humanism, secularism, and individualism.
- Artists began to produce work based on secular themes, in a more realistic style.

Section 3: The Spread of New Ideas

- Scholars and students spread the Renaissance ideas across Europe.
- Key thinkers in northern Europe — such as More, Erasmus, and Rabelais — used Renaissance ideas to promote reform.
- The development of printing and advances in literacy helped spread Renaissance ideas.

Section 4: The Renaissance Legacy

- Renaissance art, architecture, and literature left a legacy for the modern world.
- Artists and architects like Brunelleschi, Leonardo, and Michelangelo revived classical forms and developed new techniques.
- Writers such as Dante, Shakespeare, and Cervantes helped develop language and literary forms that influenced world literature.

Chapter 18: The Reformation

Section 1: The Origins of the Reformation
- Abuses by the Catholic Church generated criticism and dissent in Europe.
- The ideas of Protestant reformers spread, giving rise to the Reformation.

Section 2: The Counter-Reformation
- Catholic reformers started new religious orders that improved the Church's reputation and attracted new followers.
- The Council of Trent answered Protestant challenges and affirmed Church authority.

Section 3: The Division of Christendom
- Lutheranism and Calvinism spread through much of northern Europe. Henry VIII formed the Church of England.
- Catholics and Protestants fought wars throughout Europe. Catholicism remained strongest in southern Europe.

Section 4: The Political Impact of the Reformation
- Protestant-Catholic wars increased the power of Europe's secular rulers.
- Europeans turned to new forms of government after the Reformation.

Chapter 19: The Age of Exploration

Section 1: The Voyages of Discovery
- Improved maps, navigation tools, and ships made possible the explorers' ocean voyages.
- Oceangoing explorers revealed the extent of Africa, the existence of the Americas, and a western sea route from Europe to Asia.

Section 2: The Conquest of the Americas
- The rich Aztec and Inca empires fell to Spanish conquistadors.
- The colonization of New Spain and Peru enriched Spain and devastated Aztec and Inca cultures and populations.

Section 3: The Planting of Colonies
- Europeans set up trading posts, colonies, and missions around the world.
- European exploration and colonization resulted in a worldwide exchange of plants, animals, peoples, diseases, and ideas.

Section 4: The Origins of Modern Capitalism
- At the end of the Middle Ages, capitalism, a new type of economic system, arose in Europe.
- Mercantilism, an economic theory based on overseas trade, also emerged in Europe.

Chapter 20: Revolutions in Thought

Section 1: The Origins of the Scientific Revolution
- The ancient Greeks applied reason to studies of the natural world. Muslim scholars later preserved much of this science.
- During the late Middle Ages, Europeans combined Greek and Muslim science with Christian teachings.
- Renaissance humanism, global exploration, and new scientific tools sparked renewed interest in science.

Section 2: The Rise of Modern Science
- Beginning with Copernicus in the 1500s, scholars proved that the sun is the center of the universe.
- Newton reinforced the sun-centered model of the universe by developing the law of gravity.
- The work of Bacon and Descartes led to the development of the scientific method.

Section 3: The Enlightenment

- Enlightenment thinkers developed key ideas about natural rights, balanced government, and the social contract.
- Enlightenment thinkers applied reason to the study of society and the economy.

Section 4: The Influence of Enlightenment Ideas

- American colonial governments were influenced by English law and Enlightenment ideas.
- Inspired by these principles, colonial leaders signed the Declaration of Independence and separated from Great Britain.

Section 5: Linking the Past and Present

- Many ideas and values from the Scientific Revolution and the Enlightenment continue to influence the world today.
- Enduring religious institutions and political systems shape our lives.